On the Trail of the

GOLDEN MAN

by Lisa Thompson

illustrated by Brenda Cantell

sundance
A Haights Cross Communications ⟶ Company

Published by Sundance Publishing
One Beeman Road
P.O. Box 740
Northborough, MA 01532-0740
800-343-8204
www.sundancepub.com

First published as Treasure Trackers by
Blake Education, Locked Bag 2022, Glebe 2037, Australia
Exclusive United States Distribution: Sundance Publishing

ISBN 0-7608-9333-0

Contents

SOUTH AMERICA

Equator

EL DORADO

DR. SIMMONS CAMP

BRIDGE

WATERFALL

WHIRLPOOLS

CAPTIVE ISLAND

EL DORADO

The AMAZON

Venezuela

Guyana
Suriname

Colombia

French
Guiana

mouth of
the Amazon

Ecuador

Atlantic
Ocean

Peru

Brazil

acific Ocean

Bolivia

Paraguay

Argentina   Uruguay

Amazon Rain
Forest Region

Chile

N

W   E

S

CHAPTER 1

Always Know Your Stuff

Uncle Earl raced across the top of the canyon to meet Ricky and Mia. "Up here!" he called. "You made it! I just knew you could do it! A piece of cake, right?"

Mia reached the top of the canyon, hauled herself over using her last bit of energy, and fell to the ground, exhausted. She was covered in dirt and scratches. Her teeth were clenched. Mia was more than angry. She was about to EXPLODE!

"Uncle Earl! Are you kidding me! I can't believe you made us do that! It was the most difficult . . ."

"Stop! Wait, Mia!" Ricky shouted, as he climbed the last few rocks. Ricky knew his best friend was about to say something she would regret. The four-hour hike, followed by the three-hour climb, had taken its toll.

Uncle Earl had told them that they would be jumping out of a plane. He'd told them about the parachutes. But he hadn't mentioned the long hike and the climb! Only after they reached the ground did they find a note from Uncle Earl, along with a small map.

"Uncle Earl," said Ricky breathlessly, "that hike was a killer!"

Mia cut in sharply. "Uncle Earl! What were you thinking? That was no ordinary hike. The jungle was so thick we could have been lost forever!"

"Oh, come on. I knew you two could do it," he beamed. "I never doubted you for a moment!"

Ricky was still trying to catch his breath. The hike had been a test. He knew how Mia's uncle's mind worked. Uncle Earl wanted them to get a taste of what the Amazon jungle was like. Uncle Earl wasn't the expert's expert in archaeology by chance. Ricky had heard his motto many times. *It's all in the details!*

Mia wasn't giving in that easily. "Dropping us in the middle of NOWHERE and making us hike out? Have you gone NUTS? Look at me, I'm scratched from head to toe! Anyway, I know all about jungle survival. I didn't need to go through that again. I've read *101 Tips If You Get Lost in the Amazon* THREE times!"

Ricky laughed. Mia could be such a drama queen. "I told you to follow me," he said. "But no—you had to go your own way. That spiky bush you walked into had your name written all over it."

"Now, Mia," said Uncle Earl calmly, with just a hint of a chuckle, "if you are coming with me on this expedition, you must learn how to look after yourself. You must be prepared—even though nothing can *really* prepare you for the Amazon. It's another world. It's no ordinary jungle. Everything about it is so big."

"Like spiders as big as my head," teased Ricky.

"With bigger brains!" Mia snapped back.

Uncle Earl continued, "When you are going as far into the jungle as we are, you need to know all about survival. And not just from books, Mia. If you get lost, I need to know that you have the will to survive— just in case."

"In case of what, Uncle Earl?" asked Ricky cautiously.

Mia cut in. "In case you get bitten on the knee by a scorpion, or wrapped up tight by a huge boa constrictor, or giant termites bite you all over, and you have to beg me to save you!"

Ricky laughed. "Mia, you crack me up when you're angry."

Uncle Earl glanced at his watch. "I must say you two got here in very good time."

"That's because I had a little help." Mia grinned and pulled out her gadgets—a compass and a high-tech, state-of-the-art global positioning system.

"Hard to get lost with those," said Uncle Earl.

Mia nodded. "Always expect the unexpected."

Uncle Earl laughed proudly.
He had taught Mia well.

Ricky felt his energy creeping back. "So when do we head for the Amazon?"

"Why, this very moment!" Uncle Earl pointed to a helicopter flying over the canyon toward them. "Here's our ride. Dr. Simmons and his team are waiting for us. We should be there by nightfall."

CHAPTER 2

On a Mission

The view from the air was amazing. Tall trees made a canopy blocking any view of the ground. Occasionally an even taller tree reached up higher toward the sun. From the chopper, the forest looked like a carpet of trees with rivers winding through it like long snakes. They found a clearing and landed the helicopter. The rest of the journey had to be made by boat.

As they went deeper and deeper into the rain forest, Uncle Earl, Ricky, and Mia left their world behind. Strange sounds, plants, and smells surrounded them. Ricky and Mia had an eerie feeling that a thousand pairs of eyes were watching them as they motored upriver.

After rounding another bend in the river, Dr. Simmons's camp came into view on the riverbank. It was basic—just a few tents, some hammocks with mosquito nets, a table sheltered by a roof of leaves, and some giant fallen logs for chairs.

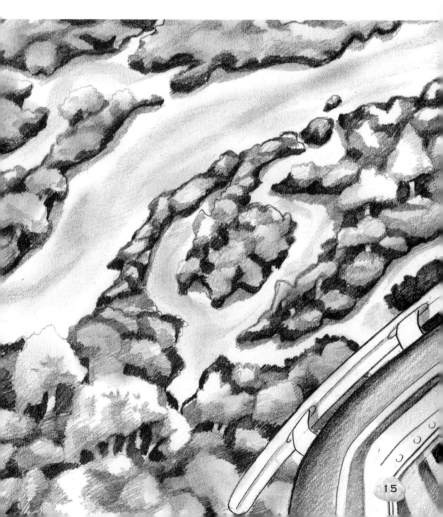

They pulled the boat onto the shore and saw
Dr. Simmons sitting at a table studying some
stone carvings. Dr. Simmons believed that the
carvings belonged to a tribe of Indians who had
lived here long ago. But that was not the reason
that Dr. Simmons had called Uncle Earl. He
needed Uncle Earl's help with a much more
important matter.

Dr. Simmons was a fidgety man with a lined and weathered face. He had spent most of his life outdoors. He talked rapidly as they entered the camp. It was obvious he wanted to explain things quickly.

"Thanks for coming, Earl, and thanks to you, too, Ricky and Mia. What do you think of the jungle so far? It's amazing, isn't it?"

"Your message sounded truly fascinating, Dr. Simmons," said Uncle Earl. "A sighting of the Golden Man from El Dorado? If it's true, and you can find him—wow! It would be one of the richest and rarest finds ever!"

Dr. Simmons nodded in excited agreement, his eyes wide. Sweat trickled down his face. In fact, sweat trickled off all of them. And for the first time, Ricky and Mia noticed how hot and heavy the air was. A few seconds later, it started to rain. Big, heavy raindrops pelted down and started bouncing off them.

"Let's take cover," Dr. Simmons said as he moved them toward the sheltered table. "You'll get used to being wet soon enough." He cleared the table and spread out a large map. "Come, sit down. Let me explain."

Mia studied the map closely before whispering to Ricky, "There's the camp marked on the map. Look how many rivers crisscross this area."

"Yeah! And by the looks of things, we're a long, long way from civilization," Ricky replied.

Dr. Simmons began his story. "About a month ago, I was walking alone in the jungle. I came upon an Indian man from a tribe I had never

seen before. He looked unusually tall and
strong. A large, golden breastplate was hanging
from chains around his neck. It was exquisite!
As I glanced at it, I realized that it was engraved
with the symbol of El Dorado. Here, look."

Dr. Simmons handed the golden breastplate to Uncle Earl.

"How on earth did you get it?" Uncle Earl asked.

"When I showed interest in it, the man gave it to me. Then he ran off," Dr. Simmons answered. "When I returned to camp with it, some of my team believed it was a sign of bad luck, and they fled. Many had heard terrible stories about the fierce warriors of El Dorado. I had to get a whole new team out here. Luckily, I met Sipu. He agreed to be my headman, and he found some men to help me."

"Who is Sipu?" asked Uncle Earl curiously.

Dr. Simmons pointed to a strong and proud Indian who wore gold crescents through his ears. The man was busy talking to his team, but he had one eye on the new members of the camp.

"Have you seen the man from El Dorado again?" asked Mia.

"Yes. I saw him about a week ago, by a river not far from here. I was alone again." Dr. Simmons dropped his voice and began to whisper. "I saw him washing gold dust off himself! When he saw me, he ran off—but he left this behind." Dr. Simmons handed Uncle Earl a small, golden figure of a man. Mia and Ricky were completely spellbound.

"So, what do you think about it, Earl?" asked Dr. Simmons.

"Well . . . it has similar markings to other gold figures believed to be from El Dorado." Uncle Earl smiled and said, "Dr. Simmons, I have a very good feeling about this!"

"What exactly is El Dorado?" asked Ricky, barely able to take his eyes off the gold.

Dr. Simmons still spoke in a whisper. "It is believed to be an ancient kingdom where everything was made of gold."

Uncle Earl broke in. "Legend has it that once a year the king covered himself in gold dust and became the Golden One. *El Dorado* means *Golden One*. The king sat upon a raft laden with gold and precious stones and was rowed to the middle of a great lake. The Golden One then threw his riches into the lake as an offering to the gods."

"Is that who you think you saw in the forest?" asked Mia.

"Yes." Dr. Simmons's eyes were gleaming.

"Awesome! Sounds like my kind of kingdom!" said Ricky.

"Hang on." Mia had found a hitch. "Has anyone ever been to El Dorado and returned? Or is it some sort of secret, lost city?"

"Young lady," Dr. Simmons replied curtly, "the jungle holds many secrets that it does not give away easily." He waved his fingers across the map of the jungle and pointed to a dark green, uncharted area. "I believe El Dorado and all its riches lie in this area. But enough excitement. You must rest now. Tomorrow we will begin our search for the golden kingdom of El Dorado."

CHAPTER 3

Jungle Trek

They left the camp the next morning, just after first light. It was early, but it was hard to tell because the forest canopy blocked out most of the sunlight. There was a thick fog on the ground that Sipu called a "cloud forest." They couldn't even see their feet as they walked.

Dr. Simmons led the way, slashing a path through the leaves and vines with his machete. Sipu, Mia, Ricky, and Uncle Earl followed behind. It didn't take long for the giant, hungry mosquitoes to come out and start biting them. Ricky couldn't stand it.

"They're chewing me up! There's going to be no blood left in me if they don't stop," he cried.

"Here, rub some of this on yourself." Mia handed him some insect repellent. She had stashed it in her survival belt, along with a compass, a fishing line, two flares, some waterproof matches, a pencil, and some chocolate.

"Thanks, Mia. I should've known you'd have something to help."

Suddenly, Sipu sank down to the ground and signaled for them to do the same. He had heard a noise up ahead. They all hugged the ground, not making a sound. Ricky's mind raced. Was it a jaguar, a monkey, that giant boa constrictor Mia had told him about—or was it the Golden Man? His thoughts were broken by the crack of a twig. It was coming closer, whatever it was. Ricky held his breath and watched Sipu.

Sipu was as still as a rock, his head forward like a lizard's so he could hear every sound. An army of giant-sized ants moved up and down Sipu's arm, biting him. They were making lunch out of him, but Sipu didn't flinch. Finally, Sipu gave the all-clear signal and waved them on.

"What was that all about?" asked Mia.

Sipu pointed to the ground. There was a large paw print.

"Jaguar?" asked Uncle Earl, taking a look.

Sipu nodded. "We were lucky. He didn't smell us because we were downwind."

"Lucky for him or for us?" said Dr. Simmons unpleasantly. "Now let's get moving. This isn't a walk in the park, Sipu. Come on! Let's not waste more time." He marched off, setting a fast pace. "Hurry up, the rest of you!"

"I don't know what his hurry is. He's in a terrible mood," said Uncle Earl. "I'll go ahead and try to calm him down. You two walk behind us with Sipu."

"I think you should walk with us," said Sipu. "It will be safer. I will take good care of you."

"Don't you worry about me, Sipu. I'll be all right. I'll see you when you catch up!" Uncle Earl said. They watched as he disappeared into the jungle.

"Sipu," said Mia, "your arm must be killing you. Those giant ants were eating you alive!"

Sipu just smiled. He broke off a branch and squeezed the sap onto the bites. Then he crushed some red berries from another plant and smeared the red pulp on his arm.

"You should wipe some of this on your skin, too," he said, giving them some berries. "It will keep most bugs away. It works much better than that cream you have."

Mia rubbed the berries evenly over her skin. Ricky painted himself with red stripes down his arms and legs and across his face.

"How do I look, Sipu?" asked Ricky. "Like a jungle boy?"

Sipu nodded and laughed. "Sure—but now come follow me. I will show you how to survive in the jungle. We will go this way."

Sipu made walking through the jungle look easy. This was his home. He had grown up here. He thought nothing of climbing over tree roots double his height, breaking vines for a quick drink, and climbing up a tree for a bite to eat. He walked so lightly through the forest that his feet barely left any marks on the ground. He showed Mia and Ricky how to walk through the rain forest without being seen or heard.

Sipu showed them how to recognize tracks of different animals. He showed them things to look for, such as a flick of dust left by a snake or a mark on a tree left by a monkey. He also told them important things to listen for, like the sounds of different birds and the noises made by various insects.

Sipu could tell just from the rustle of leaves which animal was passing by. He pointed out that the sounds made by a monkey in a tree were different from those made by a jaguar hunting for food.

Sipu showed them the plants to avoid. Some plants were as sharp as razor blades. Others were soft and smooth, yet very, very strong. He showed them which vines and leaves to use as rope. And as they kept on walking, they began to feel more at home in the rain forest.

"Oh, look at this. How cute!" Mia bent down to pick up a tiny green and black frog.

"No!" yelled Sipu. "Do not touch it!"

Mia froze.

"Sipu," said Ricky, "relax. It's just a little green frog. How dangerous could it be?"

Sipu moved them away. "That is a poison arrow frog. It's very dangerous. We use the poison from this frog on our arrow tips. It is deadly."

"That little frog?" asked Mia in disbelief.

"Come," said Sipu. "It's not far now. Just over this bridge."

"What bridge?" asked Mia. "I don't see any bridge."

"You mean that bunch of vines?" cried Ricky. "Cool! It looks just like a tightrope."

The bridge of vines stretched over a deep ravine in front of them. The roar of water echoed around them.

"Man, that has to be at least a hundred-foot drop!" Ricky shouted, taking a look over the edge.

"There's no way I'm walking across those vines, Sipu!" cried Mia. "Can't we go another way?"

"There is no other way," said Sipu, pointing to the bridge. "This is the only way."

"It'll be OK, Mia. I'll be right behind you, and Sipu will be in front," said Ricky.

Mia stepped onto the bridge. She didn't look down. "No pranks, OK, Ricky? This isn't the time to horse around!"

Ricky took one of her hands, and Sipu reached out and took the other. They walked along the bridge, step-by-step. Suddenly the vines beneath them swung wildly. They lost their footing and fell down into the deep water below.

"AHHHHHHHHHHH!" cried Mia and Ricky.

Sipu just smiled as he plunged after them into the gushing river.

Chapter 4

The Surprise Visit

The water carried them at a rapid pace over the edge of a roaring waterfall. Mia and Ricky tumbled and turned with the white water, gasping for air when they could, until the river carried them onto its bank.

"Awesome!" cried Ricky, shaking water out of his ears. "That waterfall drop blew away every roller coaster I've ever ridden. Hey, Mia?"

Mia was on her feet, searching the riverbank in a panic. "Oh no! I've lost my survival belt. My compass! Help me look, Ricky. Hang on. What's this?" She dug a golden figure out of the mud.

"Look, Ricky, it's another of those golden figures." This time the figure was standing on a raft.

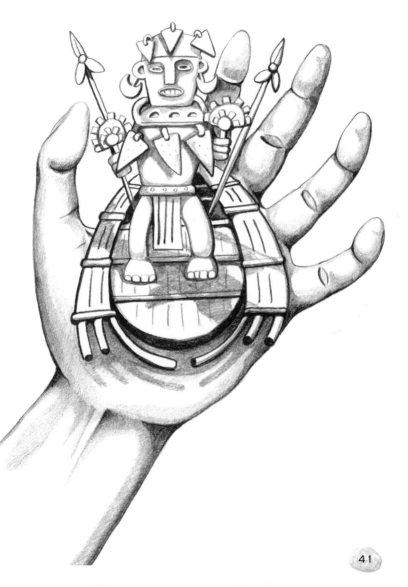

"Did you enjoy your little ride?" asked Sipu from the bank above them.

"Oh! That was unreal. That bit just before we went over the edge . . ." Suddenly Ricky noticed what Sipu was wearing. "Hey, where did you get that crazy gold headdress, Sipu?"

"Your body is covered in gold," gasped Mia.

"Welcome to El Dorado." Sipu smiled. "I'm sorry about the bridge, but there really is no other way to get here."

"YOU'RE the Golden Man who Uncle Earl and Dr. Simmons are looking for!" gasped Mia.

Sipu laughed and nodded. "Come, let me show you around. If you don't mind, I must cover your eyes while I lead you into the village." He wrapped a blindfold made of spun gold around each of their heads.

They could still recognize the chirps and whistles of the forest animals and birds, but they couldn't see a thing. Ricky heard a rustle of leaves following them. "What's that?"

"Just the monkeys that live around the village. They are rushing to tell the villagers we have visitors. You will meet them soon."

After Sipu allowed them to remove their blindfolds, Ricky and Mia saw that El Dorado was even more amazing than Dr. Simmons's description. Everything around them was made of gold and glittered brightly in the sunlight.

Gold statues surrounded the doorway of each dwelling. Golden pots and water jugs could be seen hanging inside homes. Baskets woven with gold fibers sat on the ground. Men, women, and children wore necklaces and earrings made of gold. And all over the ground, nuggets of gold and precious gems lay like pebbles.

45

"I can't believe how much gold is here!" cried Ricky. "You guys are loaded!"

"Here in El Dorado, we do not see gold in the same way as you do, Ricky."

"What do you mean, Sipu?" asked Mia.

"We have so much gold, we don't see it as something of great value. But we do see it as a thing of great beauty. Be careful, Mia. Leaning on our sun god could bring bad luck."

"Oh, sorry," said Mia, standing up straight.

"You see, the riverbeds and mountains that surround us are full of gold. As long as there is gold, the great sun god will protect our home— the rain forest. We bring gold to the sun god, and this pleases him." He picked up a nugget that lay at his feet. It was the size of a tennis ball. "As long as we keep the sun god happy, my people and the rain forest will be protected."

"So, what's more valuable than gold in El Dorado?" asked Ricky.

Sipu smiled, and his eyes widened. "Let me show you the great treasures of El Dorado!" He clapped his hands. Immediately, three servants dressed in golden cloth brought golden plates laden with food and golden jugs spilling over with juice.

They dined on all sorts of rain forest delicacies, including fruit salad with peach palm, papaya, and honey. There were fish of every size, flowers you could eat, and nuts the size of apples. They drank all kinds of exotic juices. Everything was fresh and ripe, and each mouthful was delicious.

"I can't believe you get all this from the rain forest," said Mia.

"I can't wait until Uncle Earl gets here. He's going to love this place," said Ricky.

Mia had forgotten about Dr. Simmons and Uncle Earl.

Sipu's happy face turned grim. "Your uncle and Dr. Simmons must *never* find this place!"

Mia and Ricky looked at each other. What did he mean?

CHAPTER 5

The Promise

After they ate, Sipu showed them through the village. It was alive with activity. Women were cooking and playing with their children. Men were busy melting and hammering gold. There were cautious but friendly looks from the natives. Ricky and Mia could not understand the language, but there was lots of laughter and chatter. Some children who were returning from the forest giggled and pointed at Ricky and Mia.

"What's so funny?" asked Ricky.

"The children are laughing at your berry stripes," Sipu said. "They think you have been bitten all over."

Ricky went a shade of pink and looked down at his stripes. Even the rushing water of the river hadn't washed off the pulp from the red berries.

As they walked through the village, Ricky couldn't keep his eyes off the bows and arrows the villagers carried. They were almost as big as the men themselves.

"Would you like to try one, Ricky?" asked Sipu, noticing his longing look.

"Awesome! I'd love to."

Ricky picked up a bow and arrow. Struggling, he said, "This is much heavier than it looks!" He tried to pull back on the bow, but it didn't move. "Are you sure this thing isn't locked?" he asked, pulling again without success.

"Give it up, Muscles," teased Mia.

Sipu took the bow, lifted it into the air, and shot an arrow with ease, high and far into the forest.

"It takes practice," said Sipu. "The strength of a great hunter is more than muscle."

They sat in the center of the village in an open dwelling. It was obvious Sipu had something important to tell them.

"For hundreds of centuries, men from outside the forest have tried to find El Dorado. They do not care for the forest, for my people, or for the way we live. They do not care for our culture. They only want to steal our gold. Dr. Simmons is one such man. He has been in this area for many years looking for El Dorado."

"But I thought he was studying stone carvings," said Ricky.

"Dr. Simmons is a man whose word cannot be trusted. He does not understand the ways of the forest. He does not care for the people of El Dorado. You have to understand the power of gold. Dr. Simmons cares only for the wealth the gold will bring him back in your world.

The gold breastplate that he showed you was not given to him. He stole it from one of my people. Dr. Simmons is a greedy man. If he finds the gold, he will take it all. Then the sun god will no longer protect us, and the rain forest and our home will be destroyed. We cannot let him find us."

"But, Sipu, you work for Dr. Simmons. What were you doing in the camp in the first place?" asked Mia.

"I joined Dr. Simmons to make sure he would never find us. Then you and your uncle arrived. That night the sun god sent me a dream and told me it was you two who could help save my people."

Ricky was confused. "What can we do?"

"You can try to convince Mia's uncle to lead
 Dr. Simmons away from this area," said Sipu.

"Where is my uncle now?" asked Mia quietly.

"He and Dr. Simmons are being held captive on
an island," answered Sipu.

"Captive!" cried Ricky. "They're prisoners?"

"They have been captured by our warrior
guards who protect the kingdom. Everyone who
tries to enter El Dorado faces the same fate. I
tried to warn your uncle, but . . ."

Mia shivered. "Fate? What do you mean, Sipu?"

"When the sun sets tonight, the guards will look
for a sign. If the sky turns golden, they will die.
If the sky does not turn golden, Dr. Simmons
and your uncle will be set free." His voice was
matter-of-fact.

"Sipu!" cried Mia. "The sky here is golden at EVERY sunset."

"He's Mia's uncle! You have to help, Sipu," demanded Ricky.

"I will help you save what you love, if you will help me save what I love. I cannot stop this myself, but I will show you how you can. What happens to Mia's uncle and Dr. Simmons is then up to you. But you must promise me one thing."

"Anything, Sipu!" cried Ricky. "Anything!"

"I want your word that when you get back home, you must do everything you can to protect our rain forest. You must NEVER tell anyone what you have seen here. If you do, our world will surely be destroyed."

"You have our word," said Ricky, shaking Sipu's hand. "We promise to do everything we can."

Mia nodded in agreement. "Yes, and we will never breathe a word to anyone that we have been here. Please, Sipu, take us to Uncle Earl. The sun is getting low, so we don't have much time left."

CHAPTER 6

Their Only Chance

The three crouched behind a rock and looked at the island. Ten fierce-looking warriors stood around its edge. Dr. Simmons and Uncle Earl were bound to two trees by thick vine ropes.

Mia murmured softly, "How are we going to get them out of this?"

Sipu lowered his voice to a whisper. "Listen carefully, my friends. In a short time, the sky will turn the color of gold. All the warriors will drop to the ground to give thanks to the sun god. This is called the Golden Time, and it is your only chance to free them. You must be as silent and as quick as possible, for it only lasts a few minutes. You must be like a jaguar eyeing his prey. Use these two pieces of sharp stone to cut the vines. There's a raft under those bushes. Jump on it, and leave immediately!"

"But will we be safe on the raft? Won't the warriors come after us?" Mia asked nervously.

"In this part of the river at Golden Time, the tide rises very quickly, creating great rapids and whirlpools around the island. If you reach the raft as the tide is rising and push it into the rapids, you have a good chance of making it downstream to safety. The warriors will not enter the water because of the whirlpools. But you must get to the raft as quickly as you can. If you take too long, the whirlpools will trap you on the banks of the island. Good luck, my friends. I will be watching. Remember—not only does the fate of Uncle Earl and Dr. Simmons rest in your hands, but also that of my people."

Sipu handed them two strawlike reeds. "Use these to get air when you are swimming underwater to the island. Hug the bottom like a slippery eel, and remember everything that I have shown you. Listen carefully, and keep your eyes open. Go quickly now! Here comes the Golden Time."

Ricky and Mia slid into the water without making a ripple. When they stepped onto the island, the warriors were all kneeling to the sun god. Uncle Earl spotted Mia and Ricky instantly. Ricky moved silently as Sipu had shown him, cut the rope, and swiftly led Uncle Earl to the raft. Mia freed Dr. Simmons, showed him the raft, and led the way.

The Golden Time was almost over. Mia reached the raft. The tide was rising. Whirlpools and rapids started to appear.

"Where is Dr. Simmons?" asked Ricky.

"He was with me a minute ago," said Mia.

Mia turned and gasped. "Oh, no!" Dr. Simmons was kneeling on the ground, stashing gold nuggets into a bag and into his pockets as fast as he could. He collected the last of the gold nuggets and heaved the bag onto his shoulder. The warriors saw him and angrily gave chase.

"They're going to get him!" yelled Mia. The raft swirled in the water with the force of the whirlpool. The warriors heard Mia's voice and turned toward them.

"Cut the vine, Mia! Cut the vine!" cried Ricky.

Mia cut the vine and set the raft free. "But what about Dr. Simmons?" yelled Mia, as arrows and spears flew toward them.

"He made his choice," yelled Uncle Earl. "Now, lay low and hang on tight!"

CHAPTER 7

Treasure to Protect

They clung desperately to the raft as it tossed and turned in the rapids.

"I think I hear a waterfall," shouted Ricky.

The water roared, and they shot over the edge. After being tossed about by the current, they landed on the bank of the river. Uncle Earl lay motionless on the muddy riverbank.

"Uncle Earl! Are you all right?" Mia cried.

Ricky looked over Mia's shoulder waiting for Uncle Earl to stir. Slowly, Uncle Earl opened his eyes and let out a little laugh.

"Oh, my. Wasn't that a ride and a half?" Uncle Earl said as he struggled to get up.

"Don't move, Uncle Earl," instructed Mia. "You have a cut on your head that I'm going to fix." She applied some mud from the riverbank to the cut. "There, that should be OK for now."

Uncle Earl felt his forehead. "You are quite a jungle girl after all, Mia. And Ricky . . ." He laughed a little harder. "Next time we shoot over a waterfall, try to act a little scared. You loved it so much, anyone would have thought you'd done it before!"

Ricky looked at Mia for help. "Only at an amusement park, Uncle Earl," she said.

But Uncle Earl wanted answers to bigger questions. "How did you two find us on the island? Where did Sipu go? How did you know about that raft?"

Mia did what she did best and quickly changed the subject. "What about Dr. Simmons?" she asked.

"Hmmmmmm." Uncle Earl shakily got to his feet. "Oh, yes, Dr. Simmons." He looked at the two of them. "Dr. Simmons was very . . . well, let's just say he wasn't exactly after what he said he was after. Greed is a terrible thing.

It can make great treasures worthless and
destroy wonderful discoveries."

"I guess some treasures aren't meant to be
found," said Mia.

"How true that is, Mia," sighed Uncle Earl.

Ricky noticed that the river had become calm. "We had better get going. We have a long way to go."

They set the raft afloat again and started down the river, listening to the whistles, chirpings, and clickings of the rain forest. The sounds made by animals hidden in the jungle reminded Mia and Ricky just how wonderful and mysterious the rain forest truly was.

"Hey, look, guys!" cried Ricky, pointing to the sky. It was dark now, and the moon sat full in the night sky. It looked strangely golden. "Doesn't that look awesome?"

"Look at our skin," said Mia, lifting her arm to show them.

The strange-colored moonlight was making them all look golden. El Dorado was with them. Ricky and Mia thought about Sipu and his secret tribe and the great gift that he had given them. He had shown them some of the real treasures of the rain forest. They would keep their word and do whatever they could to protect it. Their visit to El Dorado would remain a treasured secret forever.

The Legend of
EL DORADO

When the Spanish reached Colombia in the 16th century, they found the land inhabited by native people they named Indians. The Spanish first heard of the legend of El Dorado from the Indians.

Legend said that somewhere in the jungle was a kingdom rich in gold and precious stones. When a new ruler was appointed, he would cover himself in powdered gold and appear before his people by a lake. He would float on a raft to the center of the lake. Then he would throw gold and precious stones into the water as offerings to their god.

Today it is believed that the legend was based on a ceremony performed by the people who lived around Lake Guatavita.

Many tried to find the riches of El Dorado, but the kingdom was never found. Although El Dorado remained undiscovered, large quantities of gold and jewels were plundered and taken from other native peoples. Entire tribes and cultures were wiped out.

Glossary

breastplate armor worn to protect the chest

canopy the leafy branches of rain forest trees forming a dense cover

canyon a narrow river valley with steep sides

crescents curved shapes that taper to two points

El Dorado a legendary city of South America containing great treasure

exotic strikingly unusual, strange

exquisite of rare beauty, superbly made

fate destiny; fortune

flares devices that produce a brightly colored flame; used as a signal in an emergency

global positioning system a device that can work out exact coordinates of where you are in the world. It works by bouncing your signal off a satellite.

hammocks pieces of net or canvas hung between two supports

machete a large, heavy knife with a wide blade

motto a phrase or sentence that is a rule for a person's behavior

nugget a small lump of gold

ravine a long, narrow valley shaped by water

ripple little waves on the surface of calm water

spellbound fascinated, entranced

survival able to go on living in spite of great danger or difficulties

tribe a group of people of the same race, who have the same language, beliefs, and customs

whirlpools small areas in a river or sea where the water swirls quickly around and around. Objects floating nearby are pulled into the center.

Titles in This Series

Quest for the Cup

On the Trail of the Golden Man

In Search of the Egyptian Queen

Digging for Buried Treasure

Diving for the Ghost Galleon

Racing for the Birdman

Decoding the Mayan Marvels

Saving Atlantis

To Larry L. Meyer, *Editor of* Westways
and his Staff

Contents

IT IS EASIER TO SAY what is Californian than what is a classic. By Californian is meant books which treat of the State, not necessarily written by natives. Of the thirty-one authors represented, only four were born in the Golden State: Gertrude Atherton, Jack London, Lincoln Steffens, John Steinbeck. Place of birth and literary genius are rarely connected. Dana and Stevenson were transient residents, and yet what books are more Californian than *Two Years Before the Mast* and *The Silverado Squatters?*

What is a classic? It could be defined as a book read by more than a single generation. What gives a book long life? Style, I say. And what is style? I see it as a mysterious fusion of fact and imagination, of vision and vigor, present in a writer's mastery of language. If this occurs—and it does so only with unpredictable infrequency—then the result has lasting power to attract and to hold readers, whether the work be novel, poem, narrative essay, or history.

Throughout these books is the dominant element of California itself, the Golden State, whose history and lore, landscape and weather, of country-side and cities, have inspired my chosen writers.

Because of the many ways that California has affected writers, the state has fostered numerous classics. From them I have selected these few to write about. My choices are arbitrary, determined by my own temperament and tastes. They are not exclusive. Readers with other biases may add or subtract. My preference is for literature. I have chosen only a few works of historical Californiana, and then only when they could also be classed as literature, as in the case of Bolton, Cleland, Bell, and Lummis. The way is clear for someone else to make a selection of the classics of history, such as the books by Alfred Robinson, Walter Colton, Edwin Bryant, William Heath Davis, Harris Newmark, and Susanna Dakin.

My work is based on original sources, that is, on the authors' books, manuscripts, journals, and letters, as well as on biographies and other reference works. I have also talked with kinfolk and friends of the writers. Nothing has been invented or imagined. I have probed into the sources of each classic, seeking what led to its creation.

The mysterious creative process interests me the most. In no two writers does it work in the same way. Literary inspiration can be understood, if at all, by working backward from its results, by following ways leading to that secret place where mind and heart, reason and emotion, met in fruitful marriage.

In the interests of readability I have fleshed over the bones of whatever scholarship is mine. There are no footnotes. Brief reading lists at the end of each chapter do not include all of the previous citations to books and articles. I have retained the specific data on the reading and research each chapter entailed. If readers are curious about sources of my statements, they may write to me in care of my publisher. Eventually this data will go to the Bancroft Library.

This book therefore is for reading not reference, and I hope it will find readers of all ages. Young people disillusioned with the present will find here evidences of a creative past worthy of respect. Older readers who do not recognize much of what passes today for literature as relevant to their experience and needs will be grateful for these literary legacies. The writers and their books represent a literary tradition of which all Californians may be proud.

I have not written a history of California literature. Such a work would include all the writers, major and minor, would describe foothills as well as mountains. I have dwelt only on some of the summits. A few omissions require comment. George Sterling and Ambrose Bierce are remembered more for their personalities and influence on others than for their own poetry and prose; Joaquin Miller and Edwin Markham for a single poem each. Except for Charis Weston, living writers are not included, although it was hard to omit Kenneth Rexroth, California's leading man of letters, William Everson (formerly Brother Antoninus), our greatest poet since Jeffers, and William Saroyan's boyhood autobiography *My Name is Aram*.

Chapter arrangement is roughly by region, then chronologically. It proceeds from the desert to the mountains and seacoast, the Bay region and coastal valleys, thence to pastoral Southern California and its urban transformation. A theme common to several chapters is the journey, beginning with the greatest of all, the Anza expeditions.

Active work on this book began in 1967, although I have been preparing for it all my reading life which began about 1912. Retirement in 1966 from academic and professional life, during which my writing was a side-line, meant that I was free to devote full time to it. "Concentration is what a man needs to bring his mind to harvest," wrote Dr. William Carlos Williams. "To drain off the good we must find quietude."

In 1967, thanks to a Guggenheim Fellowship, I travelled 20,000 miles around California in a nimble Porsche, visiting and revisiting the locales of the books to be written about. The great lengthwise roads were long familiar; new were some of the lesser crossroads that traverse the mountains, valleys, and deserts. It was a wonderful year, during which I followed book trails from the hot southeastern corner at the Yuma Crossing, where the Colorado River divides Arizona and California, to the cold northwestern corner at Crescent City, near where Oregon begins. Although parts of the state are overpopulated and the air polluted, greater parts remain unpeopled and unspoiled. The future is veiled as, fortunately, the future always is. I have become reconciled to creation and destruction being eternally coupled. Unless the grain perish. . . .

Although not a native son—I was born in the District of Columbia, hence am a man without a state—I have lived in California since December, 1906 (I had then reached the age of four months), and I have long regarded the Golden State as my homeland. I have no patience with sectional Californians who suffer from regional myopeia, or with feuding Angelenos and Franciscans.

The writing has been done in various places—Middletown,

Boston, London, Malibu—and such is the power of the imagination, that California was with me wherever I went. If I were exiled from California, I could draw a topographical map from memory, so deeply have its configurations entered my consciousness. Seen from the air or seen from the ground, in all seasons and weathers, California's beauty never palls; and it has been blessed with great writers to praise its beauty. They have done for California something of what Yeats called on Irish writers to do for Ireland. "I would have our writers and craftsmen master this history and these legends," he wrote, "and fix upon their memory the appearance of mountains and rivers and make it all visible again in their arts, so that Irishmen, even though they had gone a thousand miles away, would still be in their own country."

Reading books is good, re-reading good books is better. Although they seem to have changed, it is we, their readers, who change, as we learn more about life by living it. California too has changed, is changing, will change, and not always for the good. Old landscapes and seascapes become unrecognizable. Even the cities are not safe, as the sound of the bulldozer is heard in the land. This is bewildering and sad to those who have affection for fixed landmarks.

In these creative books, however, California will never change. This is the untarnished gold, the immutable treasure of literature, and the priceless heritage of each generation of readers. Those who cherish in memory a vanished land, their own California, will find it forever inviolate in these books.

L.C.P.

Casa Dos Vistas
Malibu, California

Acknowledgements

MUCH OF THE PLEASURE in writing this book has come from fellowship with people who have helped me. In addition to aid of a fellowship from the John Simon Guggenheim Memorial Foundation, Gordon N. Ray, president, I profited as a Fellow of the Center for Advanced Studies, Wesleyan University, Middletown, Connecticut. Its director, Philip Hallie and staff and director emeritus, Paul Horgan, became cherished colleagues. In a Wesleyan seminar in Southwestern literature, I read several chapters to my students, all four of them—Larry Gross, Charlie Hill, Jack Michel, and Ian Vickery—and I shall not forget their responsiveness during those wintry evenings together in my study at the CAS. The staff of Wesleyan's Olin Memorial Library was ever helpful, and I wish to thank Librarians Wyman W. Parker, Joan Jurale, Gertrude McKenna, and Brian Rogers for their kindness. At nearby Yale University's Beinecke Library, Librarians Herman W. Liebert, Kenneth Nesheim, Donald Gallup, Archibald Hanna, and Marjorie Wynne, aided me. In London I was also well served by K. C. Harrison, City Librarian of Westminster, and by Stanley Gillam and Douglas Matthews of the London Library in St. James's Square. My niece, Marcia Powell Lawrence, helped us find Bret Harte's grave in Surrey.

Anyone working in the field of Californiana soon becomes a debtor to five great California libraries—Bancroft, State, Huntington, Southwest Museum, and UCLA. I owe much to the knowledge and courtesy of the following associates of these institutions: James D. Hart, director, John Barr Tompkins, chief of public services, William Roberts, his assistant, and J. R. K. Kantor, university archivist, all of the Bancroft Library; Allan R. Ottley, chief California librarian and his assistant, Mary Ellen Bailey, California State Library; James Thorpe, director, Robert O. Dougan, librarian, Carey S. Bliss, curator of rare books, Mary Isabel Fry, reference librarian, Edwin H. Carpenter, Jr., bibliographer, at the Henry E. Huntington Library; Carl S. Dentzel, director, Ruth M. Christensen, librarian, and Joan L. West, assistant librarian, Southwest Museum; Wilbur J. Smith, head, and Brooke Whiting, assistant head, and their winsome and willing staff, Department of Special Collections, University of California, Los Angeles, as well as members of UCLA's Research Library reference department, headed by Robert L. Collison, and the College library staff, directed by Norah E. Jones, especially Sylvia Gear.

I was aided also by these libraries and librarians: Tyrus G. Harmsen, Occidental College; Linda L. West, Monterey Bay Area Cooperative Library System; Donald L. Davidson, University of California, Santa Barbara; John E. Smith, University of California, Irvine; Richard H. Dillon, Sutro Library; Alice Matthiesen and staff, Tehama County Library; Frances C. Richardson, 20th Century Fox Studios; Frances Holbrook, UCLA Law Library; William H. Bond and Carolyn Jakeman, Houghton Library; Robert D. Hart, Santa Barbara Public Library; Warren Roberts and Mary Hirth, Humanities Research Center, University of Texas; Marion L. Buckner, San Diego Public Library; Robert L. Talmadge, University of Illinois; Gordon R. Williams, Center for Research Libraries, Chicago; David A. Randall, Lilly Library; Stephen T. Riley, Massachusetts Historical Society.

By correspondence and in person the following individuals aided me in a variety of ways: Rev. John Francis Bannon, S. J.; Duncan Brent; Paul Brooks; Ralph Cassady, Jr.; John Walton Caughey; Dwight L. Clarke; Robert S. Cleland; Mrs. Nat Deverich; Glen Dawson; Philip Durham; David Dworski; E. I. Edwards; Marjory and Francis P. Farquhar; Dudley C. Gordon; Leland Hawkins; Franklin K. Hoyt; Harry C. James; Olive Jones; Elizabeth Coffman Kieley; William F. Kimes; Alfred A. Knopf; George Kummer; Mrs. Harrison Leussler; Jay Martin; Don Meadows; Frank Moore; Margaret Nordhoff Morrison; Blair Gordon Newell; Doyce B. Nunis, Jr.; Scott O'Dell; Rodman W. Paul; Paul Popenoe; Wilkie H. Powell; J. E. Reynolds; Wilmer R. Shields; Norman B. Shoemaker; Walter de Steiguer; Brett Weston; Richard P. Wheat; Thurman Wilkins; Mary Nordhoff

Williams; Charis Wilson; Leon Wilson; Ella Winter; Jake Zeitlin; Dr. Henry G. Bieler.

I owe much to my old friend, W. W. Robinson. He relieved me as book reviewer for *Westways*. For many years his counsel has guided me. The final manuscript of this work benefitted from his critical reading of it.

The book's dedication indicates my gratitude to Larry L. Meyer, whose original idea got me started and whose encouragement kept me going for three years. His staff, Davis Dutton, James Gebbie, and Ruth Powell, in particular, are also to be thanked.

Anna Marie Hager of the Automobile Club's Public Relations department, went to far lengths in gathering the illustrations. I am grateful to her. She and Everett Hager merit thanks for the Index.

Cordial and efficient help was unfailingly given me by Ellen Cole and staff of UCLA's Central Stenographic Bureau.

My publisher and lifelong friend, Ward Ritchie and I acknowledge permission of the Automobile Club of Southern California to reprint these chapters, all of which appeared first in *Westways*. Readers of that periodical offered corrections, suggestions, and encouragement, all of which has been helpful in the revisions I have made. This book culminates a long relationship with *Westways'* editors, beginning in 1934 with Phil Townsend Hanna, continuing with Patrice Manahan, and flourishing now with Larry Meyer. My fruitfulness as a writer owes much to them.

My wife Fay was with me all the way, at home and abroad, during the seemingly endless reading and re-reading, the writing and re-writing. She heard all the chapters read aloud and repeatedly clarified their meaning. Without her there would have been no book.

Bibliographical Note

A SEPARATE PUBLICATION would be required to list all the books, pamphlets, periodicals, and manuscript sources I have read and referred to. Instead, I have concluded each chapter with a reading list of the essential works by and about that author. In addition I offer here a few references to some general works I have found helpful.

There is no bibliography of California literature, as there is of California history, nor is there a history of California literature such as Van Wyck Brooks's monumental work on New England. The nearest things to it are Franklin Walker's three volumes: *San Francisco's Literary Frontier* (New York, Alfred A. Knopf, 1947), *A Literary History of Southern California* (Berkeley and Los Angeles, University of California Press, 1951), and *The Seacoast of Bohemia, An Account of Early Carmel* (San Francisco, Book Club of California, 1966). In *Libros Californianos* (Los Angeles, Jake Zeitlin, 1931, revised 1958), Phil Townsend Hanna wrote perceptively of literary as well as historical Californiana. *The Zamorano Eighty* (Los Angeles, Zamorano Club, 1945) is an annotated bibliography of books about California which several members of Los Angeles's Zamorano Club chose as the best. The Book Club of California has published many items of literary interest, some of them edited by James D. Hart. *California's Literary Heritage* by John and La Ree Caughey is a discriminating anthology (Los Angeles, Ward Ritchie Press, 1962). Carey McWilliams's *Southern California Country* (New York, Duell, Sloane and Pearce, 1946) and Richard G. Lillard's *Eden In Jeopardy* (New York, Alfred A. Knopf, 1966) are provocative and illuminating books on the lands south of Tehachapi which have given me new insight into our past and present.

Paperback publishing has been a boon to readers. Most of the popular California authors are now represented in these inexpensive reprints, often introduced by contemporary authorities.

xvii

I hope my work will revive interest in and lead to the reprinting of less popular titles that have become rare and costly. California's libraries and bookstores are among the country's best. Readers in search of the books I have written about will be rewarded by visits to these centers of light and life.

California Classics

Anza's California
Expeditions

HERBERT EUGENE BOLTON

1

EVERYTHING ABOUT IT is classic, epic, legendary; the venture and
its leader, the chroniclers, and lastly the historian who, a century and a half later, discovered, translated, and published the
records of this great achievement.

What was it? The first overland colonizing expedition into
California, an heroic trek in 1776 from Sonora, Mexico through
what is now Arizona, across the Colorado River at Yuma, over
desert and mountains to Mission San Gabriel, the Monterey
Presidio, and finally to journey's end, at the site of San Francisco's beginnings as a presidio and pueblo.

Led by Captain Juan Bautista de Anza, one of the greatest of
all frontiersmen, and recorded in diaries by him and the Franciscan fathers, Pedro Font and Francisco Garcés, the colonists to
the number of two hundred forty men, women, and children,
plus a thousand head of stock, made this journey of 1600 miles
in drought, cold, rain and snow, with the loss of only a single
human life, that of a woman in childbirth. Not only did her
offspring live, two others were born en route, one on Christmas
Eve in the mountains above the Borrego Desert, and all survived
to become Californians.

Too much of the discovery, colonization, and exploitation of
the West is fraught with violence—dispossession and butchery

3

of the natives, civil strife, rampant greed and rape of resources—so it is with relief that we come upon the peaceful motivation and creative realization of Anza and his band. No Indians were killed, no one was cheated or robbed; the arduous journey was disciplined and orderly.

The intention in planting the colony was to secure California for Spain against the encroachment of Russians and English. Hitherto the colonies at San Diego and Monterey, and the few other missions, were supplied by sea, a long and uncertain voyage on which precious vessels were often lost. Urgently needed was a land link between Mexico and Alta California, which would serve also as a market for Sonoran crops.

In the late 1760's and early 1770's Father Garcés had made almost solitary *entradas* into the desert regions, and later as far as the southern San Joaquin Valley, commemorated today by the noble statue of this hardy Franciscan which stands in a traffic circle at Bakersfield. As early as 1769 and again in 1772, Anza proposed to seek an overland route. Then in 1774, with Garcés and an Indian guide, Sebastián Taraval known as El Peregrino (The Pilgrim), Anza volunteered to lead a small pathfinding group clear to the coast. His far-seeing sponsor was the Viceroy of Mexico, Don Antonio Bucareli, one of Spain's ablest colonial administrators.

Anza was no tenderfoot. He was born, raised, and seasoned on the northern Sonora frontier. His grandfather had come there from Spain, and his father gave his life in the wars to keep the Apaches at bay. Before his death he had imparted to his son a dream of an overland route to the Pacific.

Anza was born at Fronteras in 1735 and educated in Mexico City by the Franciscans. He rose steadily in the frontier forces which were constantly engaged in holding the line against the raiding savages. As a member of the presidial aristocracy, he represented all that was best in Spain's New World empire—a man cultured, brave, strong yet compassionate, far-seeing, and of incorruptible character, a peer of Coronado and Portolá, a pathfinder and leader matched in the American expansion only by Lewis and Clark.

In order to convince the Viceroy of the practicality of his vision of an overland route, Anza and his companions kept diaries of the two expeditions, the first made to mark the route, the second to lead the colonists into the promised land. These diaries were forwarded to Bucareli in Mexico City, and by him to the King of Spain.

By nothing short of a miracle, they (or copies) and the correspondence between Anza and Bucareli survived Spain's loss of Mexico and the subsequent revolutions and violence. Then in the early years of this century they were discovered, correlated, translated and published by a young American professor in one of the greatest achievements in all of western historiography.

Anza's California Expeditions was published in 1930 by the University of California Press in five stout volumes, edited by Professor Herbert Eugene Bolton, and subsidized by Regent Sidney M. Ehrman. Everything was included in the set—Bolton's narrative of the saga, Anza's, Font's, and others' diaries, the documents and correspondence between the principals, and field photographs taken by Bolton in retracing the route of the colonists. Not only did he carry out research in the archives, he trailed Anza by horse, auto, and on foot, devoting more than two decades to this rugged field work.

From 1908 to 1930 Bolton toiled to perfect his edition of Anza, and in volume three his preface called "Retracing the Trail" is a laconic summary of his labors. "I think it safe to say," he wrote, "that no pioneer routes of such great length have ever been so thoroughly explored and identified. Anza travelled twice and back from Mexico City to Monterey (and once to Suisun Bay), a distance of more than ten thousand miles. Between these points I have retraced exactly or approximately his entire journeys."

Upon its appearance in 1930 *Anza's California Expeditions* was recognized as the classic it is. The University Press failed, however, to keep it in print, and it became a costly item on the secondhand market. Then in 1966 it was reprinted by Russell and Russell at $75 for the five volumes, a large sum but still a bargain. In 1939 Alfred A. Knopf issued volume 1 only as *Outpost of Empire*, consisting of Bolton's narrative of the expeditions.

Herbert E. Bolton

6

Many libraries have this volume, or a reprint, on their shelves, and it is a good way to enter the sea of the great work.

How easy it is now to retrace Anza's trail, requiring only a couple of days to make the journey that took him 130 days, including 88 of actual travel! Good roads, the Colorado dammed and bridged, the desert cooled by air conditioning, vehicles that don't break down, plus thermos jugs and taped music. Only by reading and imagination can one regain the past and experience the achievement of Juan Bautista de Anza and his followers.

Thanks to his and Font's diaries we can relive the epic in all its extraordinary detail. If the moviemakers should ever decide to go deeper into history, beyond their obsession with frontier violence, a great film could be made of the Anza expedition, one with the sweep of Flaherty's classic *Nanook of the North*. Authenticity of clothing and equipment could be ensured by using the outfitting lists for the expedition. Anza left nothing to chance. Success was the result of meticulous planning and attention to details of clothing, provisions, and travel gear.

All the elements of epic are present, held in balance by the strong captain. At the crossing of the Colorado the Yuman Indians might have destroyed the immigrants. They were one of the bravest of the southwestern tribes, a people never subjected by the Spaniards. Father Garcés had been there earlier and made friends with them. Garcés was capable of quickly "going native." According to his fellow priest, Pedro Font, when he was with them Garcés lived as an Indian, squatting on his hams around the fire, and sharing their unsavory messes without benefit of knife or fork.

Anza was more civilized. He came as peacemaker not conqueror, and he was fortunate in finding as the Yuman chief one of the most remarkable of all American Indians. Though he was called by the Spaniards Salvador Palma, the asthmatic chief's Yuman name was Olleyquotoquiebe, which translates roughly as Old Wheezy. Like Anza, Captain Palma was a natural leader and administrator. He liked Anza and the Spaniards, and aided and protected the hazardous crossing of the river. Imagine taking 240 people and their animals safely across the Colorado, then three or four feet deep even at the ford, without benefit of bridges or boats! Palma also served a watermelon feast, digging up from sandy storage a couple thousand of the ripe gourds and inviting the parched travellers to gorge on them.

Then came the sand dunes, there to this day, followed by the wasteland and the snowy Laguna Mountains. The time was December. The crossing was perilous. Anza had to divide his party in order not to exhaust the waterholes where they made camp. Many cattle and horses were lost from thirst and later from freezing.

Font was a fussy Franciscan, a mathematician with a passion for precise, rational behavior. Anza had a deeper understanding of the people in his charge. At the end of a hard day's march, or when the divided parties were safely reunited, he issued brandy and let the colonists rejoice. His only rule was that drunkenness be confined to the tents. When Anza's and the priest's cook got drunk and couldn't prepare dinner, Font was angry. The next morning he scolded the commander. Anza replied with moderation Font wrote in his diary, "although somewhat offended, and without any signs of repentance." Anza was abstemious in food and drink, whereas poor Font never got enough to eat. Font also was ill throughout the journey, and this made him more critical and cross. Still he wrote one of the best of all travel diaries, full of precise and accurate observation, lavish in detail, and spiced with gossip.

At another reunion the colonists celebrated with a fandango. "It was somewhat discordant," the blue-nosed Font recorded, "and a very bold widow who came with the expedition sang some verses which were not at all nice, applauded and cheered by all the crowd." Whereupon the sweetheart of Feliciana Arballo, the merry widow, began to beat her. Anza restrained him. Font declared she deserved a beating. "Perhaps she does," admitted Anza, "but not that hard a one."

"He guarded against such excesses," Font noted, "but not against the scandal of the fandango, which lasted until very late." That must have been a wild night in camp.

Another annoyance to Father Font was the Yumans' practice

of painting their bodies. The girl he chose to reproach was one of Palma's several daughters, a strong swimmer who led all the others. She apparently clad herself in only a thick coat of red ochre. When Font suggested that she wash herself, she countered that she did not know how and that he should do it for her.

This was a challenge Font could not ignore. "To her great pleasure and that of those assembled I did give her a good soaping and succeeded in removing the paint. Then I gave her a mirror in order that she might see that this was good; and looking at herself, she broke out laughing, 'Ajot, ajot,' which means 'Good, good.' "

The Yuma chapter ended in tragedy. Although upon his return after leaving the colonists in California, Anza hoped to consolidate his good relations with the Yumans and establish a permanent colony on the Colorado, he was ordered to New Mexico as governor, to pacify the warring Apaches, Utes, and Comanches. But first he took Palma to Mexico City to meet the Viceroy.

Father Garcés and other Franciscans remained at a mission on the river below Yuma, and in 1779 a colony of soldiers and settlers arrived. Anza never returned—Anza the wise administrator who in 1774, upon his first encounter with the Yumans, had written to Viceroy Bucareli, "those people are incapable of doing any evil if they are treated with the kindness which is due their simplicity."

The illiterate Spaniards dispossessed and brutalized the Yumans. Captain Palma felt betrayed. After two years of suffering, he led the revolt of 1781, in which several dozen priests and soldiers and settlers were killed, their women and children enslaved. Palma wished to spare Garcés, but was dissuaded. Later the Spaniards recovered the martyred priests' bodies and reburied them at Tubutama in Sonora. They were never able to subjugate the Yumans, even by the treacherous tactics of Captain Pedro Fages. Palma bore a charmed life, even surviving shots fired at him at close range. A few years later he was reported living on an island in the river at the mouth of the Gila. Then he vanishes from history. To this day although Garcés' death is annually observed with a mass, there is no remembrance of Palma.

These happenings and Anza's career in New Mexico are not told in the Bolton work. They are the subject of Jack B. Forbes' *Warriors of the Colorado*, and of *Forgotten Frontiers* by Alfred B. Thomas, a Bolton disciple, who tells the story of Anza's decade, 1777-87, as governor of New Mexico, during which he forged a defensive alliance between Ute and Apache against the Comanche scourge. Thomas ends his book with a moving peroration:

"Spain's North American frontiers are forgotten frontiers. The sweep of the Anglo-Saxon has blurred their silhouette and fathered the illusion that western history runs only with the nineteenth century. This delightfully simple legend summed up in the 'Westward Movement' is unjust. Indian civilizations, submerged in the glorification of the pioneer, project their significance. The shambles of extermination graced the Nordic westward-ho. No such imprint mars the scutcheon of Spain in the West. There the Indian bears the mark."

"Apache, Comanche and Ute, riding with the other three horsemen, drouth, famine and disease, bade fair to destroy the Pueblo. For them the Spaniards came as saviors. Against starvation the padre's prayer and Spanish grain supported them; barbarian inroads met the steel of Spanish courage. The unwritten record of this heroic defense of New Mexico is limned with Spanish blood that alone saved the distinctive Pueblo Southwest and dulled the edge of surrounding savagery. Indians whose lush lands the English coveted have struck their tipis. Enchanted Zuñi still warms the desert skyline where the Spanish standard lifted."

Juan Bautista de Anza towers above his time, dwarfing such johnny-come-latelys as Frémont and Carson and such scum as Billy the Kid and his ilk. There is no widespread remembrance or honor rendered him in California, although there are Anza statues in Riverside and San Francisco, and the vast Anza-Borrego State Park, through which he trekked toward mountains and sea, perpetuates his name. If he had faults time has obscured them. His courage, wisdom and compassion remain clear.

His diary of the California *entradas* is mostly prosaic, lacking

the liveliness and humor of Font's. There is however one entry
of moving emotion which affords insight into the soul of this
frontiersman. It was written on Sunday, April 14, 1776, after
leaving the presidio at Monterey where the colonists were resting
before Lieutenant Moraga was to lead them on to the bay of
San Francisco:

"This day has been the saddest one experienced by this presidio since its founding. When I mounted my horse in the plaza,
the people whom I have led from their fatherlands, to which I
am returning, remembering the good or bad treatment which
they have experienced at my hands while they have been under
my orders, most of them, especially the feminine sex, came to
me sobbing with tears, which they declared they were shedding
more because of my departure than of their exile, filling me
with compassion. They showered me with embraces, best wishes,
and praises which I do not merit. But in remembrance of them,
and of the gratitude which I feel to all, and the affection which
I have had for them ever since I recruited them, and in eulogy
of their faithfulness, for up to now I have not seen a single sign
of desertion in anyone of those whom I brought to remain in this
exile, I may be permitted to record this praise of a people who,
as time goes on, will be very useful to the monarchy in whose
service they have voluntarily left their relatives and their father-
land, which is all they have to lose."

After a decade as governor of New Mexico, Anza returned to
the Pimería Alta as captain of the Tucson presidio, then died
suddenly at Arizpe, Sonora, at the age of 53. In 1963 his remains
were disinterred and reburied in a marble sarcophagus under
the floor of the church of Nuestra Señora de la Asunción.

We have thus accounted for Anza, Garcés, and Palma—Font
died in 1781 at Pitíque, Sonora—leaving only Bolton, who died
at Berkeley in his 83rd year. There is no statue of him on the
Berkeley campus, but there might well be one, for he is among
the titans who by intelligence, imagination, persistence and
stamina made it into a great university. Greatness has a price,
and there have always been those at Berkeley who were willing
to pay it. Presidents Benjamin Ide Wheeler and Robert Gordon

Sproul, Provost Monroe Deutsch, regents Phoebe Apperson Hearst, James K. Moffit, and Sidney Ehrman, professors Henry Morse Stephens, Charles Mills Gayley, and Herbert Eugene Bolton, to name a few, are such heroic figures in the university's hall of fame.

The Bolton saga at Berkeley began in 1906 several years before he arrived, for it was then that the University acquired the Bancroft Library. This proved the research magnet that drew the young professor from Stanford to Berkeley, as two years earlier Stanford had lured him from the University of Texas.

There is no accounting, however, for the earlier transformation of the Wisconsin farm boy, born in 1870, into the foremost Western historian of all time, although certain influences are apparent. In what he called "Random Memories of an Admiring Brother," Professor Frederick E. Bolton wrote in *Arizona and the West* of Herbert's formative years as farm laborer, student, and neophyte teacher. At the University of Wisconsin he was turned from Law to History by the inspired teaching of Professor Frederick Jackson Turner. At the University of Pennsylvania, where he took his Ph.D., he was further motivated by Professor John Bach MacMaster. Various steps led him to the University of Texas in Austin. There Bolton taught himself Spanish in order to spend his summers researching in the archives of Mexico. As a researcher he proved both bulldozer and fine-toothed comber.

Legend has it that once when he was laboring in the archives of Juarez, Pancho Villa and his guerillas swept into town. Everyone vamoosed but Bolton and two peons. Villa shot the peons, then turned to Bolton. The young academic not only talked Villa out of shooting him, but he persuaded the bandit leader to appoint him the official archivist of Juarez, with a bodyguard to ensure his safety.

Bolton was always a great talker. By the time I reached Berkeley in 1936 as a graduate student in librarianship, Bolton was 66 and still talking. One tuned in on his monologue and then tuned out; it apparently never ended, and it was redolent of sand and sage and musty archives, of a lifetime's consecration to the writing and teaching of history.

12

Bolton spent the last forty-three years of his life on the Berkeley campus, at least based there, as he mined the Mexican and Spanish archives and rolled up mileage in the southwestern field. He served as Sather Professor of History and Director of the Bancroft Library. The latter became known as the Bolton Factory, turning out M.A.'s and Ph.D.'s in vast numbers. He was a great teacher as well as researcher. Let him tell the story of his most popular course:

"I brashly announced a lower division lecture course in the history of all the Americas in one synthesis. I did not expect any students in such an unheard of course, and made no preparation for it. The first day 772 registered, to my dismay, and the second semester 1248. There were no textbooks, no maps, no apparatus. That year I worked harder than ever before. I spent day and night reading, made a day-by-day syllabus of one mimeographed page, and later published the syllabus and maps in a 300-page book. For a quarter of a century I lectured to more than a thousand students twice a week."

Graduates and books were not his only products en masse. He and his wife Gertrude had six daughters and one son. Legends have gathered around his memory. One is that he was standing on the curb one evening, waiting patiently, when one of his daughters drove up beside him and said, "May I take you home, Dr. Bolton?" "Thank you," he replied, "I am waiting for my daughter."

The light in Bolton's office burned into the small hours. When accused of overworking, Bolton said that he always left his light on while he went to the movies. A friend planning to drive from Berkeley to Boston asked Bolton to make up an itinerary. The historian did so, in a series of one-day stops. At every stop a Bolton disciple was teaching. Bolton said of himself that he had to behave throughout the United States because he had a former student in every city and town.

UCLA's John Walton Caughey is one of the most prolific of Bolton's protegés and the author of a lively memoir of his teacher which concludes:

"Bolton's ideas may have been rebuffed, but his writings have

Outpost of Empire. New York, Alfred A. Knopf, 1939. Vol. 1 of the above set. Also, Russell reprint, 1966.

JOHN FRANCIS BANNON, editor
Bolton and the Spanish Borderlands. Norman, University of Oklahoma Press, 1964.

J. N. BOWMAN and ROBERT F. HEIZER
Anza and the Northwestern Frontier of New Spain. Los Angeles, Southwest Museum, 1967.

JACK B. FORBES
Warriors of the Colorado; the Yumas of the Quechan Nation and Their Neighbors. Norman, University of Oklahoma Press, 1965.

ALFRED B. THOMAS
Forgotten Frontiers; A Study of the Spanish Indian Policy of Juan Bautista de Anza, Governor of New Mexico, 1777-1787. Norman, University of Oklahoma Press, 1932; reissued in 1969.

Photograph of Herbert E. Bolton, courtesy of Bancroft Library.

The Journey of the Flame

WALTER NORDHOFF

2

"RIPENESS IS ALL." The words are Shakespeare's in *King Lear*, an example of the poet's genius for succinct utterance. A reading of California's literary classics affords differing instances of that time of ripeness when a writer creates his masterpiece; sometimes early in his career, more often in the middle time of life, rarely at the end. Extreme examples are *Two Years Before the Mast*, Dana's book, written when he had barely broached his twenties, and *Ramona*, completed by Mrs. Jackson at the end of her life, in a winning race with death. The fortunate writer dies at zenith, as Helen Hunt Jackson and Frank Norris did, and is spared the sad fate suffered by Bret Harte, Raymond Chandler, and Robinson Jeffers, for example, all of whom lived beyond their literary prime.

Which brings us to Walter Nordhoff, whose masterpiece, an historical novel called *The Journey of the Flame*, was published under the pseudonym, Antonio de Fierro Blanco. Begun after Nordhoff had reached his seventies, it appeared in 1933 when he was seventy-five. Is there another example of a writer's first book ripening so late in his life?

If it is true that wisdom comes late, after much experience and long reflection, it is also true that it is usually accompanied by diminished creative strength. This was not the case of Walter

17

Nordhoff, whose long life stretched from 1858 to 1937. He was not the man described by Browning in lines from "Andrea del Sarto": *In this world, who can do a thing, will not; and who would do it, cannot . . . and thus we half-men struggle.*

Walter Nordhoff was a whole man to the end of his life, and a fortunate man in that his will and power and creative imagination remained equally strong in that final period when ripeness was all. He was fortunate also in being able to retire at sixty-five. In 1923 he settled in Santa Barbara, and proceeded to demonstrate the truth of Dr. William Carlos Williams's dictum: "Much of the world's greatest writing has waited on a removal from the world of affairs for its doing."

It should not be assumed that Walter Nordhoff was a beginning writer at sixty-five. On the contrary. Born of a writing father, he fathered a writer, and in young manhood he worked throughout Europe as correspondent for the *New York Herald*. We are concerned with three generations of accomplished writers: Charles Nordhoff (1830-1901), sailor, adventurer, newspaper correspondent, author of romantic sea stories and many other books. He also wrote the most popular California booster book of all time—*California for Health, Wealth, and Residence* (1872), which sold three million copies and stimulated a never ending flow of immigration to the Golden State. Charles Bernard Nordhoff (1887-1947), Walter's older son, achieved his fame as half of the writing team of Nordhoff and Hall, authors of the trilogy, *Mutiny on the Bounty*, *Men Against the Sea*, and *Pitcairn's Island*. Still another son, Franklin (1894-1956) was a Buellton rancher and author of *Fruit of the Earth* (1955), a book of sketches published first in Santa Barbara and Santa Ynez newspapers, about outdoor life on the West Coast and the Nordhoff ranch in Baja California.

All of the Nordhoffs led travelled, adventurous lives. Why did Walter alone adopt a pseudonym? Why did he seek to conceal, at the same time that he was compelled to reveal?

For various reasons, the most obvious of which was that he did not wish to trade on a name made famous by his father and his son. Another was his character. He was an old-fashioned gentleman of formal courtesy and deep reserve which served to protect a sensitive nature from worldly intrusion. Although he was a born writer, with a compulsion to record and communicate, he wanted also to keep the world at arm's length.

There was still another reason for his not wishing *The Journey of the Flame* to be known as the work of Walter Nordhoff. It had to do with land, with the Rancho Ramajal in Baja California, a feudal tract of 50,000 acres, including the cape called Punta Banda on the Bay of Todos Santos, fifteen miles south of Ensenada. It had been deeded to Charles Nordhoff in 1888 by the Mexican International Company, an Anglo-American group which had acquired most of northern Baja from the Mexican government, with the intention of developing it commercially. After the success of Charles Nordhoff's Alta California book, the company engaged him to write *Peninsular California*, hoping it would do as much for Baja. Title to the huge ranch was their way of compensating him.

After graduation in 1879 in mining engineering from Yale's Sheffield Scientific School, Walter Nordhoff went abroad as a newspaper correspondent in his father's footsteps, and there during postings to various European capitals, he developed extraordinary linguistic ability, as well as a life-long passion for all things Spanish.

Thus it was natural for him to respond to his father's invitation to help him manage the new ranch in Lower California. Walter was then thirty-two years old, married to Sarah Cope Whitall of Philadelphia, and the father of baby Charles, who had been born in London. Theirs was an adventurous move to the primitive country south of the border. Writing years later, Sarah Nordhoff recalled what it had been like in 1890:

"I never forget the arrival in San Diego, after dark, and the luxurious bedroom at Hotel del Coronado recently opened, with the sound of the surf outside. The next night we took the small steamer for Ensenada and arrived at daybreak. How strange and wild that arrival was! The beautiful bay, the Mexicans speaking Spanish, the dusty little town, the point with its very agreeable colony of English people—and the lovely long drive on the mesa and through the river bottom to the ranch house on the flat. I had a very sleepy little boy of three and a half years on my lap during that rough drive, and I wondered how I should manage to make a home there where he might flourish. It was a strange experience for a young woman who only knew housekeeping in London and Berlin; to be put down in our lonely settlement, with everything to organize, sources of supply very vague or distant, little knowledge of country life and hardly any knowledge of cookery. Father was wonderful in his sureness and hope—and somehow we made a home and were fed and washed and had a good time, with little Charles the life of the place."

In F. W. Nordhoff's book are descriptions of life on the ranch, such as the following: "Our home stood three quarters of a mile from and seven hundred feet above the Estero del Maneadero. On clear nights we could see the distant lights of Ensenada and on the far horizon the glow of San Diego's illumination, nearly one hundred miles north. Life at Ramajal, in the early 1900's, was unhurried. We got most of our food from the sea and brush area that surrounded our home."

Until the Mexican Revolution of 1910 compelled him to return to the United States, Walter Nordhoff lived for twenty years as the *patrón* of a great hacienda. During that halcyon time, he absorbed the legends and the lore of Baja California by being a good listener. He observed and retained all that he saw and heard, he was sensitive and perceptive, he had power over words; and perhaps most important of all, when it came years later to create his masterpiece, he had the stamina to sustain and complete it. He was blessed with a creative old age such as few writers enjoy.

Although Nordhoff left the ranch after the Revolution, his land was not confiscated. He kept title to it for the rest of his life. It was a tenuous title, however, and Nordhoff did not wish to jeopardize it by having his true name appear on a book about that area. Hence the disguise of "Fierro Blanco."

The compound surname was cunningly chosen. *Fierro* (iron) evoked Cortes's soldiers, clad in shining armor, which led to the Indians hailing them as white gods. *Blanco* was also a reference to the blonde Norseman who came early to Spain and founded a dynasty, and it represented the Nordhoffs' Norwegian origin. Walter himself was a blue-eyed, blonde Viking.

On leaving the ranch, Nordhoff did not go far, just over the border to National City, a suburb of San Diego, where the former mining engineer-journalist-rancher entered a new incarnation as a businessman. Not an ordinary one, however, for whatever Walter Nordhoff did, an unusual element was always present. He established the California China Products Company—a glazed tile factory wherein were fashioned the colored tiles that embellished the buildings of the San Diego Exposition of 1916, whose architect was Bertram Grosvenor Goodhue. This venture flourished until World War I cut off the supply of fuel oil required to fire the kilns.

It was here at the tile works that Walter Nordhoff employed a young mining engineer and geologist named Walter de Steiguer, Missouri-born in 1884, an M.I.T. graduate, who became the older man's literary confidant.

Nordhoff's retirement to Santa Barbara, where he and his wife lived at 104 East Padre Street, set the stage for the final acts of his life. If the Mexican overthrow meant paradise lost, life in Santa Barbara, from 1923 until his death fourteen years later, saw paradise regained—regained by an act of the creative imagination, which resulted in a book unique in our literature. Its title-page was given over to copious information in the manner of earlier centuries. Let me transcribe it in full:

"The Journey of the Flame; being an account of one year in the Life of Senor Don Juan Obrigón, known during past years in the Three Californias as Juan Colorado, and to the Indiada of the same as The Flame. Born at San José del Arroyo, Lower California, Mexico, in 1798, and, having seen three centuries change customs and manners, died alone in 1902 at the Great Cardón, near Rosario, Mexico, with his face turned toward the South. Written down by Antonio de Fierro Blanco, and Englished by Walter de Steiguer. With illustrations by Alfredo Ramos Martínez. Houghton Mifflin Co., The Riverside Press, Cambridge, 1933."

21

Although the mystery of Fierro Blanco's identity was always a rather transparent one in Santa Barbara, the eastern publishing and reviewing establishment was long deceived. The book's success was immediate. *The Journey of the Flame* was a Literary Guild selection, thus giving it wide distribution and critical attention. It was hailed as an authentic Southwestern masterpiece which of course it was and is.

Mary Austin's review in the *New Republic* was one of the last things she wrote. "The story is admirably told," she concluded, "with enough detail to give the proper feeling of authenticity and freshness to the unfamiliar background, with many fine touches of veracity in the setting and portraiture. How much of the entertaining and freshly described anecdote of the story is fictional and how much the product of the rich imagination of the *mestizo* mind, it is not possible for the reader unacquainted with that mind's capacity for invention to determine, but it is by the reading of such books that our knowledge of the processes of history is enlarged."

The Literary Guild devoted the November issue of its magazine, *Wings*, to comment on the novel by several writers, including Carl Van Doren. "Englished by Walter de Steiguer" was a puzzler. Some library catalogs identify him as the translator of a work written in Spanish by Señor Fierro Blanco. Others, including the Library of Congress, list De Steiguer as another of Walter Nordhoff's pseudonyms.

Although I have never met the gentleman, I can vouch for his individuality from correspondence with him where he resides in his native Missouri. One may learn also from the *Cumulative Book Index* that he is the author of a mystery story with the sinister title, *Jewels for a Shroud*.

In *Wings*, De Steiguer offered this explanation of his role in the work: "The English of the text which comes to me generally contains complexities which are difficultly understandable to the Anglo-Saxon mind not familiar with Spanish-American methods of thought. Don Antonio is kind enough to think that I afford him some assistance in bringing these to more easily understood form. His mention of me on the title-page of the book is a gesture of courtesy, and at his own insistence. 'Englished' was pitched upon as perhaps the nearest word to indicate with fair accuracy my efforts, in its somewhat antique sense of 'to interpret or set forth plainly.' "

Wings also contains a profile by De Steiguer which describes the character of the true author: "Antonio de Fierro Blanco is a man approaching eighty years of age, who retains all the mental brilliancy, and much of the physical vigor, of his prime. His books which he has only recently begun to write, embody the accumulation of a lifetime of patient and tactful listening and observation."

De Steiguer goes on to offer a searching commentary on the writer's style: "The author's text will be found to comprise, in many instances, two separate though related surfaces, of which the lower is deducible from, or visible through, the first. The upper surface is one of apparently uncomplicated narrative, but actually of subtle implication. For those who can see, there lies glimmering below, a sub-surface on which the suspicions, vanities, fears, and passions of his characters blend or clash in shifting patterns of color."

"Fierro Blanco" himself also contributed an autobiographical note to this issue of *Wings*, a tongue-in-cheek vignette, in which Nordhoff scattered a few deceptive leads, concluding thus:

"It has happened to me to be accused of having an imagination. This is an untruth which always irritates my usually placid temper. In my books I merely repeat that which I have heard. It may be that what I write is from the imagination of someone. That may be correct. I never write from my own imagination, because I have none."

Although he be dead, Nordhoff's book lives, and is more alive than ever, as it gains new life from being read and reread. With the passage of time, a vital book's author recedes into unimportance. He gave his life that his book might live. In Emerson's blunt words, he jumps into his book and leaves not a pinch of dust behind. "All fades and disappears," laments the old narrator as *The Journey of the Flame* draws to a close, "vanishing forever with that past I knew. So must I also disappear."

23

24

Which is just what Walter Nordhoff wanted to happen. With the reserve and formality with which he lived and which prevented him, Walter de Steiguer declared, from ever calling even such a long time friend as De Steiguer by his first name or even to shaking hands with him, any personal publicity in connection with his book would have been abhorrent to him.

Years after the appearance of the book, when his publisher's western representative, Harrison Leussler, tracked down Nordhoff and reported that word of his authorship was spreading, "Fierro Blanco," protested in these words, "My barber asked me this morning about my books, and when one begins to get barbershop notoriety, it's time to shut it off. I wish to avoid being made ridiculous by permitting publicity because of a novel. I object to having my old friends think I am suddenly senile."

It was not until eighteen years after Nordhoff's death that Houghton Mifflin republished the book under his true name, with a preface by Scott O'Dell.

When he insisted that he had no imagination, Nordhoff was merely saying that his novel holds more truth than fiction. It is a rearrangement and a fresh perception of old elements, a re-creative work of the highest order of imagination. A true work of fiction is always a better guide than a false work of fact, and thus it is that we have come to rank Nordhoff's novel as the best of all books about Baja California.

It is not incorrect to rank it as a California classic, for in olden times the Californias, Baja and Alta, were a single outpost of Spain's empire. All but the last few pages of the book is laid in Lower California for, as the narrator explains, all is so well known about Upper California.

As Walter de Steiguer observed in *Wings*, Nordhoff's work exists on different levels. It represents a deep and distant vision of time and space. Within the limits, temporal and spatial, of its formal conception, the book glitters with brilliant scenes and violent action. It is classical in form and style, employing the ancient device of a narrated journey, one made by a boy of twelve, recalled and retold by him as an ancient of 104 years, to a gathering of his people. Thus what we have is a refracted vision, a double view of life as seen by a lad and told by a very old man, marked by the naiveté of the one and the sophistication of the other.

In reading it we recall another old man's book of remembered history, that greatest of Mexican epics, the *True History of the Conquest*, by Bernal Díaz del Castillo, written in his old age by a member of Cortés's conquistadors.

Nordhoff's style is deliberately archaic, echoing classical Spanish literature which is rich in philosophical dicta. It is characterized also by sensuous details of life on a primitive frontier, and permeated with an elegiac nostalgia for a vanished era. "Now that I am old," the narrator reflects, "all men study in books. And who make books? Only those who are too lazy to rise before dawn and see for themselves how night and day meet in twilight. Then, for one short moment of least light, those who have gone before and those who are to follow us converse together, giving of their knowledge some slight hint to him who rises betimes and waits with open mind."

This leads to the question, did Nordhoff have a prototype for his ancient narrator? An old-time San Diegan believes that he might have had one. In 1919, Wilmer R. Shields was in the port of Cabo San Lucas, at the very tip of the peninsula. There he encountered a legendary octogenarian known as Colonel Yldefonso Greene, the pioneer Irish-Mexican *mestizo* of that area, who boasted of having fathered scores of children by several wives and also of having walked the length of the peninsula as a boy. Shields photographed Colonel Greene there on the wharf, the *S. S. Alliance* in the background. Years later, upon reading *The Journey of the Flame*, Shields remembered that encounter and the picture that he took.

Don Meadows, the Orange County historian, told me of another possible prototype, old Captain Tom Richie, who died in 1875, and is written about in Henry Edwards's book, *A Mingled Yarn* (1883).

"The Flame's" journey began in 1810 and took eighteen months to cover the fifteen hundred miles between Cape San Lucas and Monterey. It was made by the "Viceroy" of Baja

26

California, Don Firmín Sanhudo, his wife, Doña Ysabel, their small son, and retinue, for the purpose of taking ship back to Spain to report to the king on the state of the province.

As a boy, Juan Colorado, the red-headed *mestizo* son of a Mexican mother and an Irish sailor, accompanied the expedition to look after the leader's little boy, Inocente. Two boys on a long peninsular journey recalls a boy and a runaway slave on a river raft, *Huckleberry Finn*, to be sure. Recalled also is the Anza expedition, the details of which, translated only a few years earlier by Bolton, were known to Nordhoff. Nordhoff displays particular affection for the mule, that indispensable frontier animal. Juanito's hinny is one of the book's most memorable characters.

What is the meaning of "The Flame?" "I am known in my age as Juan Colorado from my red hair," the narrator explains, "but Indians also call me 'The Flame,' not from my head color, but because I have at times used fire against those enemies who trust rather to numbers than to valor."

From the quietude with which Nordhoff's retirement rewarded him, he looked back nostalgically on his years of ranch life and recalled the legends and lore of the desert and the Vermilion Sea, which he had partly gained from listening to his peons. It was a knowledge difficult to come by, Walter de Steiguer wrote me, because of the wariness, suspicion, and evasiveness of these people in discussing their affairs with others. "Mr. Nordhoff has told me that in his talks with them, he had to pretend indifference and inattention, since any show of curiosity at once dried up all flow of information."

Details of landscape and weather, the flora, fauna, and lagoon life, were preserved in his memory. A dominant characteristic of the book is Nordhoff's love for his adopted land. This homesickness for a landscape lost moved him throughout the writing of *The Flame*. By his genius he transformed what to most is a desert into an earthly paradise.

A lifelong love of history, shared by his wife Sarah, had led him to accumulate thousands of books of history, travel, biography, and literature. To supplement them and to ensure historical accuracy, Nordhoff corresponded with the State Library in Sacramento. Alas, his letters were not preserved, coming as they did from a then unknown writer, nor did he keep the Library's replies. He worked at his typewriter late into the night, his daughter told me, and then slept until noon. In his book-lined study was a big roll-top desk deep in papers. In one drawer was always a box of chocolate caramels, which he rationed to his daughters Margaret and Mary.

In his introduction Nordhoff wrote, *"The Journey of the Flame* is in fact an historical novel in which certain deviations from the truth are essential. In the main, every statement made therein is truthful, though some are founded on legends and family traditions. Every statement regarding Missions, roads, animals, fish, or plants is taken directly from histories, private letters of that time, or from conversations with descendants of those who then lived. I felt that accuracy was so much to be desired that I had a map drawn from old sources [this is repro-duced as the book's end-papers], giving each day's travel as that which a well-tended mule-train could easily make."

Throughout the book, as *leit motif*, is a lament for the expul-sion of the Jesuits from Baja California, which occurred seventy years after their arrival in 1697, and of regret for the Franciscans, led by Padre Junípero Serra, having stripped the Missions in order to commence their own chain in Alta California, thus leav-ing the Indians to starve. Nordhoff's heroes were the Jesuit fathers, Ugarte and Salvatierra, his villains the distant bureau-crats and the soldiers who spread disease among the natives.

I am not alone in holding that *The Journey of the Flame* is that rarity, both good fiction and good history. In a review of it written in 1934, Herbert Eugene Bolton declared, "This is a remarkable book on a fascinating subject. As the author clearly states in his preface, and as is plain from the contents, it is a work of historical fiction and not of history. But it is excellent historical fiction, and is highly illuminating of the little known subject of Lower California, its geography, history, and folklore." After correcting the author on several minor errors, including his use of "Three Californias," Bolton concludes, "But after all is said,

The Journey of the Flame is a thrilling narrative. There is no other book about Lower California which will give the general reader so much information and 'atmosphere' in so agreeable a form."

What Bolton did not say is that many works of so-called pure history are vitiated with errors in greater number than the comparatively few made by the novelist.

Walter Nordhoff's ripe years yielded a harvest of writing. "Readers of *Journey of the Flame*," wrote Walter de Steiguer in *Wings*, "will be interested to know that Don Antonio has completed five books, and is working on a sixth."

Only one other was published, a year after "The Flame," and also under the same pseudonym. *Rico, Bandit and Dictator* is a fictional satire on government, sardonic, biting, witty, and reminiscent of Voltaire's *Candide*. A lesser book than *The Flame*, *Rico* has nevertheless the essential Nordhoff flavor.

In the last two years of his life, Nordhoff's publisher rejected two of his manuscripts, *Wine of Wrath* and *The Gift of the Three Virgins*. Still another, which he apparently never submitted, was called *The Valley of the Singing Cranes*. These manuscripts have been preserved by the author's descendants.

Rico's illustrations, a half-dozen powerful wood-engravings printed in red, are credited to no one. They appear, however, to be by the same illustrator whose name appears on the title-page of *The Flame:* Alfredo Ramos Martínez. A note in *Wings* identifies him merely as a Spanish-American artist, and on the jacket of the 1955 edition his name is misspelled. He was a member of the Mexican Renaissance school of fresco painting. His last years were spent in Southern California where he died in 1946, leaving an unfinished fresco of Mexican flower girls on a garden wall at Scripps College, Claremont. Perhaps Nordhoff came to know the artist and admire his work when Ramos Martínez was painting the Easter Murals in Montecito's Church of Our Lady of Mount Carmel. These are said to be his finest work.

For a short time during his ranching years on the bay of Todos Santos, Nordhoff established a home in Redlands, California, in order that his children, Charles, Franklin, Margaret and Mary, might have proper schooling. They also had a summer home on Terminal Island, when that now great Los Angeles port center held only a dozen houses. There Mary was born. The spacious Redlands dwelling still stands at Cedar and Pacific Streets.

Numerous Nordhoffs are buried in the Redlands Hillside Memorial Park: Walter and Sarah, their sons Charles and Franklin, and their daughter Mary's husband, Allen Hamilton Williams, M.D. *In Silentio et Spe* is carved on the stone that bears their names and life spans: *In Silence and Hope.*

I do not believe that the spirit of Fierro Blanco haunts that park. A more likely place to seek him lies south of the border, on the bay beyond Ensenada, roaming his beloved Rancho Ramajal. For did he not write, in *The Journey of the Flame*, "Where a man has worked and helped others, that is home"?

Reading List

WALTER NORDHOFF (1858-1937)
The Journey of the Flame . . . by Antonio de Fierro Blanco, and Englished by Walter de Steiguer. Boston, Houghton Mifflin, 1933. Also with Literary Guild imprint. Reissued in 1955 as by Walter Nordhoff, with Preface by Scott O'Dell.
Rico, Bandit and Dictator. By Antonio de Fierro Blanco. Boston, Houghton Mifflin, 1934.

CHARLES NORDHOFF
Peninsular California; Some Account . . . of Lower California. New York, Harper, 1887.

FRANKLIN W. NORDHOFF
Fruit of the Earth. New York, Vantage Press, 1955.

SARAH COPE WHITALL NORDHOFF
"Reminiscences," an Unpublished Manuscript in the family's possession.

Photograph of Walter Nordhoff, courtesy of Margaret Nordhoff Morrison.

Death Valley in '49

WILLIAM L. MANLY

3

THE AMERICAN WESTERING of the early 19th century was motivated by economics and politics. The mountain men trapped beaver pelts. The Yankee sailors came for cowhides. Lewis and Clark pathfound the Oregon Trail in order to establish our political claim to the Northwest.

Such pioneer activity was largely individualistic. Then in 1848 the discovery of gold in California avalanched the greatest western movement of all times and places. In a single season 100,000 men, women, and children, and their animals, rushed for Eldorado. Their impact and that of their descendants on our history, literature, and western ways is felt to this day.

Many of their diaries have been published, and new ones keep turning up. While all have mosaic value, few have literary merit. If we were to establish by logical processes the most likely author of a gold rush literary classic, we would probably seek an emigrant with writing experience, a trained observer and reporter possessed of energy and imagination and the art of transfusing his prose with those qualities.

We would surely not wait half a century after the gold rush and then choose an unschooled Yankee who had come west in 1849 with an emigrant train, now a shaky old man with only memory to aid him. We would not identify him as the author of a classic of the gold rush, a chronicle of death and disaster, survival and heroism, distinguished by narrative power, specific event, and precise observation.

Such nevertheless is *Death Valley in '49* by William Lewis Manly, published in 1894 at San José by the Pacific Tree and Vine Co., and thrice reprinted, in 1927, 1928, and 1949. A transcription of its title page reveals that it is more than its main title would indicate, that it is not just another item in the bibliography of Death Valley. The sub-title reads:

"Important Chapter of California Pioneer History; the Autobiography of a Pioneer, detailing his life from a Humble Home in the Green Mountains to the Gold Mines of California, and particularly Reciting the Sufferings of the Band of Men, Women, and Children who gave 'Death Valley' its Name."

The magnetic power of gold is constant. The Forty-Niners responded to it in many organized and unorganized ways. No greater contrast can be imagined than that between the disciplined Anza Expedition and the motley congregation of wagon trains gathered at South Pass in the winter of 1849-50. Instead of continuing over the Oregon Trail and being impeded by snow in the Rockies, many of the trains turned south together in search of a more temperate route to the gold fields. Lacking accurate maps and informed leaders, disorganization soon occurred and the large train broke up into bands of several wagons each.

Young Lewis Manly was the hunter and ox driver with a small train that grew even smaller. By the time it had blundered into what is today known as Death Valley, it consisted of only a few families, their wagons, oxen, and a deerhound called Cuff. Lack of a wagon route out of the valley, uncertainty as to where they were, shortage of food and water, were factors that decided the group to stay camped while Manly and another young man, John H. Rogers of Tennessee, went ahead on foot to seek relief. Instead of the ten days they estimated they would be gone, they were nearly a month in reaching Los Angeles and returning with food and knowledge of the route.

Heat was not the problem, for it was the winter season when Death Valley is at its least deadly. If the group had entered the valley in summer, it would never have emerged.

Their misadventure had a fortunate ending. All reached Los Angeles in safety, although the going was arduous. Manly went on to the mines, made a stake and returned east. He came west again, mined for several years, then finally settled at San José and married. He died in 1903 at the age of 83, and was buried in Woodbridge Cemetery near Lodi.

Why did Manly wait forty-four years to publish his book? How does it give the impression of having been written at the very time of the happenings it chronicles? Let me begin to answer by saying that of all the classics herein, *Death Valley in '49* is the most puzzling. I am unable to reconcile Manly the frontiersman with Manly the Homer of the gold rush.

First, the long time between the happening and the telling. According to Manly, this was not intended. In 1851 upon his return to Wisconsin, from where he had first set out for California, he found himself snowed in and unable to travel the final three hundred miles to where his parents had emigrated from Vermont.

"I grew lonesome," he wrote years later in his book, "for the enforced idleness, on account of the stormy weather, was a new feature in my life, and grew terribly monotonous. I concluded to write my parents in Michigan and give them a long letter with something of the history of my travels, and to refresh my memory I got out my memorandum I had kept through all my journey."

"As my letter was liable to be quite lengthy I bought a quantity of foolscap paper and began. I took my diary as my guide, and filled out the ideas suggested in it so they would understand them. I soon ran through with my paper and bought more, and kept on writing. The weather was cold and stormy, and I found it the best occupation I could have to prevent my being lonesome; so I worked away, day after day, for about a month, and I was really quite tired of this sort of work before I had all the facts recorded which I found noted down in my diary. I found over three hundred pages of closely written foolscap paper, and I felt very much relieved when it was done."

As soon as spring came, Manly stored his narrative in a trunk and went off trapping in northern Wisconsin. Then deciding to return to the gold fields, he had the trunk's owner send the manuscript to Manly's parents. They in turn loaned it in the neighborhood until it was nearly worn out from reading. Finally their farmhouse burned down, and that was the last of Manly's manuscript.

"When the news of this reached me I resolved to try to forget all the trials, troubles and hardships I had gone through, and which I had almost lived over again as I wrote them down; and I said to myself that I would not talk about them more than I could help, the sooner to have them vanish, and never write them down again, but a few years ago an accident befell me so that I could not work, and I back-slid from my determination when I was persuaded so earnestly by many friends to write the account which appeared a few years ago in the *Santa Clara Valley* [from 1887 to 1890]. The diary was lost, and from memory alone the facts have been rehearsed, and it is but fair to tell the reader that the hardest and worst of it has never been told nor will it ever be."

Thanks to E. I. Edwards, bibliographer of Death Valley and the desert lands around, I have read a photographic copy of this second version of Manly's story. It is similar to but not identical with the book which appeared soon after. The general form and style are the same in the two versions.

There was yet another attempt to tell his tale which, like the foolscap manuscript, has apparently not survived. Writing in 1884 to the *Inyo Independent*, Manly refers to his lost diary— "left it East in 1852 and now cannot find it"—then states, "I have given Bancroft a history of the trip as near as I could recollect it, after trying to forget it for 34 years, and I suppose it will appear in his history of the Pacific coast when published."

Manly's supposition was wrong; it never appeared, nor is it today in the Bancroft Library. Was it a written history, or was it one of the dictated memoirs that Bancroft employed shorthand stenographers to go about the state and take from pioneers such as Manly and which were both cited by Bancroft in his published works and preserved in his library?

So we see that *Death Valley in '49* did not suddenly appear by magic in 1894. According to Manly, he was a writer from his earliest years as an argonaut. And yet from 1852 for the next thirty years, he seems not to have written anything. Then, perhaps stimulated by Bancroft's request, he began to write again. In *The Jayhawkers' Oath*, Arthur Woodward collected sketches contributed by Manly to the *San José Pioneer* during the 1880's and '90's. None of them has the richness and style of his single published book.

The riches of the book are not found only in those chapters about the Death Valley episode, but mark the narrative throughout. Manly observed and recalled his surroundings with an eye for the extraordinary, as in this vignette of Wisconsin Territory in the 1840's:

"Near sundown I came to a small prairie of about 500 acres surrounded by scattering burr-oak timber, with not a hill in sight, and it seemed to me the most beautiful spot on earth. This I found to belong to a man named Meachem, who had an octagon concrete house built on one side of the opening. The house had a hollow column in the center, and the roof was so constructed that all the rain water went down this central column into a cistern below for house use. The stairs wound round this central column, and the whole affair was quite different from the most of settlers' houses."

This sounds like there was a progenitor of Wisconsin's great architect, Frank Lloyd Wright.

In most of the literature about Manly's book, the emphasis is on Death Valley and the routes followed by Manly and Rogers and their charges, and on how Death Valley got its name. I have less concern for such topographical matters than for the book's literary power and human interest. It possesses a low-key fascination, as in this description of a corpse:

"We came to where the dead body of Mr. Fish lay, just as he died more than a month before. The body had not been disturbed and looked quite natural. He was from Oscaloosa, Iowa."

Another characteristic of Manly's style is a modulating from wide lens to close-ups, and of proceeding from the sublime to the ludicrous. When he and Rogers finally regained their stranded comrades, Manly describes a scene of deep feeling in which Mrs. Bennett clung to him with wordless, maniacal emotion. Then "the morning came and the women were as usual, and their appearance would remind one of half-drowned hens. Hair snarled, eyes red, nose swollen, and out of fix generally." They walked as if they had corns, Manly noted, careful never to take a step backward.

Although as a hunter, Manly killed only to eat, and usually displayed a tough attitude toward animals—as when, on their return with succour and unable to get their horses out of a rock-walled canyon, he and Rogers left them to die—he had affection for the dog Cuff, and for his little black-eyed lady of a mule who surefooted out where the horses failed; and also for Old Crump, the sturdy ox who bore the children to safety in a pair of saddle-bags. This was one of the few of their beasts the emigrants did not have to kill for food. Manly recognized Old Crump later in the 1850's, near French Camp in the San Joaquin Valley. "I got off my horse and went up to him, and patted my old friend." Upon inquiring he learned that the ox's new owner knew of the animal's devoted role and was allowing him a life of ease.

Manly did not share the Yankee contempt for Californios. It was the del Valle family at the ranch near Castaic that welcomed Manly and Rogers and outfitted them for their return. To each of the children left in Death Valley, Señora del Valle sent an orange.

Throughout the literature of the farthest west there runs a golden thread of California seen as the promised land. So it seemed to Anza and his people, to Dana and Stevenson, Muir and Lummis, and to Smeaton Chase and Steinbeck's Joads. Manly too describes the emotion they felt on first seeing the fertile land along the Santa Clara River near today's Newhall:

"As we reached the summit there appeared before us as beautiful a rural picture as one ever looked upon. A large green meadow of a thousand acres more or less; its southwest side bounded by low mountains, at the base of which oak trees were plenty, but not brush or undergrowth. It was like a grand old park, such as we read of in English tales. . . . We tarried here perhaps two

36

hours, till the cattle stopped eating. Never again would any one of the party go back over that dreary desert, they said, and everyone wondered why all places could not be as green and beautiful as this one. I cannot half tell how we felt and acted, nor what we said in our delight over this picture of plenty. The strong contrasts created strong impressions, and the tongues so long silent in our dry and dreary trouble were loosened to say everything the heart inspired."

Manly's account of early Los Angeles is valuable. Then he proceeded north along El Camino Real. It was springtime after a season of heavy rain, and he observed how tall the mustard had grown, and how ground squirrels climbed to the top of the stalks in order to spy out danger.

Dana's first view of California was from the *Pilgrim* off Santa Barbara. Manly's naive view of the Pacific was the reverse of this:

"As we journeyed along we came to the sea shore, the grandest sight in the world to me, for I had never before seen the ocean. What a wide piece of water it was! . . . There was no wind and I could not see what it could be that so strangely agitated the water. Here the waves kept coming, one after another, with as much regularity as the slow strokes of a clock. This was the first puzzle the great sea propounded to me, and there under the clear blue sky and soft air I studied over the ceaseless, restless motion and the great power that was always beating on the shore. I tasted the water and found it exceedingly salt . . . why did it keep so when the great rivers kept pouring in their torrents of fresh waters? I did not understand, and these are some of the thoughts that came to the boy who had been raised upon the prairie."

I do not find it hard to account for the fact that although he was writing of places and events of nearly half a century earlier, Manly was able to evoke precise happenings and exact details. This is a phenomenon of aging whereby the immediate past is lost and the remote time recoverable and real. "Every point of that terrible journey," he wrote, "is indelibly fixed upon my memory and though seventy-three years of age on April 6th 1893 I can locate every camp, and if strong enough could follow that

37

weary trail from Death Valley to Los Angeles with unerring accuracy."

Manly's book was recognized from the beginning as an important contribution to western Americana. In a review in 1897 in his *Land of Sunshine*, Charles F. Lummis first struck a blow for better typography: "Printed by 'blacksmiths' who have disfigured its every page with mis-spellings and letters upside down . . . a pity it is that a narrative of so much worth historically should have fallen to the tough mercies of (let us hope) the most incompetent printers in California." Lummis then continued in characteristic vein to award Manly the palm:

"And speaking of the Great American Desert, those arm-chair geographers who today rather sniff at the title, because they can traverse that desolation in a Pullman, might learn something by study of this plain tale. I also have trudged the breadth of that desert, and can vouch that Mr. Manly does not overstep the truth."

In spite of its blemishes, this first edition remains the most desirable of all those issued, although later ones have editorial matter, maps, and illustrations not found in the 1894 printing. In 1927 it was issued in the Lakeside Classics, edited by M. M. Quaife of the Detroit Public Library. Quaife not only shortened the text by ending it with the Manly party's safe arrival at Los Angeles, he "excised freely and frequently throughout the course of the story, which in the original is endowed with much of verbosity and repetition . . . solely with an eye to presenting the story as the author would, no doubt, have wished to present it had he been trained in the art of narration." The ultimate in editorial patronizing!

The next year Wallace Hebberd of Santa Barbara republished Manly, with a fulsome introduction by John Steven McGroarty, pretty illustrations by Alson Clarke, and a map by Richard I. Kelsey. Although not abridged nor improved in the manner of Quaife, the Hebberd edition does rearrange some of the chapters.

The Centennial Borden edition of 1949 has an introduction by Carl I. Wheat, the cartographical historian. Although he pays tribute to Manly's Homeric quality and his photographic accu-

39

racy, Wheat is not concerned with Manly as a writer or his book as literature.

Needed is a definitive text which will correct the errors of the first edition, supply annotations, maps, and an index, plus a bio-critical introduction.

What was Manly like at the time of writing his book? In addition to photographs of him in old age, there is other evidence. He and his handwriting had become shaky. In the Huntington Library there is a copy of his book once owned by Banker M. E. Morgan of Los Angeles, in which is tipped a pencilled letter from Manly, dated March 18, 1896, which reads in part, "It is strictly true in every respect. The work all done in San José and under the author's care. I am now an old man and hands very shaky, so excuse me."

Also in the Huntington Library is another copy which belonged to John B. Colton, the last survivor of the companion Jayhawker Party, which suffered its worst privations not in Death Valley but in the more deadly Searles Lake region. On an inserted envelope Colton pencilled, "When this old man found our trail, and came into our camp, trying to get out, and get succour for the women and little children, he was a skeleton, but did not look older than 25 years, but he had the nerve of a catamount."

The Bancroft Library has a copy of Manly, accompanied by a letter of presentation written by the author on February 3, 1895, to University Librarian J. C. Rowell. Although the handwriting is not as shaky as it was a year later, the mode of expression reveals an unlettered writer, very different from the stylist of the book published only a year before.

A contemporary account of Manly is found in Rockwell D. Hunt's *Personal Sketches of California Pioneers I Have Known*, published in 1962 when Hunt was 94. This goes back to 1895 when Hunt was teaching at the University of the Pacific, then located in College Park, a suburb of San José, where Manly lived. Hunt recalled Manly's silent nature, bent form, and trembling hands, patriarchal beard, and his stage-fright when invited to speak to Hunt's history class.

40

A psychological study of Manly's character is in E. I. Edwards' *Death Valley's Neglected Hero*, a searching examination of big John Rogers's co-equal role in the Death Valley rescue, consistently played down by Manly in his book.

After rereading Manly and the literature about him and his book, and visits to the Huntington and Bancroft libraries, I went to Yucca Valley on the High Desert, to talk with E. I. Edwards. By then I had answers to all questions but one, and this I put to the learned bibliographer:

"Who was it that helped Manly write his book?"

"The same question has occurred to me," Edwards admitted.

"Although it is not mentioned by those who have written on him and edited his book," I continued, "I am certain that the old man he was in 1894 could not alone have written such a powerful narrative. There is a wide gap between it and the shorter pieces and the letters written at the same period."

Edwards nodded in agreement. "There is some evidence to support us, but I have forgotten where I read it."

We were in Edwards' study, shelved to the ceiling with his collection of desert Californiana. The hours passed while we talked and he sought to recover the reference to Manly's "ghost writer."

Finally I saw Edwards light up, smile broadly, then pull open a drawer in his desk. Still smiling he handed me a sheet of paper with typing on it. "I knew it was somewhere in this room," he said, "It was found after Carl Wheat's death among papers relating to Death Valley. Be so kind as to read it aloud."

It was a memorandum from Ranger-Naturalist Bernarr Bates, dated December 20, 1939, addressed to Naturalist Curry of the Death Valley National Monument, and sent to Wheat with the suggestion that it might prove useful to him in his historical research.

This is what I read aloud:

"On the evening of December 18th, before the naturalist's lecture at Furnace Creek Ranch, it was my pleasure to meet a Mr. C. P. Franklin who was a young plumber in San José, a neighbor of Mr. Wm. Lewis Manly when he was writing his

41

articles and the book, 'Death Valley in '49.' Mr. Franklin tells of Manly coming into his shop en route to the post office where he would sit and tell of his experiences in Death Valley. Mr. Franklin described Manly as, '. . . a small man, about 5 feet 4 inches in height, bent over and walking with a manzanita cane held in a palsied hand, palm outward. His eye was clear and keen with a snow-white beard and his mind was like a basket, filled only with the events of his trip through Death Valley. He had the reputation of having been the keenest rifle shot in the entire party. I am sorry, now, that I hadn't the interest in the old man's stories, but I was young and courting my wife and what had I in common with this old man?"

I paused and said, "This is certainly evidence of Manly's condition in his mid-70's, but it doesn't answer my question."

Edwards smiled and said, "You haven't come to the end."

I resumed my reading of Ranger-Naturalist Bates' memorandum.

"Mr. Franklin lives with his daughter, Ellen, on the Silver Auto Trail in Napa, California . . . Miss Ellen Franklin told me of a Mrs. Margaret (Munn) Smith who lives at Stinson Beach near Muir Woods National Monument. Her father assisted Manly in the preparation of the manuscript for *Death Valley in '49*."

I looked at Edwards. His face was questioning.

"You're right," I said. "There is the answer. I knew he must have had a collaborator. Now who's going to find out who *he* was, that man named Munn?"

"Let's leave something for the young ones," Edwards laughed.

"That's not all we'll leave them," I said. "Does that lost diary still exist in some Wisconsin attic? And according to L. Burr Belden of San Bernardino, writing in *Westways* as recently as November 1964, when Manly died in 1903, his nephew Henry J. Kelsey of Ventura, who was his executor, sold a chest of drawers containing Manly's papers to a second-hand furniture man. The buyers threw out the priceless records and sold the chest. Who will find those papers? Ventura's not too large for a house-to-house search!"

Driving home to Malibu, I had time to think about the research on Manly and Death Valley, done and undone. I concluded that it was and would always be peripheral. Only the book is central. That William Lewis Manly lived it and never lost it, in spite of all that time did to destroy him, and that a man named Munn probably gave it the form and the style that make it so lastingly readable, only serves to deepen the mystery of the creative act.

Reading List

WILLIAM L. MANLY (1820-1903)
Death Valley in '49. San José, Pacific Tree & Vine Co., 1894; Chicago, Lakeside Press, 1927; Santa Barbara, Wallace Hebberd, 1928; Los Angeles, Borden, 1949.
The Jayhawker's Oath and Other Sketches. Edited by Arthur Woodward. Los Angeles, Warren F. Lewis, 1949.

E. I. EDWARDS
The Enduring Desert, A Descriptive Bibliography. Los Angeles, Ward Ritchie Press, 1969.
"Death Valley's Neglected Hero," in *Brand Book* Vol. 12, Los Angeles, The Westerners, 1966.

Photograph of William L. Manly, courtesy of Huntington Library.

The Land of Little Rain

MARY AUSTIN

4

WHERE IS IT, that land of Mary Austin? Southwest of the Rio Grande all the lands receive little rain. People, even critics who should know better, often think it is Arizona or New Mexico. Theirs is an understandable mistake, for Mary Austin did live there during the last two decades of her life, and those two states are indeed semi-arid.

Her land is California, the high desert country at the eastern base of the Sierra Nevada, merging with sagebrush Nevada. It should probably have been included in the state of Nevada, for it does not resemble the characteristic California of seacoast, forested mountains, and fertile valleys.

It is a more subtle land to which Mary Hunter Austin came before the turn of the century. There in the county of Inyo she put down roots and absorbed the lore of the Paiute and Shoshone Indians and of the shepherds, ranchers and miners. With her feet on earth and her head in the sky, she gave voice in singing prose to the soul of a hitherto unsung land.

From birth and education in Illinois and young womanhood spent on her family's homestead in Kern County on the northern flank of the Tehachapi Mountains, Mary Hunter was determined to be a writer. Friendship with General Edward Fitzgerald Beale, owner of Rancho Tejón, and with his *majordomos*, aroused her interest in the history and lore of early California.

44

Stories and sketches came first. Her debut as a western writer was in the *Overland Monthly*. By the time she had married Stafford W. Austin, an educated rancher, and crossed the mountains with him to Inyo, she had the necessary equipment to write a masterpiece: precise knowledge and deep love of a land and its people, capacity to absorb and convert experience into literature, and stamina to persist. She also had a strong drive for recognition.

The Land of Little Rain was published in 1903, the first of thirty-five books Mary Austin was to write before her death at Santa Fe in 1934. It had the advantage of the New England imprint of Houghton Mifflin, one of the country's most distinguished publishers. She went on to become a successful writer and lecturer, a feminist spokeswoman, and a Fabian Socialist.

One might think that such an active writer would produce books of increasing quality and popularity. This was not the case. *The Land of Little Rain*, a young writer's first book, remains her best book. It is also the only one of her many books that has remained in print.

What makes it more than a California classic, truly an American classic, is its fidelity to the landscape and lore of its region. Although not a guidebook, *The Land of Little Rain* is true to the look and the feel of that desert country, to the lay of the land. She was one of the first writers to exalt the desert.

Its overtones are philosophical, and yet it is not theoretical, speculative, or impressionistic. Evidence of what might be called its mirror quality is the beautiful edition of 1950, introduced by Carl Van Doren, and with dramatic photographs by Ansel Adams which are captioned with passages from the book.

Here we see a perfect conjunction of life, landscape, and literature. In this book Mary Austin found the words which precisely expressed what she saw and felt and wanted to say. The register of her language is fully as sharp as that of Adams's photographs.

The first edition of 1903 owed some of its charm to illustrative line-drawings by E. Boyd Smith, although I have not seen evidence that Mrs. Austin ever acknowledged this. The Doubleday paperback edition reproduces these Smith drawings. They are most happily married to her prose.

if he might seat a man with her. "Yes," she said, "on condition that he does not speak to me." Whereupon a young man came to table and the meal proceeded. Several times he appeared on the verge of speaking, and each time she cowed him with a look. Finally she could stand it no longer. "Young man," she said, "I do not believe that you know who I am." "Indeed I do," he said, "but please, Mrs. Austin, may I have the salt?"

In 1924 Mary Austin settled in Santa Fe and for the remaining decade of her life she was its eccentric high priestess, a safe distance removed from Mabel Dodge Luhan, her Taos counterpart. It was in Mrs. Austin's home, La Casa Querida, that Willa Cather wrote the latter chapters of *Death Comes for the Archbishop*.

Two good books came from her New Mexican residence, and although they do not reach the level of her masterpiece, they rank high in Southwestern writing. *The Land of Journeys' Ending* is based on reading and on a six-weeks field trip in Arizona and New Mexico. Among the Mary Austin papers in the Huntington Library is a notebook which she kept on this field trip. Comparison of it with the finished book reveals her creative power. Bare notes are expanded by knowledge, illumined by imagination, and transformed into literature.

Its high point is the chapter on Inscription Rock called by the Spaniards El Morro, that great buff-colored sandstone battlement on the road between Acoma and Zuñi on which centuries of passing travellers have carved their names. "Here I shall haunt," she wrote, in a beautiful peroration; and although her ashes were cemented into the rock on a mountain above Santa Fe, El Morro is the place to seek this woman's spirit, there and in her Land of Little Rain.

In *Taos Pueblo* her prose and Ansel Adams's photographs are again wed. This essay is free of the crankiness, self-conscious admiration, and careless writing that flawed her later work. For example, her autobiography, *Earth Horizon*, begins with a richly detailed account of her earliest years, and then thins out in slovenly writing.

Just as her first book of nature essays remains her finest book, so Mary Austin's first novel, *Isidro*, is the best of several she wrote. Published in 1905 and inspired by the vaquero stories heard when she lived in Kern County, it is compact, lyrical, and faithful to the landscape and seasons of a country she knew and loved. *The Basket Woman* is a book of Paiute Indian tales retold for children. "All of these stories are so nearly true," she teasingly wrote, "that you need not be troubled in the least about believing them." Later, when her fiction became turgid with causes and prophecies, sounding like D. H. Lawrence at his worst, its fate was sealed. Mary Austin had the zeal and the stamina of Helen Hunt Jackson, and yet she never wrote a novel to match *Ramona*. Only when she forgot her own abnormal ego was she able to write beautiful, lasting prose, and this happened all too rarely.

After leaving Inyo and before settling in Carmel, she returned to Kern County, near Bakersfield, and there she wrote *The Flock*, a book of sketches in the same vein as the Inyo book, rich with sheepherding lore of the San Joaquin, the Grapevine, and the Tejón Ranch. It also is embellished with E. Boyd Smith's delicate, strong drawings. *The Flock* has never been republished, and is difficult to find outside of libraries which specialize in Californiana.

One of her California books had an unlikely English origin. While living briefly in London in 1913, Mrs. Austin was asked to write chapters to accompany Sutton Palmer's watercolor paintings of California—the opposite of the process whereby Ansel Adams took photographs to illustrate her prose. *California, Land of the Sun* was published in England in 1914, an American edition being postponed because of the war.

Not until 1927 did it appear in the United States, as *The Lands of the Sun*, and lacking the Palmer paintings. It is a lyrical hymn to California, its contours and configurations of seacoast, valleys, and mountains. This book holds a special place in my remembered reading because of the circumstances in which I discovered it. The place was Paris on a rainy afternoon in May, mild and yet too wet for walking. I sheltered under the umbrella of a bookstall on the Quai des Orfèvres—the Quay of the Goldsmiths—and there I chanced upon a worn copy of *The Lands of the Sun*.

Reading it in my dreary hotel room was a radiant experience. It made me homesick. I could hardly wait to return to California, from which I had been absent for several years. Never had my home state appeared more golden than in Mary Austin's evocative chapters on the Mothering Mountains—the Sierra Madre of my boyhood—the Port of Monterey, the Twin Valleys, the High Sierra, and the Sagebrush Country.

That reading in 1933 did not have the ironic thrust felt upon re-reading it in 1968, as embodied in this passage from her preface:

"Too much of what I describe has utterly vanished, too much more has utterly changed, so blatant and bristling with triumph over the unresisting beauty of the wild, that it would be difficult indeed for one to lose himself in that delighted sense of the whole which was the special privilege of those who came to California in the last quarter of the last century and before it."

Though disheartened by change, she did not end on a hopeless note. Reading the final paragraph of her preface, there in that dripping Paris spring, I heard it as a clarion call. Then and there I determined to go home and become a California writer.

Here is how she ended: "In two or three generations, when towns have taken on the tone of time, and the courageous wild has re-established itself in by-lanes and corners, a writer may be born, instinctively at one with his natural environment, and so able to give satisfying expression to that wholeness. In the meantime let this book stand as a marker, if for no more than the sketched pattern of a suggested recovery."

In the centenary of Mary Austin's birth, I read or re-read all of her books, and revisited the lands of which she wrote. The central and southern Sierra passes all lead to the Land of Little Rain; and of these, the southernmost Walker Pass affords the least dramatic ingress. Once through its low crossing, the road runs from creosote to sagebrush, skirting the China Lake complex of the U.S. Naval Ordnance Test Station, with Death Valley invisible to the east. In the west, so steep as almost to fall on the road, rises the granite escarpment of the Sierra Nevada, John

Muir's Range of Light. Mile after mile the landscape is pure Mary Austin.

On another trip I chose the more dramatic crossing over Tioga Pass in the short season when it is free of snow, thrilled by that nearly vertical drop down Lee Vining Canyon to the desert. "The Streets of the Mountains" is the chapter in *The Land of Little Rain* which has the look and the feel of these high places overlooking the Owens River Valley.

I arrived in Bishop without my copy of the paperback, having been earlier to visit my nonagenarian mother-in-law in Tehama County. She too had lived in Kern and Inyo counties as a girl, though she did not know nor had ever read Mary Austin. After sampling my copy of *The Land of Little Rain*, she confirmed the book's fidelity to the land she had once known. "Yes," she kept murmuring, "this is the way it was." And so I left it with her.

I went to the drugstore in Bishop that was said to carry paperbacks, and there I asked for *The Land of Little Rain*. "We don't carry no books on the weather," the clerk said, deadpan. Nevertheless I spun the rack until I found it, and in bed that night, I re-read Mary Austin with renewed delight. This is indeed the way it was and, thankfully, much of it still is.

Mary Austin's house still stands in Independence. There is hope that it will become a memorial museum. The state of California has declared it an Historical Monument and caused to be placed a bronze sign bearing these words from her book:

"If you ever come beyond the borders as far as the town that lies in a hill dimple at the foot of Kearsarge, never leave it until you have knocked at the door of the brown house under the willow at the end of the village street, and there you shall have such news of the land, of its trails and what is astir in them, as one lover of it can give to another."

Her house still stands under the willow tree at the end of the street. Today if one should heed those words and knock on the door, I am sure he would be made welcome.

MARY AUSTIN (1868-1934)

The Land of Little Rain. Boston, Houghton Mifflin, 1903. Illus. by E. Boyd Smith; same publisher, 1950, with Ansel Adams photographs & an Introduction by Carl Van Doren; also in Doubleday's Natural History Library, including the Smith illus., Anchor Books, 1961.

The Flock. Boston, Houghton Mifflin, 1906. Illus. by E. Boyd Smith.

Isidro. Boston, Houghton Mifflin, 1905.

California, Land of the Sun. London, Black, 1914.

The Lands of the Sun. Boston, Houghton Mifflin, 1927.

The Land of Journeys' Ending. New York, Century, 1924.

Mother of Felipe & Other Early Stories. Edited by Franklin Walker, San Francisco, Book Club of California, 1950.

Taos Pueblo. Photographs by Ansel Adams. San Francisco, Grabhorn Press, 1930.

Earth Horizon; Autobiography. Boston, Houghton Mifflin, 1932. Also with Literary Guild imprint.

HELEN MACKNIGHT DOYLE

Mary Austin, Woman of Genius. New York, Gotham House, 1939.

T. M. PEARCE

The Beloved House. Caldwell, Idaho, Caxton, 1940.

Mary Hunter Austin. New York, Twayne, 1965.

Photograph of Mary Austin, courtesy of Huntington Library.

The Wonders of the Colorado Desert

GEORGE WHARTON JAMES

5

IN THE BEGINNING the desert was only a perilous obstacle to those who sought to enter the Promised Land of Southern California. The Anza expeditions in the 18th century were classic demonstrations of how the wasteland could be safely crossed by organization and leadership. Nearly a century later the disorganized American argonauts blundered through, suffering privation and death, as recorded in Manly's Death Valley epic.

By the 1870's the coming of the railroad assured safe passage, and thereafter the immigrants poured into Southern California through the mountain passes of Cajon and San Gorgonio. Then, after 1900, the desert became the subject of a new kind of literature, of descriptive, lyrical, and mystical appreciation. By the middle of the 20th century, rapid transportation, air-conditioning, jeeps, and dune-buggies enabled the tide of immigration to flow backward through the passes and spread out over the desert. Parts of the area even became urbanized.

This change of viewpoint is described by Franklin Walker in "The Desert Grows Friendly," a chapter in his *Literary History of Southern California*. Beginning with a young eastern art professor, John C. Van Dyke's prose poem, *The Desert* (1901), an aesthetic appreciation of the colorful beauty of what had been merely a dreary land to traverse with utmost speed, there appeared a number of desert books as celebrations.

These included Mary Austin's *The Land of Little Rain* (1903), Idah Meecham Strobridge's *In Miners' Mirage Land* (1904), Arthur J. Burdick's *The Mystic Mid-Region* (1904), and in 1906, *The Wonders of the Colorado Desert* by George Wharton James. More than half a century later, and despite a rising flood of desert literature, James's book has not been surpassed as an authoritative and readable source book on the area. Its only rival in scope and style is *California Desert Trails* (1919), by another Englishman, J. Smeaton Chase. These two writers were sons of the spirit if not the soil of California, living out their lives and dying there in the same year, 1923.

Why do I rank James's desert book a classic? Because it embodies more information about the region, its natural and human history, than any other single book; and because it is written in masterful prose, an expression of its author's virile character; and finally because it is embellished with hundreds of accurate drawings by Carl Eytel, making the book a pictorial as well as a prose encyclopedia.

It was not for gold that George Wharton James, born on September 27, 1858, emigrated in the 1870's from his native Lincolnshire to the sagebrush desert of Nevada. He came in search of health. And find it he did, although he remained nervous and highstrung until his death at 65 on November 8, 1923, at a sanitarium in St. Helena, Northern California.

James was tall, dark, and handsome. A full black beard and a noble head of fine black hair, plus a strong resonant voice, made him a magnetic preacher. For several years he led an adventurous life on the Methodist circuit in frontier Nevada. In 1905 there appeared a novel, *The Sagebrush Parson*, based on James's Nevada years. Its author, Alice Bailey, a Smith College graduate, took the pen name of A. B. Ward. Her novel had a wide success, and James readily admitted to being the prototype of its hero. A copy of the book preserved in the UCLA Library bears this signed note in James's characteristic bold hand: "While there is much of fiction in this book, in the chapters I have marked there is far more of truth than of fiction, for these were actual chapters in my own life."

54

The definitive bio-critical book on James is yet to be written. The nearest to it is a UCLA doctoral dissertation by Roger J. Bourdon, a study deserving of wider dissemination than its niche in the research archives.

The cross in James's early life was his English wife, a shrew of a woman afflicted with pathological jealousy. When the Jameses moved from Nevada to a pastorate in Long Beach, California, his wife soon accused him of gross immorality, including such unlikely feats as having carnal relations in a single night with several women of the same family ranging from young to elderly. After a messy divorce proceedings and accompanying "yellow journalism," James was expelled from the Methodist Church. His wife and three little children returned to England to stay, leaving him broken in health, purse, and spirits.

Even as Charles F. Lummis found healing in New Mexico for physical and emotional suffering, so did James regain his well-being in the Land of Enchantment. Many years later, when he came to write a book on New Mexico for the L. C. Page Co.'s See America First series (it was Lummis who coined that phrase), James declared in his foreword:

"It was here that I came over thirty years ago, broken in health and spirits, and gained the renewing impulses and courage that ultimately won for me a fuller enjoyment of life than I had ever had before. With my roll of bedding I was ready to sleep on station-platform, when deposited, solitary and alone, often in the dead of night, from the irregularly running trains. I was free to wander at my own sweet will, making my bed under piñon tree, cliff, or on sandy plain, wherever my patient burro might bring me."

With health restored, James proceeded to capitalize on his talent as a preacher. He became a successful public lecturer. It was the great age for such, and he captivated lucrative audiences throughout the Midwest and East, employing modern equipment of slides, projector and screen, heralded by striking posters and sumptuous brochures. He was a natural showman.

While in Chicago James engaged in social reform work, joining the war against prostitution, gambling, and drinking, with which activities his frontier pastorate had somewhat acquainted him. He edited a municipal commission's proceedings called *Chicago's Dark Places*.

Back in Southern California, where the divorce scandal had made him *persona non grata*, James found that the mud had been somewhat washed away by time. He returned in 1892 as Social Director for Professor Thaddeus Lowe's Echo Mountain Railway and Hotel. In his spare time he compiled a volume of "Nature Sermons." In 1895 he made a second marriage, to Emma Farnsworth, a minister's widow with two daughters. This proved happy and lasting, and brought James particularly close to his stepdaughter Edith. Henceforth his books were copyrighted in her name, probably to keep his divorced wife from attaching their earnings. The James home at 1098 North Raymond Avenue in Pasadena became a kind of museum salon in the same way that El Alisal served as the center for his rival booster Lummis's Los Angeles followers. Throughout subsequent books, James paid loving tribute to his wife and their homelife.

James showed courage in returning to the scene of his earlier disgrace, and living it down to become one of the Southland's noted citizens. He was its number one booster, surpassing even Lummis in publishing, lecturing, and a bewildering variety of cultural activities. The fact that the rest of his life was morally exemplary leads one to blame his earlier troubles on mismarriage with a vindictive woman. Although he never returned to the Methodist Church, James practiced a sturdy Christian idealism, unrestricted by any particular dogma. He did not share the widespread prejudice against the Chinese and Japanese in California.

A sampling of his enormous output of Californiana indicates his versatility. *A Tourist's Guide Book to Southern California* (1894) is one of the best of the pre-automobile works on the region. *In and Out of the California Missions* (1905) remains a valuable book. *Through Ramona's Country* (1908) is the outstanding volume about Helen Hunt Jackson's classic novel, its setting and characters. Charmingly sentimental is *The Story of Scraggles* (1906), a book about a pet sparrow that would perch on his left hand while he wrote with his right. *The Lake of the Sky, Lake Tahoe* (1916), is the only one of James's books in print today.

Lectures were given to such disparate groups as a realtors' convention and the girls of Ramona Convent. He founded the Pasadena Browning Society, devoted to study of the Victorian poet. Housework for women was recommended in an article in *Good Housekeeping* called "Housekeeping as Physical Culture." He also penned pamphlets on how to treat rattlesnake bite and on sex education for children, plus a guide to the Lick Observatory. He served as secretary-treasurer of the Chuckawalla Valley and Palo Verde Mesa Irrigation Association. A history of the U.S. Reclamation Service was another of his good works.

James championed contemporary California writers. Although he did not overlook those authors who are read to this day—Frank Norris, Jack London, Gertrude Atherton, Mary Austin, for example—he placed losing bets on others long since unread and forgotten. The climax of James's efforts came at the San Francisco and San Diego expositions, where he gave daily lectures on California literature. The record of the latter is preserved in his *Exposition Memories* (1917), a hasty compilation now somewhat embarrassing to read. Yet his motives were of the best, to recognize and reward talented writers during their lifetime. He left uncompleted a major work on California literature.

In a copy of his London slums book, *People of the Abyss*, sent by Jack London to James, the fiery young Socialist wrote on the title-page, "With the facts of these pages before me, I may agree with you in your favorite quotation from Browning, that 'God's in his heaven,' but I cannot agree with you that 'all's right with the world.' "

One of the oddest of James's ventures was the Anti-Whispering Society, with its own publication, devoted to the suppression of (1) talking audiences, (2) peanut fiends, and (3) crying babies. He grew more eccentric and demanding as a lecturer, given finally to announcing before he started that those who were not prepared to sit through the entire lecture should get up and leave forthwith. If he approved of an audience, he was

58

apt to invite them afterward to a cook-out supper. He did the cooking; all they had to provide was their own knife, fork, and plate.

In addition to established eastern publishers, James's works appeared under his own imprint, The Radiant Life Press. Two of its characteristic products were his own *Quit Your Worrying* and *Living the Radiant Life* (both 1916), inspirational works that anticipated Dale Carnegie and Norman Vincent Peale.

All the while that James was providing his public with hundreds of articles, pamphlets, and books about California, he was also producing nearly as large a body of writing on the wider Southwest. It is not composed, as one might think from the author's rapid pace, of superficial works. On the contrary. Of the critics of Colorado River literature, none is more severe than Francis P. Farquhar, the Berkeley historian, bibliographer, and mountaineer. Of the books listed in his river bibliography, James's *In and Around the Grand Canyon* (1900) is described by Farquhar as being "in many respects one of the best." It was also favorably reviewed in the *American Anthropologist* by no less an authority than Frederick Webb Hodge, the ethnologist destined to become director of the Southwest Museum.

James was no armchair writer. In his preface to the Grand Canyon book he tells of making notes for it on the descending trail, in the bottom of the canyon, on foot and horseback, in bed and cave. A photograph shows him at work in his cave study, "Under the shelter of an overhanging rock with piñon boughs piled up and canvas stretched to exclude the sun, my paperweights pieces of limestone, my shelf a rude pine box. This is where the tangled threads of description are being woven into the warp and woof of connected story."

Dramatic? Romantic? True. Yet thereby heightened in readability. James's book was fittingly dedicated to the greatest of all Grand Canyonites, Major John Wesley Powell.

James's father was by trade a basket-maker, and thus it came naturally for the son to write on Indian basketry. His several manuals and a periodical on the subject have not been superseded. He likewise wrote with authority on Indian blanketry.

For the same series that included the New Mexico book, he wrote works on Arizona, Utah, and California, broad in scope, authoritative, and readable to this day. He left unfinished a companion volume on Nevada.

Which brings us finally to *The Wonders of the Colorado Desert*. I am not the first to rank it a classic work on that arid southeastern corner of California. E. I. Edwards, whose bibliography of the California desert's Mohave and Colorado areas extends to 300 pages, puts the James book at the top of the pyramid. Francis P. Farquhar calls it "the best starting point for any study of the Colorado desert." Phil Townsend Hanna, longtime editor of *Westways* and as critical a scholar as Farquhar, wrote in *Libros Californianos* that James's book "is as good a guide to the mysteries of the great wasteland today as it was in 1906, and would need very few modifications to bring it up to date."

If a book is to live and last, to be read and loved beyond its writer's lifetime, it must contain more than facts. It must be animated by its author's spirit, so that it has in it something more vital than paper and ink.

This is what Wharton James did in *Wonders of the Colorado Desert*, composed as it is of learning and love, and fashioned on the several levels of history, science, topography, and visionary idealism. That movement of desert adoration launched by John C. Van Dyke in 1901 culminated later in Mary Austin and Wharton James, she the mystic, he the earthy idealist.

"The close proximity of the desert to the growing cities of Southern California is one of the greatest blessings," James wrote. "Though, as yet, unappreciated and largely unknown, it is waiting to pour out of its largeness into the hearts of the few men and women who will ultimately come to learn from it the lessons that will better fit them to lead the people of Southern California to higher and nobler things."

Not a bad idea, to send our civic leaders into the desert for refreshment and inspiration.

Even as he wrote his Grand Canyon book in the field, so did James compile the Colorado Desert book "far from the madding crowd." In his preface, after acknowledging the help of Dr. Welwood Murray, Palm Springs' patron saint, and of Dr. Walter Swingle, Physiologist of the United States Department of Agriculture's Bureau of Plant Industry, James goes on to state:

"The desert itself, however, has been my chief inspiration. Upon its northwestern edge I have a camp of my own. Within five and a half hours' ride from my Pasadena home, where library and pictures and piano and flowers and birds and congenial society all conspire to keep me (even were there no loved ones in the home itself), I have found this desert a resting place. Up in a canyon [Chino] on the northeastern slope of the great San Jacinto range, where seeping water makes a 'cienega' and gives life to a good sized patch of grass; where someone, sometime, planted a fig tree, which has grown to rugged maturity and rich bearing; where there is a hot spring to bathe in, and a cold spring to drink from; sheltered on one side by one of the steepest, if not the steepest and highest wall in the world, and on the other with an outlook over illimitable wastes of desert land, here is where I love to come and rest, think, and write."

Then in thirty-nine solid chapters James writes about every aspect of that desert area, ranging from Twentynine Palms to Yuma, and from the crest of the San Bernardino-San Jacinto-Laguna mountains to the Colorado River. As Bibliographer Edwards notes, James left precious little for subsequent writers to write about. The growth of desert communities and the development of the river's resources did not come in James's time, but they would not astonish him. I am not sure that he would approve of the Palm Springs Aerial Tramway up his beloved San Jacinto, although as he aged and his legs weakened, he might have been grateful for it, loving as he did the prospect from on high.

As Smeaton Chase was to do a decade and a half later, Wharton James explored the desert on foot and with pack burros. His two favorite companions were Lea Van Anderson, who drew the book's maps, and Carl Eytel, who made the drawings which add so beautifully to the book's authority and charm.

A writer's character is revealed in his book's acknowledgements. It is characteristic of James's nature that at the very first of this desert book he devotes a chapter to "Carl Eytel, the Artist of the Colorado Desert," concluding:

"While Mr. Eytel (with the modesty that is one of the flowers of his character) would disclaim any right to be regarded as other than the artist of the book, I cannot do him the injustice to allow its readers to assume that I am the sole author of its literary contents. While I have done the actual writing, many pages of that which is written belong to Mr. Eytel, and I wish him fully to share in any praise which that portion of the book receives just as much as I wish him to be the sole recipient of all the praise for his beautiful sketches."

The book's first edition was in two volumes, priced at only $5; then in 1911 it was reissued, unabridged, in a single volume on thinner paper at half the price. The work is a beautiful example of typographical layout, in the harmonizing of the hundreds of Eytel drawings with the printed text. Both editions today bring a premium price in the second-hand market.

James's book was on the seat beside me when I made an unarduous trip around his desert country, travelling by automobile rather than on foot and burro. Beyond San Gorgonio Pass and bypassing Palm Springs, I stopped to gaze on the granite upthrust of San Jacinto, Southern California's noblest mountain. While resting I turned to the chapter, "The Mountains of the Desert," and read the paragraph wherein James urged teachers in Southern California's schools and colleges to bring their students into the field for lessons not to be learned from books.

I pressed on south by the Salton Sea, formed at the time when James was writing, and then turned off into the solitude of the Anza-Borrego State Park. There is an oasis at the Casa del Zorro near the settlement of Borrego Springs. There after lunch I savored a sample of James's prose, on the contrast between the desert's aridity and its verdure:

"And coming back to this oasis, as I have done several times after weeks of weary travel on the wide expanse of desolation beyond, how sweet and blessed it all is. The leaves of the trees, with the waxen blossoms of the orange and lemon, or the blush-

62

ing blossoms of the almond and apricot, touch one as with tender hands bathed in sweetest perfume. The waters of its tiny creeks whisper of the cooling draughts they will give to mind as well as body. The gentle zephyrs kiss one's face and lips and hands as in tenderest caress, and the skin the fierce desert sun and winds have tanned and scorched is soothed and refreshed. Yet it is not all external, what the oasis gives. The heart beats easier, the pulses are less strong and masterful, the nerves are more under control, and the inward fever of body and brain seems quenched almost as soon as one reclines under the shade of the oasis. And then, penetrating farther, mind and soul are soothed and quieted, and one is able to see how to use the added strength and rugged power he has absorbed from the rude and uncouth, but loving and generous bosom of the desert mother."

Approaching Yuma the highway traverses the honey-colored dunes, the same dunes that impeded Juan Bautista de Anza and his people in 1776 on their trek to California. Today the All American Canal flows through the sand in a concrete channel, bringing life to the crops and people of the Imperial Valley. The dams upriver, beginning with obsolete Laguna, and Imperial where the Canal's water is desilted and diverted, are subsequent to James's time. Since then man has so tamed the Colorado that its lower reaches are now a chain of placid lakes. Nor would James recognize neonized Yuma and its irrigated environs.

Crossing the Imperial Valley toward San Diego and the coolness of ocean, I observed the dry channels through which the river poured in 1905-06 to form the Salton Sea. Up from the desert floor the divided highway climbs in a few miles to 4,000 feet, a marvel of road engineering. At the summit I turned off to rest again and leaf through my book, finding those pages describing the place where I was parked, on the route where James and his companions trudged through from San Diego to Yuma. Such is the magic of a classic that the author's experience is ever transferable to the reader, so that I imagined myself sweating and thirsty.

My final quest of the man and his book took me to the Southwest Museum, on the hill above the Arroyo Seco. There, in one of those reconciliations time has a way of effecting between rivals, I found shelved cheek by jowl the archives of George Wharton James and Charles Fletcher Lummis, the former given in 1939 by James's step-daughter Edith. James's reference library on the West is also housed there. A smaller collection of his manuscripts is in the Huntington Library.

Book reproduction in reduced size and clarity of the Carl Eytel pen and ink drawings is a pale substitute for sight of the originals, mounted in a large portfolio. Delicate and dazzling in black and white, they are the finest drawings of their kind ever made. This was the judgement of my host, Director Carl S. Dentzel, whose qualifications include that of being an authority on Southwestern art and artists.

In speaking of the twin titans of regional culture, James and Lummis, Dentzel observed that their achievements were the more remarkable in that they were done entirely on their own, without benefit of either foundation fellowships or university grants.

I stayed on to pore through the manuscript relics of George Wharton James's abundant life, in themselves so fragile and ephemeral unless transmuted into the more lasting life of print. Of supreme interest to me was the original manuscript of *The Wonders of the Colorado Desert*, a wondrous bundle of odd pages of incoming business letters, hotel stationery from a dozen cities, invoices, circulars, invitations, and announcements, all thriftily used by James in the same way that Robinson Jeffers composed his poetry, by writing on the blank versos.

Reading List

GEORGE WHARTON JAMES (1858-1923)
The Wonders of the Colorado Desert. Boston, Houghton Mifflin, 1906. 2 vols. Reissued in 1911 in 1 vol. Line drawings by Carl Eytel.

ROGER J. BOURDON

George Wharton James, Interpreter of the Southwest. University of California at Los Angeles, Ph.D. Thesis, 1966. Xerox copy available in the UCLA Library.

Photograph of George Wharton James, courtesy of Southwest Museum.

LOUISA SMITH CLAPP

6

THERE IS NO dearth of Californiana. Although thousands of books about the state crowd the shelves of libraries and bookstores, only one short shelf is needed to hold the classics. Such a work cannot be written to order. The conception and birth of lasting literature remain a mystery. All we know is that the right writer must be in the right place at the right time. *Who, where, when,* are unpredictable factors, never the same twice.

The Shirley Letters did not become a book until 1922, nearly three quarters of a century after they were first serialized in a monthly magazine. This was not because they were overlooked by readers. From their first appearance in 1854-55 in *The Pioneer*, a short-lived San Francisco literary periodical, these letters from a young bride to her sister in New England were recognized by Royce, Bancroft, and other authorities, as among the best of all descriptions of life in the gold regions of the Sierra Nevada. From them Bret Harte took incidents used in "The Luck of Roaring Camp" and "The Outcasts of Poker Flat." Some believed that Mark Twain's "Jumping Frog" was inspired by mention of a miner's tame frog that hopped around on the bar.

Their author, who signed herself Dame Shirley, wrote other things, before and after her famous letters, but everything else by her was not only unclassical, but downright bad, then and now. Why was this? Why are these twenty-three letters, written

66

from the Feather River country in 1851-52, extraordinary not only in their author's work, but in all California literature as well? The law of averages should have produced more than one classic of that time and place for, although I lack statistics, there are probably more books about the Gold Rush than about any other aspect of California's history.

Bayard Taylor's *Eldorado?* Interesting historical journalism. Sarah Royce's *A Frontier Lady?* Authentic, surely, but written in ordinary prose. Not until Manly's *Death Valley in '49* do we encounter a work to rival *The Shirley Letters*, and then if there were only one palm to award, the lady would win it for the sparkle of her prose, wine to Manly's beer—both good drinks, depending on one's taste.

These two books also represent antipodal ways of writing, Shirley's penned at the time of the happenings, Manly's half a century after. Each has its advantages, supremely demonstrated in the woman's ability to mirror history-in-the-making, the man's to employ a powerful memory in total recall. Each achieved perspective and authenticity.

The story of Dame Shirley and her letters is altogether romantic. Thanks to Thomas Russell, Carl Wheat, and Rodman Paul, much is known about her, and it should all be brought together in an introduction to a new edition of the *Letters*. After we have read everything about her, and than reread the *Letters*, we end with the question, why was it Shirley who wrote *the* classic of the Gold Rush? It was an inauspicious debut for an immortal work, strung out in the small-print columns of an ephemeral periodical, most of the issues of which were destroyed in the fires that were always ravaging San Francisco. Today those twenty-three issues of *The Pioneer* are of great rarity and corresponding value.

In 1922 San Francisco printer Tom Russell resurrected Shirley's letters and gave them new life in a book. Next, in 1933, Carl I. Wheat, the lawyer-bookman, edited them for the Grabhorn Press. Then in 1949 Alfred A. Knopf republished this limited printing in popular format. Today all of these editions are out of print and coveted by collectors of Californiana.

Who was she, this woman who signed her letters Dame Shirley? Her true name was not nearly as fitting. Christened Louisa Amelia Knapp Smith, and adding later the married name of Clapp, no wonder she adopted a pseudonym! Louisa became Louise, and an "e" was added to Clapp. Whence came "Shirley"? Her mother's maiden name was Lois Lee, and the daughter sometimes signed her work "Shirley Lee." Could Shirley have been one of her mother's other names? Or did she take the name from Charlotte Bronte's novel, *Shirley*, published in 1849?

She was born of genteel parents at Elizabeth, New Jersey on July 28, 1819, was early left an orphan and raised by a family friend in Amherst and educated in languages and literature. She travelled frequently, was attractive to men, and was married at thirty to a young medical doctor, Fayette Clapp, five years her junior. Also growing up in Amherst, though ten years younger than Shirley, were two other women destined for literary fame, Emily Dickinson and Helen Hunt Jackson.

Louisa was naturally restless. She wrote later to her sister, "In good sooth I fancy that Nature intended me for an Arab or some other nomadic barbarian, and by mistake my soul got packed up in a Christianized set of bones and muscles." Gold Rush fever caught her and her husband, both given to hypochondria, and they rounded Cape Horn in 1849 in the ship *Manila*. Their health suffered in San Francisco's weather, and eventually they made their way to a mining community, deep in the nearly sunless canyon of the east branch of the Feather River's North Fork.

There in that turbulent, gold-seeking hive of mostly men, Dr. Clapp hung out his shingle, while his wife diverted herself by penning a series of fortnightly letters to her sister, Mary Jane, called Molly, back home in Amherst. Although no one dreamed it at the time, least of all the writer, that rare conjunction of factors had occurred—the right person in the right place at the right time. Fate arranged it thus, in the way that a random twirling of the dials might arrive at the one-in-a-million combination to open the vault.

Mrs. Clapp was practiced as a writer. Poems, essays, letters

68

had come from her pen in earlier years. No green schoolgirl, for nearly a decade she had engaged in a romantic correspondence with an older man, the distinguished American statesman and editor, Alexander Hill Everett (brother of the orator), who encouraged her efforts. In a letter dated October 31, 1839, her mentor wrote, "If you were to add to the love of reading the habit of writing, you would find a new and inexhaustible source of comfort and satisfaction opening upon you." This was indeed what happened. There was something about young Amherst literary women that attracted older men. Both Emily Dickinson and Helen Hunt Jackson became protégées of Colonel Thomas Wentworth Higginson.

Since coming to California Mrs. Clapp had contributed sketches and poems to periodicals, yet all of her writing, up to the mining letters, was in the artificial style of the time, flowery and false, then bad enough, now utterly unreadable.

Here is the creative mystery at its most unfathomable. What was it that purged and purified her style, so that suddenly her letters soared to the realm of lasting literature? It is not enough to say, as some have said, that it was because she was writing informally to her sister, rather than for publication. She was too knowledgeable a writer to confine her expression to a single reader. It was as though she had prescience of her letters' ultimate destiny and was writing both to and through her sister to the world of time-out-of-mind. Today we read the letters as though they were addressed to us.

What became of the originals? Are they packed away in a trunk in some Amherst attic? Even if some of them never reached their destination, Shirley's wisdom in keeping copies ensured their publication. When she returned to San Francisco in 1852 and her marriage ended soon thereafter in divorce (Dr. Clapp had gone off to practice in the Hawaiian Islands), she gave the copies to Ferdinand Ewer, editor of the newly founded *Pioneer*, which was modelled on the *Knickerbocker* of eastern fame, just as two decades later the *Overland Monthly* was patterned on the *Atlantic Monthly*.

Shirley's letters were no careless effusions, dashed off between household tasks, but were composed with skillful art. It would seem that the personages, sights, and happenings of the violent mountain community were of such vividness and power as to catalyze this sensitive woman's latent talents and bring them into perfect focus on that highest level where literature is achieved. Only once was she thus transformed.

Form and content were inseparably wedded, as they must be if prose is to rise above the level of journalism. From what we knew of Shirley and her earlier writing, we would have expected her letters home to be marked by shock and dismay at the roughness and squalor of the miners' life, and that she would evade or gloss over such unpleasantness.

Not so. Before leaving New England she had vowed to reflect and report on the whole picture of mining life as she saw it: "I am bound, Molly, by my promises, to give you a *true* picture (as much as in me lies) of mining life and its peculiar temptations, 'nothing extenuating nor setting down aught in malice.' I know how deeply you are interested in everything relating to California—and therefore I take pains to describe things exactly as I *see* them, hoping that thus you will obtain an idea of life in the mines *as it is*."

Most New England brides would have sought refuge from the brutality of everyday life in rhapsodies to Nature. It is true the letters are sometimes rhapsodical, especially when spring brought the flowers, but Shirley did not flinch from reporting the troubles of the "hot summer" of 1852. Here is how she began her 19th letter, *From our Log Cabin, Indian Bar, August 4:*

"We have lived through so much of excitement for the last three weeks, dear Molly, that I almost shrink from relating the gloomy events which have marked their flight. But if I leave out the darker shades of our mountain life, the picture will be very incomplete. In the short space of twenty-four days, we have had murders, fearful accidents, bloody deaths, a mob, whippings, a hanging, an attempt at suicide, and a fatal duel."

The letter goes on to elaborate on these rude happenings. Her being a doctor's wife kept her close to reality. To see an amputation did not send her into a swoon. Death was a part of life to be observed and reported. Although her marriage did not last, its circumstances ensured her literary immortality.

Another appeal of Shirley's letters comes from her sympathetic eye for human types. She had compassion for the Hispanos who were grossly abused by the Yankees. She had no illusions about her countrymen, those uneducated, bigoted, chauvinistic patriots who largely formed the mining communities. She also understood that drunkenness and violence were concomitants of the unnatural, restricted, womanless life the men led, especially in the winter. Letter 12 describes a three-weeks drunk on which the miners embarked at Christmas-time. Here is how it began:

"At nine o'clock in the evening, they had an oyster and champagne supper in the Humboldt, which was very gay with toasts, songs, speeches, etc. I believe that the company danced all night; at any rate, they were dancing when I went to sleep, and they were dancing when I woke the next morning. The revel was kept up in this mad way for three days, growing wilder every hour. Some never slept at all during that time. On the fourth day, they got past dancing, and, lying in drunken heaps about the barroom, commenced a most unearthly howling;—some barked like dogs, some roared like bulls, and others hissed like serpents and geese. Many were too far gone to imitate anything but their own animalized selves."

In addition to their compassionate view of humanity, Shirley's letters have a wealth of information on the way of life in the mines: cabins and tents, food and clothing, and the modes of extracting gold from the river. Her feminine interest resulted in details unimportant to a masculine observer, as for example the uses of calico cloth and other furnishings. She had an especial eye for flowers. "Since I have commenced writing, one of the Doctor's patients has brought me a bunch of wild roses. O! how vividly at sight of them started up before me those wooded valleys of the Connecticut . . . I have arranged the dear *home* blossoms with a handful of flowers which were given to me this morning by an unknown Spaniard."

Shirley complained about the same thing Mark Twain criticized on first seeing the Sierra Nevada, that is to say, "the monotonous tone of the foliage, nearly all the trees being firs. One misses that infinite variety of waving forms, and those endless shades of verdure, which make New England forest scenery so exquisitely lovely. And then that gorgeous autumnal phenomenon one never sees here."

Shirley's letters proceed by radical turns of thought, and yet there is always a connecting thread, as when in writing about the Spaniard who brought her flowers, she went on to report that "A few evenings ago, a Spaniard was stabbed by an American. It seems that the presumptuous foreigner had the impertinence to ask very humbly and meekly that the most noble representative of the stars and stripes, if the latter would pay him a few dollars which he had owed him for some time. His high mightiness, the Yankee, was not going to put up with any such impertinence, and the poor Spaniard received, for answer, several inches of cold steel in his breast, which inflicted a very dangerous wound. Nothing was done, and very little was said about this atrocious affair."

To inquire further into the reason for the long life of the Shirley letters, we must go beyond the details they preserved of a vanished era, and also the sympathy with which they are endowed, although we recognize that without these qualities they would not be read today. Other writers of the mining age have similar factual and human interest accounts. What is unique about Shirley's, and perhaps is the secret itself, is Shirley. Style, said the Frenchman, is the man himself. How does this occur, whereby a writer becomes his work?

We do not know the answer, nor can we teach it in a course in writing. We can only observe it *ex post facto*. Open *The Shirley Letters* to any page, to any passage, and it will be apparent what I mean: that transformation of the person into irridescent prose, ever changing in mood and pace, as though in writing her letters Shirley was reflecting the water in the river upon which she looked from her cabin porch. This is the supreme gift a writer can receive from the Lord—the power to convert his personality into prose (or poetry) and at the same time to create a style of such clarity that we seem to see through it to life itself.

With Letter 23, written on November 21, 1852, Shirley comes to the end. The fluming companies had failed. Upon reaching bedrock, no gold was found. Whereupon "The mass of the unfortunates laid down 'the shovel and hoe' and left the river in crowds. It is said that there are not twenty men remaining on Indian Bar, although two months ago, you could count them up by hundreds."

Winter was approaching, and soon they would be snowed in. Shirley packed her trunks and was ready to leave, in the meantime using them for tables. Then Dr. Clapp was called away to visit a sick person and their departure was delayed. Finally he returned and they prepared to leave on the morrow. Snow was falling and the trunks had to await better weather; she could take only a change of linen in a carpet-bag. Then it was that she burst out in a moving peroration to Molly:

"My heart is heavy at the thought of departing forever from this place. I *like* this wild and barbarous life; I leave it with regret. I go from the mountains with a deep heart of sorrow. I took kindly to this existence, which to you seems so sordid and mean. Here, at least, I have been contented. The 'thistle-seed' as you call me, sent abroad its roots right lovingly into this barren soil, and gained unwonted strength in what seemed to you such unfavorable surroundings. You would hardly recognize the feeble and half-dying invalid, who drooped languidly out of sight, as night shut down between your straining gaze and the good ship *Manila*, as she wafted away from her Atlantic home, in the person of your now perfectly healthy sister."

What became of Shirley during the half-century before her life ended? She never married again. For twenty years she was a San Francisco grammar-school teacher, beloved of her pupils, and especially helpful to any who showed talent for writing. Episcopal church work also occupied her. For a time she lived in the home of John Swett, California's pioneer educator. It was said that Bret Harte, as editor of the *Overland Monthly*, snubbed her. Judging from the few examples we have of her writing subsequent to the mining letters, Harte was justified in rejecting her contributions. She may have always been the right person, but never again were the time and the place also right, never again did all three come into conjunction.

She apparently did not resent Harte's using incidents from her letters. Bancroft was wrong when he wrote, "Mrs. Clapp's simple epistolary style narrates the facts, and Harte's exquisite style imparts to them the glamour of imagination." Her style was never simple, any more than his was exquisite.

Mrs. Clapp's former pupil, Charles Warren Stoddard, who went on to some fame as a California writer, took another view of Harte's "plagiarism." In 1875 he wrote to the editor of the *Overland*, John H. Carmany, urging him (unsuccessfully) to reprint Shirley's letters from *The Pioneer*. Harte's stories, he declared, are tinsel and soapsuds, whereas Shirley's letters are gold and champagne.

Health regained during her sojourn on the Feather River was never lost. In addition to her school and church work, Mrs. Clapp enjoyed outings such as ones described by a former pupil, Mary Viola Tingley Lawrence, in a memoir Russell included in his edition of *The Shirley Letters:*

"At times we went across the bay, in various directions, but oftenest we strove through the sand to the ocean beach, stopping here and there to botanize, and gather the sweet yellow and purple lupin, and to rest on the limbs of the scrub-oaks. On the beach we roasted potatoes and made coffee, and then ate ravenously. A happy gipsying it was, and she, the queen, forgot her cares. Not a pebble at our feet, nor a floating seaweed, nor a shell, nor a seal on the rock, but opened up an instructive talk from our teacher, or started Charley Stoddard reciting a poem, or set a girl singing. Before starting homeward, the whole party, including Shirley, shoes and stockings off, waded into the surf, and afterwards rested on the warm beds of sand. A fine comradeship, and one that never died."

Another time Mrs. Lawrence and her husband took Shirley on a three-weeks' holiday to Yosemite. "Down in the meadows we came upon John Muir sawing logs. He dropped his work, and we three went botanizing, and soon were learning all about the valley's formation as he entrancingly talked. We met many

74

tourists of distinction, and Shirley forgot that she ever had a care, and on our way back she galloped along recklessly."

In 1878 Mrs. Clapp retired and left San Francisco, enriched by a two-thousand-dollar purse from her former pupils and associates. She went to New York and lived with an adopted niece, the actress Genevieve Stebbins. The Cyrus Field family gave her a trip to Europe. Later she lectured on art and literature, and wrote occasional articles, none of them with even an echo of the magical years on El Rio de las Plumas.

In 1897 fate brought her full circle, back to her native state of New Jersey where she came to live near Morristown in a small home for elderly people called Overbrook Farm, presided over by a niece of Bret Harte. Nine years later she died in her 88th year, and was buried in Evergreen Cemetery, Morristown. Her headstone reads, "Louise Clappe, wife, Dr. Fayette Clappe."

This led Rodman Paul to speculate: "Perhaps this means that in her old age, when she made known to her niece her wishes as to burial arrangements, she reverted with feelings of nostalgic affection to those exciting years in Gold Rush California, when she found herself married to a young doctor who was so impractical as to give his delicate, well-bred wife a superb opportunity to share in one of the great episodes of human history."

When Carl Wheat came to edit her letters he found, thanks to Caroline Wenzel of the State Library, that Overbrook Farm still preserved memorabilia left by Shirley. These he acquired and gratefully placed in the California State Library at Sacramento. In 1964 Rodman W. Paul, Caltech professor of history, used them brilliantly in research for his article in the *Pacific Historical Review*, "In Search of Dame Shirley." His is the most thorough account to date of her life and work. It also identifies and traces Dr. Clapp through another marriage, medical service in the Civil War, and death from disease in 1864.

I went to Sacramento one summer day to see for myself what it was that Shirley had treasured to the end of her long life. There in the cool setting of the great California Room I perused a folder of letters from family and friends, written to her during her girlhood. In another folder were the several score letters—thinly veiled love declarations—written to her from 1839 to 1847 by Alexander Everett, twenty-nine years her senior, one of them recalling their first romantic meeting on a stagecoach in Vermont; the last written from Macao en route to Canton, to where Everett had been posted as the U.S. Minister to China. It is a sad, bitter letter, written to the young woman upon hearing of her engagement to Dr. Clapp. Three months later Everett died in Canton. What became of her letters to him? They are not among his papers in the Massachusetts Historical Society.

Still another folder held dozens of photographs of women and men, none of them identified. In lieu of a likeness, we have only this description by Mary Lawrence: "Shirley was small in build, fair and golden-haired, with a thin face and a finely shaped head. Her limbs were perfect in symmetry."

And we have her letters, her book.

Reading List

LOUISA SMITH CLAPP (DAME SHIRLEY) (1819-1908)
The Shirley Letters . . . Edited by Thomas C. Russell. San Francisco, T. C. Russell, 1922.
California in 1851-52; the Shirley Letters. Edited by Carl I. Wheat. San Francisco, Grabhorn Press, 1933. 2 vols.
The Shirley Letters from the California Mines. Edited by Carl I. Wheat. New York, Alfred A. Knopf, 1949.

RODMAN W. PAUL
"In Search of Dame Shirley." In *Pacific Historical Review*, May, 1964.

The Luck of Roaring Camp

BRET HARTE

7

It was Oscar Wilde who said that Life imitates Art, rather than the opposite. If he were writing today, he would be even more sure of it, as he observed the effect of movies, radio, and television on that imitative animal called Man.

On a recent visit to Switzerland I had abundant confirmation of Wilde's pronouncement. It was in Lucerne on Shrove Tuesday, at the height of the carnival marking the advent of Lent. Bands of children roamed the streets in costume, most of them in the frontier styles of the American West—cowboy and Indian, sheriff, badman, and gambler.

It gave me a strange feeling to know that I had in my pocket a paperback whose stories, published a century ago, were probably more responsible than any other factor for the scene I was witnessing. Whereas older mummers were dressed in the traditional Swiss carnival costumes, the kids were copying what they had seen on T.V., the stereotyped westerns that have galloped out to all points of the compass.

And what were the westerns copying? Essentially the characters and situations first described in the 1860's by Bret Harte in those immortal stories of the Gold Rush and its heroes and its villains—"The Luck of Roaring Camp," "The Outcasts of Poker Flat," and "Tennessee's Pardner," to name three of the most celebrated.

I don't know of another example in American literature of an author's art having influenced life as widely as this handful of stories by Bret Harte. Why has it been so powerful and permanent an influence? Because Harte created a mythology, something more potent than mere history. In his Foreword to the paperback I was carrying, Wallace Stegner put it this way:

"He made a world . . . a world insufficiently rooted in fact to have realistic validity, and even such facts as it contained were mainly anachronisms already outlived. Yet it was at once recognizable as plausible, cohesive, self-contained, and is as much a world as Faulkner's Yoknapatawpha County, and it is peopled by creatures of a simple and enduring kind. The pilgrims who visit the 'Bret Harte Country,' and the chambers of commerce along Highway 49 who set their traps for them, have a surer instinct than the critics; they recognize valid myths when they see them."

Until I reached London, I had never read more than the few classic stories of Bret Harte; and so after settling in, I set about reading him at length and depth in a veritable book spree—his collected works in prose and poetry in ten volumes, three biographies, his letters, and miscellaneous critiques of the 19th and 20th centuries. My single paperback proved to be a kind of Aladdin's lamp, multiplying into a whole shelf of books. I read by day and by night, in libraries and bookstores, in coffee bars, on bus and in tube, and at home in our flat.

I would bet and win that Britain holds more books by Bret Harte than California, of which he wrote. The reason is that he spent the last twenty-four years of his life in Europe, mostly in and around London, and more editions of his works were published and read in England than in the United States, to which he never returned.

I admit to having become as interested in the man as in his work, curious as to the mainsprings of his life and art. What caused him to leave California at the peak of his fame, not only never to return, but also never to write to any of his colleagues on the *Overland Monthly*, which he edited and which first published his sky-rocketing stories. That was a San Francisco group of unusual talent and influence, including Mark Twain, Ambrose

Bierce, Clarence King, Prentice Mulford, Charles Warren Stoddard, and a lone woman, the beauteous Ina Donna Coolbrith. Franklin Walker's *San Francisco's Literary Frontier* tells their story.

I wanted to know whether Bret Harte's work truly mirrored his life during the seventeen formative years he spent in California. Were his settings true to the landscape, seasons, and weathers? Who were his literary descendants? I recalled that Gertrude Atherton had acknowledged the inspiration of Harte's stories in writing *The Splendid Idle Forties*. It would seem that Idwal Jones's tales were also Harte's grandchildren. Who were the women in his life? Without knowing anything about them, I assumed that there were some.

There was no dearth of answers, thanks to biographies by Pemberton and Merwin, and best of all, one by George R. Stewart called *Bret Harte, Argonaut and Exile*.

And yet much about Bret Harte's life and the ways it engendered his art is veiled. He was a Victorian, that is to say, discreet and impersonal. Except for one instance, during his youth in Northern California, he apparently never kept a diary. His published correspondence, edited by his grandson, deals mainly with daily routines, business matters, and his own bad health. His stories are objective. He was a skilled professional, machine-like in his regularity at meeting deadlines.

Although wary of the psychoanalytical approach to literature, I do say that in his life and work Bret Harte is a prime subject for a critic skilled in this method of literary criticism. He could start with Harte's first—and some say best—story, "M'liss," seemingly the most personal of all his tales, that of a schoolmaster and a twelve-year-old girl pupil, Melissa, based probably on Harte's own pedagogical experience somewhere on the Mother Lode and later near Eureka.

Why was it Bret Harte rather than Mark Twain who became the myth-maker of California? Here we enter the area of speculation, the alchemical land of literary creation, and of the unforeseeable conjunction of the elements which results in lasting literature.

80

We do know that Bret Harte's success was no accident. From age 11, when his first poem was published in the *New York Sunday Atlas*, he was determined to be a writer. Born in Albany, New York, on August 25, 1836, and christened Francis Brett Harte, of ancestry half English, a quarter Dutch and a quarter Jewish, the boy was brought up in a literary environment. His favorites were Dickens and Dumas, the writers who had the most influence on his subsequent achievement. After the death of his father, young Harte and an older sister in 1854 joined their mother who had gone to California to be married to an old family friend. This stepfather was probably the model for Colonel Starbottle, a Southern orator of the old school, who plays a role in many of Harte's stories.

As a youth, Harte had episodic experiences on the Mother Lode, which perhaps included mining, riding as an express messenger on a stagecoach, and certainly school-teaching; he also worked in a law office, and for an accountant and a druggist. Because he was fated to be a writer, with a sponge-like capacity to absorb and retain, as well as a compulsion to recreate what he saw and remembered, he succeeded in that brief time spent on the most exciting mining frontier the world has ever known, to accumulate enough material to last him a lifetime. Clear at the end of his life, after years of hackwork in the decline that followed the meteoric success of his few great stories, Harte was able once again to find the golden thread and to write "Colonel Starbottle's Client" and "A Protégée of Jack Hamlin's," tales which rank among his best.

In 1850 he worked as printer's devil and editorial assistant on the Union (now Arcata) *Northern Californian*. After two years he returned to San Francisco, the reason being a courageous editorial he wrote condemning a massacre of local Indians and which made Union too hot for him. There he became a compositor and contributor to the *Golden Era*, the city's leading literary periodical, on which his sister was already employed.

Then as he was about to leave for a better paying job in Oregon, Jessie Benton Frémont—one of the three most influential women in his life—got him a political appointment as clerk in the Surveyor General's office and later as secretary to the Superintendent of the Mint, where as someone observed, "he occupies a high, responsible, and lucrative position, with very little to do."

All the while he was writing—sketches, reviews, poems, stories. It was publication of "M'liss" that first won Mrs. Fremont's favor. She encouraged him to write about the Spanish background of California, and in 1863 she placed in the *Atlantic Monthly* his story "The Legend of Mt. Diablo." It and similar tales, such as "The Right Eye of the Commander," and his poem about Concepcion de Arguello, were what inspired Mrs. Atherton to write her best book.

Bret Harte's character was always aloof. His loyalties were to those around him, rather than to those he left behind. He tended to satire, even hoax, although he never went as far as Mark Twain in these broad forms. Harte's poem, "The Calaveras Skull," is one of his best spoofs, on the California Academy of Natural Sciences and its solemn inquiry into the origins of a skull unearthed at the bottom of a mine shaft. He teased a friend by inscribing a book "To Clarence King, author of the *Geology of the 40th Parallel* and other works of fiction."

Condensed Novels (1867) satirized the popular writers of his time. *The Lost Galleon*, published in the same year, was his first book of poems. In *Outcroppings* he edited an anthology of contemporary Californian poetry. This brought down on him the wrath of those whose poems he had left out. It marked his first disenchantment with the public, the initial step which led him finally to forsake California.

In 1862 he married Anna Griswold, an older woman who sang in his church's choir. It was not a good marriage. She had only superficial interest in his career as a writer, nor did she prove to be a homemaker, preferring instead to live in hotels and resorts. After he went abroad in 1878, it was twenty years before they met again, although Harte never failed to remit monthly drafts for the support of her and their children.

Up to 1868 Harte's career did not point to his subsequent world-wide fame. This was precipitated by Anton Roman, San Francisco's leading bookseller-publisher, who decided that California deserved a counterpart to the *Atlantic Monthly*. He turned to Bret Harte as the West's leading literary figure. Together with their wives, Roman and Harte went off on a three months' holiday to the Santa Clara Valley and the Bay of Santa Cruz. There they planned the *Overland Monthly*, the most important literary periodical ever published in California. As editor, Harte named it, and he also collaborated with artist A. P. Nahl on the symbolic vignette of the grizzly bear on the railroad track. He was not infallible in his judgement, however, for he rejected Walt Whitman's "A Passage to India."

That Roman holiday appears in retrospect as the zenith of Harte's career. Not only was the *Overland* born, the periodical destined to carry his name beyond the mountains, continent, and ocean, but also, urged by his publisher, he began to write stories of the Mother Lode and its characters, particularly one that Roman recalled from his own experience as a book-peddler, of a community of rough miners suddenly entrusted with a helpless infant.

Thus "The Luck of Roaring Camp" came to be written during the early months of 1868 by the surf and sand of Santa Cruz. Years later when a clipping reached Harte in Europe, which credited Mrs. Roman with originating the story, Harte wrote indignantly to his wife, "Do you remember the day you lay sick at San José and I read you the story of 'The Luck,' and took heart and comfort from your tears over it, and courage to go on and *demand* that is should be put in the magazine? And think—think of fat Mrs. Roman claiming to be its sponsor!!!"

What did he mean by *demand?* Simply that "The Luck of Roaring Camp," his tender story of the prostitute Cherokee Sal's baby, offended a virtuous female who was setting copy for the issue. There was an uproar over possible outrage of readers' sensibilities. A committee argued over it. Harte stood on his agreement with Roman, that as editor he should have the final word on what went into the magazine.

"The Luck" made its debut in the issue of August 1868. Writing years later, Harte made out that it had been unfavorably received in California for having discouraged immigration by portraying a rough society, and that only in the East had it been hailed. This was an exaggeration, for there were many in the West who were moved to write favorable reviews.

For years Harte had been throwing darts at the target, and he made some very good throws, as with "M'liss." Nothing he had written before, however, had the purity, the economy, and the compact form of "The Luck." The flaw in "M'liss," I think, is that Harte was troubled by it, aware that he was playing dangerously with his own emotional past. "The Right Eye of the Commander" is his masterpiece in the Spanish genre.

"The Luck" neither satirized nor patronized its characters. It is sentimental, pathetic, unrealistic, of course, and yet it is also romantic, heroic, and deeply human. Such is the stuff of myth. The story represents the poetry of life fused in literature, in a tradition that leads back to the time of Homer. This is indeed a function of the artist: to make reality more bearable by veiling its violence with poetry and humor. Life in the gold camps was savage and squalid. In transforming its characters by the device of paradox, whereby the worst are also the best and vice versa, Harte was paying tribute to his master, Charles Dickens.

Here is an example of Harte's prose magic:

"On the long summer days The Luck was usually carried to the gulch from whence the golden store of Roaring Camp was taken. There, on a blanket spread over pine boughs, he would lie while the men were working in the ditches below. Latterly there was a rude attempt to decorate this bower with flowers and sweet-smelling shrubs, and generally some one would bring him a cluster of wild honeysuckles, azaleas, or the painted blossoms of Las Mariposas. The men had suddenly awakened to the fact that there were beauty and significance in these trifles, which they had long trodden so carelessly beneath their feet. A flake of glittering mica, a fragment of variegated quartz, a bright pebble from the bed of the creek, became beautiful to eyes thus cleared and strengthened, and were invariably put aside for The Luck."

Critics have complained that Harte's Mother Lode geography is vague. This is true, in a geographer's sense. Like Norris, Jeffers, and Steinbeck after him, Harte transposed geographical features to meet his literary needs. And yet his is no never-never land. An issue of *The Bookman* in 1901 contained "Bret Harte's Country" by Will H. Clemens, which included state and county maps, showing the settings of the stories. Throughout his work Harte reveals an awareness of California's seasonal landscapes and weather, its trees and flowers, and particularly its great river, the Sacramento.

With "The Luck of Roaring Camp" Harte hit bull's eye. In writing, this is all that matters. Though a writer score only once in a hundred throws, he will be remembered for that success, his misses forgotten and read only by such as I, for comparative reasons.

Harte was thirty-two when "The Luck" appeared. He lived to nearly sixty-six, his life a slow decline from zenith, of loss of public favor in America, of failure as lecturer, novelist, and dramatist; of separation from family, debts, ill health, and finally death from cancer of the throat. All the while he kept on writing, always with meticulous care, publishing, and remitting to his wife. "I grind out the old tunes on the old organ," he wrote to her, "and gather up the coppers, but I never know whether my audience behind the window blinds are wishing me to move on or not."

Why did he leave California? He had no choice. The rocket of his fame took him with it on a glorious transcontinental trajectory. "The Outcasts of Poker Flat," a story nearly as good as "The Luck," also appeared in the *Overland*; and then the poem which gave Bret Harte more fame than anything he ever wrote, one of the most widely read and quoted poems of all time.

> Which I wish to remark—
> And my language is plain—
> That for ways that are dark
> And for tricks that are vain,
> The heathen Chinee is peculiar,
> Which the same I would rise to explain.

"Plain Language from Truthful James" was published in the

Overland for September 1870, and as "The Heathen Chinee" it swept the country.

Readers familiar with English poetry observed that its metre was wickedly that of the threnody in Swinburne's "Atalanta in Calydon." Harte was more than a frontier joker; he was steeped in literature from boyhood; and he regarded the Gold Rush as an epic movement worthy of Homeric treatment. His concept of a native Western literature is found in the "Introduction" to his collected *Works*, published a year before his death.

Harte had no particular regard for the verses which carried his name afar, and it was only at Ambrose Bierce's urging that he put them into the *Overland*, where they promptly became both his fame and his bane. "I have," he said to Ina Coolbrith, "at least I think I have, written more worthy things; things by which I, at least, would choose to be remembered—and then to have that cussed Chinaman hoisted up aloft, flourishing his pigtail in my face."

It was ironical that "The Heathen Chinee" led to the belief that Harte shared the anti-Chinese prejudice of most Californians. The opposite was true, as may be seen from his story, "Wan Lee, the Pagan." His sympathies were with minorities and the downtrodden.

The same year of 1870 also saw publication in Boston of *The Luck of Roaring Camp and Other Stories*. Whereupon Harte signed a contract to write for the *Atlantic Monthly*—$10,000 for twelve stories in one year, a fantastic price for that time. Roman had sold the *Overland* to John Carmany, who sought to keep Harte as editor. The newly-founded University of California announced that it had offered Harte a professorship and the curatorship of the library at a monthly salary of $300 gold. In vain. He had had enough. The city's newly rich disgusted him. He had mellowed somewhat when later he wrote "A Maecenas of the Pacific Coast." He despised the rising cult of pioneers and native son-ism. What was needed, he said, was a society for the suppression of local pride.

California has never accepted its greatest writers in their full stride. Steinbeck's stories of Monterey and its raffish characters,

86

and of the migratory workers, were no more acceptable to the chambers of commerce of peninsula and valley than were Harte's gamblers and whores; and it is said to have been Jeffers's virile poems of the Big Sur's passionate protagonists that kept the University of California from ever honoring him. Only after death and transfiguration are they welcomed into the official hall of fame.

Ten of his literary friends gave Bret Harte a farewell dinner. It lasted till dawn. Thereafter, during the thirty-one years until his death, he never broke the silence between them, save for a single message to Ina Coolbrith.

The next seven years, during which Harte lived in the East, marked his decline and fall. His social popularity prevented him from fulfilling his contract with the *Atlantic*, although he spent the money, and it was not renewed. Lecture tours earned him dwindling amounts, for he was a poor speaker and hated doing it. At his debut in Boston he was introduced by Richard Henry Dana, Jr.

Popular success did not make Harte gracious. He once wrote to his wife, "I hope you will not think me rude to your friends if in enclosing these autographs I cannot help saying how utterly heartless, soulless, indelicate, insincere, and vulgar I hold the whole tribe of autograph-hunters, big and little, and how I loathe them! I could tell you so many stories of them—of their insolence and brutality, and their complete want of any sentiment of gratitude, respect, veneration, admiration, or even knowledge of the people from whom they expect these favours or of any feeling that could excuse their persistence—that you would not wonder at my extravagance. Some day I may tell these things publicly."

On the other hand, one of his biographers tells of how, when Harte had thrown into the wastebasket a letter requesting his autograph, he retrieved it, saying, "I will do it; it might be for a child."

Harte knew the reason for his failure as a novelist and dramatist. "It seems I can write dialogue like an angel, draw characters like a heaven-born genius, but I can't make situations and plots."

87

Like Melville before him, who gained popular fame with his South Seas idylls, Harte wanted to be recognized as more than a local colorist. He resented the public's expecting him to personify his own characters. Actually he was slender, fastidious, even foppish, and given to overdress, as when in delivering the Phi Beta Kappa address at Harvard he wore green gloves.

Ina Coolbrith recalled a time before he had left for the East, "On an occasion of meeting some visitors of note in his *Overland* office, he said to me, quite nettled, 'I wonder what or who I am supposed to be: one of my own characters? I really asked myself when they were gone whether I were 'Jack Hamlin,' 'Oakhurst,' 'Colonel Starbottle,' or—'The Heathen Chinee,' I broke in, 'You are, Frank; you are one and all of them by turns. I never know whom I am to encounter when I come. I sometimes surprise the whole crowd of them;—and, interesting as I find them, I sometimes would really enjoy meeting you alone.' He made a face."

Add to Harte's troubles was his lack of money sense. He spent more than he earned. He borrowed and did not repay. It was gossiped that he once paid his butcher bill with stamps mailed him by fans to cover the return of autographs he failed to send. By 1878 he was broke, and yet still with wife and children to support.

The final blow was a collaboration with Mark Twain on a play that flopped. This led Twain to remark about the man who had given him his literary start in San Francisco, "Bret Harte was one of the pleasantest men I have ever known, and he was also one of the unpleasantest men I have ever known." In his posthumously published autobiography, Twain damned Harte in scathing terms. "In the early days I liked Bret Harte and so did the others, but by and by I got over it; so also did the others. He hadn't a sincere fiber in him. I think he was incapable of emotion, for I think he had nothing to feel with. His heart was merely a pump and had no other function."

Friends in Washington procured Harte the position of commercial agent of the United States at Crefeld, Germany, despite a damning letter Mark Twain wrote to President Hayes urging that Harte not be appointed. This post led to the consulship at

Glasgow. Harte distinguished himself by his absences, although he did see that his paid assistants carried on the official work. An apocryphal story tells of how, upon returning to Glasgow, Harte put his head out the train window and asked, "What town is this?"

After seven years a change of government saw his Scottish post handed out to another writer, of the party in office. For the rest of his life Harte supported himself and his absent family by writing for English periodicals and gathering his contributions into published volumes once or twice a year. Thus did he regain in Europe the popularity lost in the United States. He became a welcome figure in social and literary circles. He dressed elegantly and, thanks to a good agent and a woman patron, he lived comfortably.

The cultured woman was a French writer, the wife of Arthur Van de Velde, the Belgian cultural attaché in London, both admirers of Harte. Although they had nine children, they added the homeless American to their menage. It was Madame Van de Velde's solicitude and encouragement that kept Harte productive until the day of his death.

After Van de Velde's decease, Harte maintained the relationship with his widow. How close it was we do not know, although it appears to have been platonic. Enough to say that it made them both happy and him productive.

When after twenty years of separation, his wife came to England, they did not live together although they met from time to time and corresponded frequently.

It is regrettable that, unlike Henry James who ended his long exile and returned to the United States to write *The American Scene*, Harte never returned to America and to California, as Steinbeck did in *Travels With Charley*, or Dana, a quarter-century after *Two Years Before the Mast*. What a time that would have been by the Golden Gate and on the Mother Lode or if he had camped in Yosemite with John Muir!

If his thoughts ever roamed to California, they were of mountains not men. On a trip to Switzerland in 1895, he wrote in a letter, "And, strangest of all, I find my heart going back to the old Sierras whenever I get above 3,000 feet of Swiss altitude; and—dare I whisper it—in spite of this pictorial composition, I wouldn't give a mile of the dear old Sierras, with their honesty, sincerity, and magnificent uncouthness for a hundred thousand kilometers of this pictureque Vaud."

There was one person in California, however, that Bret Harte remembered—a woman, not a man—and for reasons we will probably never know. To someone returning to California Harte once gave the message, "Tell Ina Coolbrith I shall never forget." That she never forgot, we know from an introduction she wrote for John Henry Nash's facsimile of "The Heathen Chinee" manuscript preserved in the University of California Library, and published in 1924, four years before her death at age 87.

Bret Harte died on May 5, 1902, the year of Frank Norris's death and John Steinbeck's birth. He was then living in Madame Van de Velde's home, The Red House, in Camberley, Surrey, thirty miles southwest of London. She buried him in nearby Frimley churchyard. The service was also attended by Harte's widow, his son Frank and wife, and his daughter Ethel.

His estate was valued at £360-6s-9d, which led Professor Stewart to observe, "He could scarcely have died poorer, if thirty-two years earlier he had accepted a professorship at the University of California." Concern for his family ended at the grave, for he had sold his copyrights upon publication of each book and no royalties accrued to his heirs.

If not the first Californian to have pilgrimaged to Frimley, I am probably the only one to have placed on Harte's grave a branch of *sequoia sempervirens*, known in England as Wellington pine, brought from the great avenue of California redwoods that leads to Wellington College in nearby Berkshire.

Let serve for Bret Harte verses he wrote in 1870 upon the death of Dickens:

> And on that grave where English oak and holly
>   And laurel wreaths entwine,
> Deem not all a too presumptuous folly,—
>   This spray of Western pine.

90

Reading List

BRET HARTE (1836-1902)
The Luck of Roaring Camp and Other Sketches. Boston, Field, Osgood, 1870. Also edited by George R. Stewart, New York, Macmillan, 1928.
The Outcasts of Poker Flat and Other Tales. Introduction by Wallace Stegner. New American Library, Signet Classics, 1964.
The Heathen Chinee; Plain Language from Truthful James . . . with introduction by Ina Coolbrith. San Francisco, John Henry Nash, 1924. Includes facsimile of the original manuscript.
Letters. Boston, Houghton Mifflin, 1926.

GEORGE R. STEWART
Bret Harte, Argonaut and Exile. Boston, Houghton Mifflin, 1931.

MARGARET DUCKETT
Mark Twain and Bret Harte. Norman, University of Oklahoma Press, 1964.

Photograph of Bret Harte by Spy, courtesy of Huntington Library.

MARK TWAIN

8

SEATED BY A coal fire and further warmed by cups of tea, the wind and the rain at bay, we were discussing Californian literature. All went well until I said that I was re-reading Mark Twain. Whereupon my English friend protested, "What do you mean, Mark Twain? He's no Californian!"

"What do you think he is?"

"Even the village idiot knows he's a Missourian. He grew up on the great river, and his three best books are river books."

"Name them," I teased, well aware of my friend's wide knowledge.

"A pleasure, I assure you. *Life on the Mississippi*, *Tom Sawyer*, and *Huckleberry Finn*."

"What about *Roughing It?*"

He snorted, then filled our cups, and settled back with a smile.

"My dear boy, you know very well that *Roughing It* is five-eighths Nevada, two-eighths Sandwich Islands, and one-eighth California."

"Sorry," I said, "I was never good at fractions."

"Pay attention, please. You also know that Mark Twain remained in California only long enough to obtain work elsewhere; and when he left for the last time—I believe it was around 1868—he never returned, although he lived another forty-odd years."

"It sounds to me like you've been reading the *Dictionary of American Biography*."

Another smile, more tea, and my friend continued, "Not lately, but I have just read Justin Kaplan's *Mr. Clemens and Mark Twain*."

"What about 'The Jumping Frog,' " I persisted. "Will you grant it a Californian pedigree?"

"A mere bagatelle. You will recall Mark's contempt for 'that villainous backwoods sketch.' He didn't like taking second place to a frog."

"You must admit that 'The Frog' has been jumping for a century. It's the only story I know of to have spawned an annual sporting event."

"True, unless we call the Ramona Pageant a sporting event. I grant you that the frog population of Calaveras County probably exceeds that of France, at least when the fun starts in Angels Camp."

"You're probably right percentage-wise about *Roughing It*," I conceded, "but let me put it another way. Have we time for a short lecture?"

"Dinner's not until eight!"

"Here goes then. The fact is that California, quite as much as Missouri, was responsible for Mark Twain's becoming a classic writer. I grant you the importance of the Mississippi River and the Nevada frontier in his boyhood and youth, but it was in California—on the Mother Lode and in San Francisco—that he came to manhood, adopted his pen-name, found his own vernacular style, met his literary colleagues and mentors, and embraced his final calling as a travel writer and a lecturer. It was the newspapers of San Francisco and Sacramento that first commissioned him as their travel correspondent, paid him well, provided him with a sophisticated audience, and the opportunity to live and to write the book that launched him."

"I take it you mean *The Innocents Abroad*."

"I do."

"Have it your way. After all, you are my guest. But I warn you, don't try to make *Hiawatha* into a Chumash classic."

93

94

Upon returning to London from my friend's cottage in Berkshire, I proceeded to reinforce my California "lecture" with a massive re-reading of Mark Twain, particularly his San Francisco and Mother Lode adventures of the 1860's. There was no problem in obtaining his books. From the beginning of his career, right up to Penguin paperbacks, Mark Twain has been an Anglo-American author. Later in his life he lived long abroad, once for nearly a decade. In the 1890's both he and Bret Harte were resident in England, although the break between them, dating from twenty years earlier, was lasting and they apparently never met again.

Yet in every consideration of Californian literature to this day, their names are linked in a kind of frontier blood brotherhood. What they fell out over is what often causes human fallout: money. Twain also accused Harte of deserting his family. This was untrue, at least in a fiscal sense, for even though Harte and his wife did live apart for many years, he never failed to support her and their children.

Despite moral judgments of his onetime friend and mentor, Twain never repudiated Harte as a writer. He always regarded "The Luck of Roaring Camp" as the classic it is. Nor did he forget that it was Bret Harte who, as the literary leader of California, gave him several publishing opportunities. "He trimmed and trained and schooled me patiently," Twain wrote later, "until he changed me from an awkward utterer of coarse grotesqueness to a writer of paragraphs and chapters that have found a certain favor."

Harte proved the more loyal of the two; he never turned on Twain, either as man or writer. In reviewing *The Innocents Abroad* in the *Overland Monthly*, he generously said, "It is like an Indian spring in an alkaline desert."

Rereading the works and lives of these two kindred authors made it clear to me that Mark Twain was the greater writer, and for the reason that he embodied in his character and craft a larger capacity for development. Whereas Bret Harte never transcended his Mother Lode triumphs and was content to go on repeating himself for thirty years, Twain proceeded from

"The Celebrated Jumping Frog of Calaveras County," *The Innocents Abroad*, and *Roughing It*, to those immortal river books and to become the universally best known American author of all time.

Mark Twain's growth did not come easily. It was a struggle all the way, as literary growth always is. Success, not failure, was his worst enemy—success, of which that other nineteenth century novelist, Anthony Trollope, said, "It is a poison that should only be taken late in life and then only in small doses."

In the beginning, Twain feared that Bret Harte would outshine him. It was in the early 1870's, soon after they had both left California to work the rich eastern market; and with the publication of "The Luck of Roaring Camp" Harte's star was blazing in the sky. Discouraged by family worries, Twain abandoned work on *Roughing It*, and wrote to his brother Orion, "I plan to stay shady and quiet till Bret Harte simmers down a little, and then I mean to go up head again and stay there."

This is what happened. It recalls a comparable rivalry that developed a century later, when William Faulkner beat Ernest Hemingway to the Nobel Prize. Then we saw "Papa" rally and make it to the Swedish tape with *The Old Man and the Sea*.

Just as "Heathen Chinee" was Harte's fame and bane, so did "The Jumping Frog" plague Twain. My English friend was right. At least in the beginning, Twain did call it "a villainous backwoods sketch." The worst cut was suffered when readers confused the two writers, as when after Twain had lectured in New Orleans, one came up and said, "I have not read all of your writings, Mr. Twain, but I think I like 'The Heathen Chinee' the best of all." This recalls the Upton Sinclair-Sinclair Lewis confusion of our time.

The Gold Rush was the major factor in the development of both Bret Harte and Mark Twain, for it was this epic movement that drew the two young men west in its wake, Harte in 1854, Twain seven years later. Both looked back with nostalgia on that era of the argonauts. Twain called it "the watershed dividing an age of high morality and lofty impulses from an age of money lust, hardness, and cynicism." He was quick to glamorize it.

Whereas Bret Harte's fictional Gold Rush included women, Twain shied away from sex, as he did throughout his work. "It was a wild, free, disorderly, grotesque society," he wrote. "*Men*— only swarming hosts of stalwart *men*—nothing juvenile, nothing feminine visible anywhere."

It is true that *Roughing It* is only fractionally Californian; and yet the ambiance of the Nevada silver rush of the 1860's and the boom towns of Carson City and Virginia City which Twain chronicled, is akin to that of the Mother Lode of a decade earlier. Its opening chapters, describing the stagecoach journey from St. Joseph, Missouri to Carson City, via Salt Lake City, are as classic for that mode of travel as Stevenson's *Across the Plains* was to prove for the crossing by railroad. Both Twain and Harte deified the stagecoach driver.

Roughing It includes extraordinary chapters on the two lakes, Tahoe and Mono, which lie along California's border with Nevada. They could be extrapolated and printed together as symbolizing the bright and dark angels of Twain's nature. To the end of his life he held Tahoe to be the world's most beautiful body of water. We even find a paradisal description of it in his European travel book when, in *The Innocents Abroad*, he exalts it above Italy's Lake Como.

On the contrary, that bitterly alkaline Mono Lake is a kind of infernal Dead Sea in Mark Twain's imagination. He writes with grim intensity of how a sudden storm on it nearly cost the lives of him and Calvin Higbie, to whom he dedicated *Roughing It*.

By the time he came in 1870-71 to write his western book, Twain had achieved a strong, flexible prose style. He learned this in the best way to learn writing—by writing. As Hemingway did in his time, Twain developed his facility by writing for newspapers. We could press the parallel a bit by assigning to Gertrude Stein the role played by Bret Harte; from them Hemingway and Twain received the push that brought them to their own stylistic perfection.

In 1863 Twain quit Nevada for California. He already had an audience in San Francisco, for newspapers there had reprinted some of the grotesque hoaxes he wrote for the Virginia City

Territorial Enterprise. His reason for departure was akin to that of Bret Harte's for quitting his newspaper job in Northern California: the place got too hot for him. In writing later in *Roughing It* of his exodus from Nevada, Twain clouded his motives. "Just naturally restless" was one reason he gave. Another was that he didn't want to see Nevada pass from territory to state. Here is how he finally confessed it:

"Mr. Goodman went away for a week and left me the post of chief editor. It destroyed me. The first day, I wrote my 'leader' in the forenoon. The second day, I had no subject and put it off till the afternoon. The third day I put it off till evening, and then copied an elaborate editorial out of the *American Cyclopedia,* that steadfast friend of the editor, all over this land. The fourth day I 'fooled around' until midnight, and then fell back on the *Cyclopedia* again. The fifth day I cudgeled my brain till midnight, and then kept the press waiting while I penned some bitter personalities on six different people. The sixth day I labored in anguish till far into the night and brought forth—nothing. The paper went to press without an editorial. The seventh day I resigned. On the eighth, Mr. Goodman returned and found six duels on his hands—my personalities had borne fruit. So I thought I would depart and go abroad into the world somewhere."

Don't look for booster literature in *Roughing It*'s California chapters. Twain thought our piney forests too drab to rank with the hardwood glories of New England. He found the absence of distinct seasons a bore. "No land with an unvarying climate can be very beautiful," he wrote. Nor did the city by the Golden Gate move him to the rapture expressed by virtually everyone else who has written about it. Here is how he described it:

"San Francisco, a truly fascinating city to live in, is stately and handsome at a fair distance, but close at hand one notes that the architecture is mostly old-fashioned, many streets are made up of decaying, smoke-grimed wooden houses, and the barren sand hills toward the outskirts obtrude themselves too prominently. Even the kindly climate is sometimes pleasanter when read about than personally experienced, for a lovely cloudless sky wears out its welcome by and by, and then when the longed for rain does come it stays. Even the playful earthquake is better contemplated at a dis—."

From up close, Sacramento gets a hot blast from Twain, but when he looks down on the valley from the Sierra Nevada, he creates the classic vista seen in their time by John Muir, Frank Norris, and John Steinbeck:

"There is a transition for you. Where will you find another like it in the Western Hemisphere? And some of us have swept around snow-walled curves of the Pacific Railroad in that vicinity, six thousand feet above the sea, and looked down as the birds do, upon the deathless summer of the Sacramento Valley, with its fruitful fields, its feathery foliage, its silver streams, all slumbering in the mellow haze of its enchanted atmosphere, and all infinitely softened and spiritualized by distance—a dreamy, exquisite glimpse of fairyland, made all the more charming and striking that it was caught through a forbidden gateway of ice and snow, and savage crags and precipices."

Then occurs a nostalgic evocation of Gold Rush days: "The men are gone, the houses have vanished, even the name of the place is forgotten. In no other land, in modern times, have towns so absolutely died and disappeared, as in the old mining regions of California."

Which brings back us to that classic story of "The Celebrated Jumping Frog of Calaveras County."

Why Mark Twain quit newspaper work in San Francisco for the Mother Lode was because his pal Steve Gillis was in a jam with the police. Twain went bail for him, Gillis vanished, whereupon the law came for the bondsman, and Twain joined Steve at his brother Jim's hideout cabin on Jackass Hill. Twain hung around the local saloon, and it was there that he was said to have heard a character by the name of Ben Coon drawl out the fabled story of the frog who was so weighted down by a bellyful of birdshot that he couldn't jump. This is a more likely source than the Shirley Letters.

Back in San Francisco, when the heat was off, Twain spun the yarn for Artemus Ward, who urged him to write it out in the vernacular and send it to New York for a volume of humorous stories Ward was readying for publication. By the time Twain got around to doing this, it was too late; the book had gone to press. The editor passed it on to a New York newspaper. Ever since then, "The Frog" has continued to jump.

During his brief sojourn on the Mother Lode Twain tried his hand at gold mining, but again he failed to strike it rich, even as he failed as a silver miner in Nevada. "Our wanderings were wide and in many directions," he wrote in *Roughing It*, "and I could give the reader a vivid description of the Big Trees and the marvels of Yosemite; but what has this reader done to me that I should persecute him?"

Mark Twain found in the West something far richer than gold or silver—his literary fame; and he came eventually to regard "The Jumping Frog" for what it was, his first passport to the eastern land of gentility.

When he became fed up with newspaper work in San Francisco, Twain persuaded the *Sacramento Union* in 1866 to pay him $20 apiece for a series of twenty-five letters to be written from Hawaii, known then as the Sandwich Islands. Some of these lively reports he used later to pad out *Roughing It* to the length called for.

The success of this series led the *Alta California*, the state's other leading newspaper, to pay Mark Twain's passage as its correspondent on the European pleasure cruise of the *Quaker City*, the first in a long procession of tourist cruises that continues to this day, more often in the sky. First published in San Francisco, these letters were expanded into *The Innocents Abroad*, the book which flooded Twain with fame and fortune, and which remains one of the best travel books ever written.

When Samuel Langhorne Clemens came west in 1861, he intended to stay for only three months. He remained for seven years. In the course of his travels later to many parts of the world, he returned only once to San Francisco. That was after the cruise of the *Quaker City*, and the reason was to persuade the *Alta California* to relinquish copyright on his letters for eastern publication of *The Innocents Abroad*.

He rewrote the book in San Francisco, 200,000 words of it in two months, working from before midnight until seven or eight the next morning. Not until he came to write *Huckleberry Finn* did he again tap such a deep creative vein. He had enormous physical stamina.

Twain's shaping of *The Innocents Abroad* coincided with Bret Harte's readying of the first issue of the *Overland Monthly*. Harte found time nevertheless to read Twain's huge manuscript. Its author wrote later, "Harte read all the ms. of 'The Innocents' and told me what passages, paragraphs, and chapters to leave out—and I followed orders strictly. It was a kind thing for Harte to do, and I think I appreciated it." Two of the chapters appeared in the *Overland*, the second, "A Californian Abroad," in the same issue which contained "The Luck of Roaring Camp."

Before he left San Francisco, Twain embarked on his career as lecturer that was eventually to bring him fully as much applause and lucre as his writing did. His debut is hilariously described in the last chapter of *Roughing It:* "For other people there was facetiousness in the last line of my posters, but to me it was plaintive with a pang when I wrote it: 'Doors open at 7½. The trouble will begin at 8'. That line has done good service since. Showmen have borrowed it frequently. I have even seen it appended to a newspaper advertisement reminding school pupils in vacation what time next term would begin."

After he left for the last time in the summer of 1868, why did Mark Twain never return either to Nevada or California? It was not an aversion to traveling. His lecture tours took him as far as Australia and South Africa. He crossed the Atlantic more than twenty times. Nor was it simply a rejection of his bohemian past by one who had become the friend of presidents and kings. At his farewell lecture, to a packed house, given at Carnegie Hall on April 19, 1906, with General Grant in the chair, he opened with a fervent plea for aid to the victims of the catastrophe that had just destroyed the city of his youth.

It was, rather, the opposite of rejection. In the four decades that had passed since he left California, Mark Twain suffered disillusionment and deepening pessimism. There was family sorrow. He proved a poor business man and had to go into bankruptcy. He drained himself lecturing in order to pay his debts. Success was his in the sense of universal acclaim, but the price on it was proportionately high.

And so he came to look back on his feckless frontier days as the freest and happiest of all. Did he recall the dictum that the highest good to which man can attain is to be a genius and remain obscure? When a western friend queried him as to why he had never returned, the wise old writer replied:

"Those were the good old days! the old ones! They will come no more. Youth will come no more. They were so full to the brim with the wine of life; there have been no others like them. Would you like to have me come out there and cry?"

Halley's Comet was in the sky at Mark Twain's birth in 1835. All his life he had the premonition that his death would coincide with the comet's return, seventy-five years later. He was right. Mark Twain died at sunset on April 21, 1910, one day after Halley's Comet reached its perihelion. His literary reputation, based as it is on the Far West, remains at zenith.

Reading List

MARK TWAIN (1835-1910)
Roughing It. Hartford, American Publishing Co., 1872; also edited by Henry Nash Smith, New York, Harper, 1959.
Letters from the Sandwich Islands. Edited by G. Ezra Dane. Stanford University Press, 1938.
Autobiography. New York, Harper, 1924. 2 vols.

JUSTIN KAPLAN
Mr. Clemens and Mark Twain, a Biography. New York, Simon & Schuster, 1966.

MARGARET DUCKETT
Mark Twain & Bret Harte. Norman, University of Oklahoma Press, 1964.

Photograph of Mark Twain, courtesy Bancroft Library.

The Splendid Idle Forties

GERTRUDE ATHERTON

9

THE RABBIT must be caught before the stew can be made. Likewise a book cannot be read until it is in hand. My problem was to get my hand on a particular one of the upward of fifty books that Gertrude Atherton wrote during her long life. Born at San Francisco in 1857, she died there in her beloved city nearly ninety-one years later, the grand old lady of American literature.

The quest began in Boston on a June day of 96 degree heat and 85 per cent humidity. I sweated through three second-hand bookshops before I hit pay-dirt in the fourth. In answer to my question, "Have you any books by Gertrude Atherton?" the proprietor exclaimed, "Do I have any books by Gertrude Atherton? I've got 'em all!"

He wasn't too far off. He led me deep into the darkest corner of his huge shop that was stacked with a hundred thousand volumes of belles lettres. There he knelt as though to pray, and called to an assistant to bring him an electric light on a long extension cord. I knelt beside him, praying that the book I sought would be there.

"Why do booksellers always begin the alphabet from the bottom shelf up?" I complained.

He paid no attention, as he began to pull out, blow off the dust, and read aloud the titles of what proved to be a respectable collection of thirty-five of Gertrude Atherton's considerable output.

I kept waiting for the one I wanted most, her book called *The Splendid Idle Forties*, subtitled "Stories of Old California," and published in 1902. There were other volumes of the fiction and non-fiction she wrote about her native state, and those I put aside to take with me.

When at last every book had been unshelved, dusted, and named, I expressed disappointment at not finding my prime desideratum.

"Don't blame me," the bookseller said, "it used to be a common book. Then some nuts out west got out a bibliography of what they claimed were the best books of Californiana, including *The Splendid Idle Forties*. Then what happened? Well, there are jackasses who will buy a book only if it is on someone else's list. They never read 'em. All they want is to brag that they have corralled them all."

"Then what do they do?" I asked, innocently.

"I'll tell you what they do. They move on to another list and start all over. It's these buzzards who've made that a scarce book."

"You must be referring to *The Zamorano Eighty*," I said. "It was published by the Zamorano Club of Los Angeles about twenty years ago."

"That's it," he exclaimed. "Wasn't Zamorano an early pirate?"

"A printer," I said. "Mexican California's first printer."

"The same thing. You ought to see the last bill I got from my printer."

He packed my purchases in two shopping bags, and I trudged across Boston Common, grateful for the shade of the old elm trees and with only a passing glance at the grassy group of hippies. The next day in the Public Library on Copley Square, which from the outside resembles a Florentine palace, I found that *The Splendid Idle Forties* was kept in the rare book room. I wanted a copy "to go," and so I crossed the river to Cambridge.

All bibliographical roads lead eventually to Harvard's Widener Library, the greatest university library in the world. There at last I found a circulating copy of the book I sought. Back in my Boston digs, I eagerly re-read some of the most enchanting stories ever written about California "before the gringo came."

It was Phil Townsend Hanna who first led me to those Atherton stories. In reviewing Western Americana for *Westways*, I was annoyed by the anti-southern California bias displayed by Gertrude Atherton in her volume, *My San Francisco*, which she accurately sub-titled "A Wayward Biography"; or perhaps it was her *Golden Gate Country*, also published in the mid-1940's. I chided her for this.

Hanna called me in. "You are right," he said, "but we can't print it."

"Why not?" I demanded, still a long way off from my mellower years.

"Because no gentleman criticizes a very old lady. Do you realize Mrs. Atherton is nearly eighty?"

"I'm not writing as a gentleman," I protested.

"Maybe not," Hanna replied, gently. "but I'm editing as one. Go read her *Splendid Idle Forties*. They are the finest stories ever written about early California, and I'm not overlooking Bret Harte."

I did. He was right. They were, and still are. Although romantic, mechanically plotted, and theatrical in characterization, they are nevertheless essentially faithful to history, landscape, and human motivation. They poignantly embody the drama of that crucial decade, when the Yankees conquered California, and the pastoral era was succeeded by the golden age, the railroad, automobile, and airplane, by all of what we call progress.

Now with California's population reaching twenty million and a doubling of that figure by the year 2000, Gertrude Atherton's stories of love and death, bull and bear fights, moonlight *meriendas*, horse races and fancy dress balls, are increasingly meaningful and precious. They are truly classics of Californiana.

It is a publishing scandal that *The Splendid Idle Forties* is virtually unobtainable in an ordinary reading copy. If one seeks it in a public library, he will find it more often than not, as I did, sequestered in the treasure room as one of the coveted Zamorano Eighty. In 1960 the Book Club of California reprinted some of the stories, with an introduction by Oscar Lewis, in a beautiful edition from the press of Lewis and Dorothy Allen in Kentfield, Marin County, limited however to only 150 copies and priced at $30.00 a copy. This left the garden variety of reader as unsatisfied as ever. It is difficult to understand how the book escaped the avalanche of California centennial reprints that broke loose in the 1940's.

Let's go back over Gertrude Atherton's long and fruitful life, and see how she came to write these classic stories. Most of her myriad books are deservedly forgotten. She wrote too often from the top of her clever mind. In only a few instances did she go down deep for her material. The best source on her life and work is her own autobiography, *Adventures of a Novelist*, which appeared in 1932 when she was seventy-five years old. It is still enormously readable and only slightly less informative. If one does not demand precise dates—and I suppose that as a former librarian I am excessively preoccupied with such—one can relive the author's varied life through the six hundred pages of her memoir.

Born on San Francisco's Rincon Hill, the writer-to-be was the daughter of Thomas Lodovick Horn and Gertrude Franklin. "The marriage lasted three years. My father permitted his young wife every extravagance. But she hated him increasingly. They quarrelled incessantly; he took to drink, and as my mother was in hysterics most of the time while I was on the way, it is a wonder I was not born an idiot. Undoubtedly the abnormal conditions caused that dislocation of particles, or rotten spot in the brain, or whatever it may be that produces fiction."

Gertrude was raised by her grandfather, secretary of the Bank of California, who provided her with the books that led her ineluctably toward a literary life. Before the parents finally separated, there were lively times in the house on the Hill, her exuberant father having taught the little girl to stand on the dinner table and kick the plates into the laps of the guests.

Later, when George Atherton, son of the wealthy Faxon Dean Atherton and Dominga de Goñi, a Spanish aristocrat he had met in Chile where he was amassing a fortune in hardware, came courting Gertrude's mother (whose second marriage had also ended in divorce), it was the precocious, blonde, and beautiful Gertie who ended up marrying him. Later she described her marriage as "one of the most important incidents of my school life." George, she declared, talked a lot but never said anything.

After fathering a son (who died in childhood) and a daughter, George obligingly died, leaving his young widow firmly connected with one of California's most colorful, prestigious, and wealthy families. He died at sea on a ship returning from Chile, and in order to bring the body back for burial in Lone Mountain Cemetery, the captain pickled George Atherton in a barrel of rum. This made for discontent among the crew, as the spirits were deducted from their ration.

Apparently the story is apocryphal, and is denied by her at the same time that she repeats it, that the first that Gertrude knew of her husband's demise was when a barrel of rum was delivered to her home and rolled onto the porch. "I haven't ordered any rum," she protested, at the same time asking a servant to broach the barrel. And there was George.

It was before she was left a not unhappy widow that Mrs. Atherton began to write, first a few pieces for *The Argonaut*; and then, with a pent-up rush, her first novel which, from having read Robert Louis Stevenson's essay on alliteration and assonance, she called *The Randolphs of Redwoods*. She sold it to *The Argonaut* for $150, and promptly spent the money on books and clothes.

The novel appeared anonymously, for it was the thinly veiled story of one of the juiciest scandals of the scandalous San Francisco peninsula, that of drunken Nelly Gordon and her even more debauched mother. When it finally came out that the author was the young society matron, Mrs. Atherton, the brouhaha was enormous. Proper young ladies of twenty-five didn't write, or if they did, certainly not books about a household of drunken women. In *My First Publication*, a Book Club of California volume edited by James D. Hart, Mrs. Atherton is one of eleven California authors who describe their earliest appearances in print.

Thus was Gertrude Atherton launched on a colorful career, marked by independence, originality, and a thumbed nose at social and literary conventions. This culminated with *Black Oxen*, the most sensational American novel of the early 1920's, which told of the rejuvenation by glandular therapy of an aging woman and her subsequent love life. Mrs. Atherton was not writing from ignorance or imagination alone; she had experienced this treatment, and five novels promptly poured from her pen. *Black Oxen* was widely denounced by preachers and club-women, and as widely read.

As the Atherton books appeared year after year, they were anticipated by her friends and enemies with mingled eagerness and dread, for she had a gift for the wicked phrase, as when she described George Moore as looking like a codfish crossed with a satyr.

"Everyone secretly cherishes the ambition to be 'put in a book'," she wrote, "But no one is ever satisfied with anything save incense, butter, and honey, unrelieved by salt or spice." When she decided to write a novel about Washington, she announced her intention to choose one of the senators as her hero. The subsequent *Senator North* is said to be a portrait of Senator Hale of Maine, to which he willingly consented and advised.

After she became a widow, Mrs. Atherton flew the California nest for New York and Europe, fancying herself as a kind of female Henry James. Her autobiography is full of great ones: Thomas Hardy, with whom she talked cable cars; Winston Churchill, who came off second best; and Oscar Wilde whom she refused to meet because she didn't like the looks of his big blubbery mouth; and a whole gallery of others.

The Randolphs of Redwoods was followed by another California novel, *Los Cerritos*, written while she was living in a convent at Boulogne. In setting and theme it anticipated two California classics: John Steinbeck's *To a God Unknown* and Frank Norris's *The Octopus*.

Los Cerritos was drawn from her experiences soon after marriage, when George took her to live for a year on the family's Rancho Milpitas, in the Jolon Valley near Mission San Antonio, later part of Hearst's Rancho San Simeon and now the Hunter Liggett Military Reservation. Trouble ensued with Mexican squatters on the ranch. This was her first view of poverty, and it led to a deepening of her insight and growth as a novelist.

'She never married again. Let her tell why. "I invariably discovered that an absorbing interest in a new man afforded a mental stimulation which inspired a book; and as soon as the book was ready to be born, the man ceased to interest me; having served his purpose, he was tactfully or abruptly discarded. More enemies. It was Heine who said, 'A woman always writes with one eye on some man and the other eye on the paper, except the Countess Hahn-Hahn who has only one eye.' This may be true, but I wrote better when I grew independent of this particular form of stimulation."

In the late 1880's, while living abroad and in a barren period between books, Mrs. Atherton came upon a paragraph in the literary column of a London weekly. It ran something as follows: "Why do California writers neglect the old Spanish life of that state? Never has there been anything as picturesque and romantic in the history of America, and it is a mine of wealth waiting for some bright genius to pan out."

"I read no more," Mrs. Atherton declared. "Forked lightning was crackling in my skull. It illumined a dazzling vista. Bret Harte had barely touched upon that period and its nuggets were mine."

"There was some excuse for my past indifference. I had never visited the old Spanish towns of California, nor even read a history of the state; and when the subject came up, which was rarely, Mother Atherton had always sniffed. What were Spanish Californians in comparison with the aristocratic exiles of Chile? I had received the impression they were mere dirt."

"Now, vague references, rumors, scattered pictures by Bret Harte, floated down my memory to fire enthusiasm. A week later I was on my way to California."

The determined manner in which Gertrude Atherton set out to prepare herself for writing about early California is reminiscent of Helen Hunt Jackson's industry in gathering the material that went into *Ramona*. First of all, she read Hittell's four-volume *History of California*, as well as other standard sources found in San Francisco's libraries, most of which were destined to perish in the fire of 1906, along with her own manuscripts and papers. Her later archives are preserved in the Bancroft Library.

And she went to see her mother-in-law, Dominga Atherton. "Why you write of those peoples?" the old lady scorned. "Only Mexicans before. No come from old Spain."

Nevertheless she gave Gertrude letters of introduction to the Castros, the Argüellos, and the De la Guerras, all the way down state from Monterey to San Luis Obispo and Santa Barbara. With her half-sister, Aleece, Gertrude set out for the south. Their adventures are vividly recalled in her autobiography.

She was enchanted by the beauty of the Monterey-Carmel area, as Dana had been in the 1830's, Stevenson in the 1870's, and as Mary Austin, George Sterling, Robinson Jeffers, and John Steinbeck were yet to be. She lived for a time with the old families, particularly the De la Guerras in Santa Barbara, They were only a generation removed from the time about which she planned to write. Their memories were alive. The old people's clothes still hung in the closets or were packed in the chests. The rodeos, fandangos, and grand balls were still held. And the landscape—the tortured cypresses, the stately pines and redwoods, mountainous configurations such as Bishop's Rock at San Luis Obispo, and Zaca Lake, and the fields of yellow mustard after the spring rains—all of these were unchanged. The ruined missions haunted her, as they did Mrs. Jackson, and they came to play roles in her stories.

When Mrs. Atherton returned north to Ross in Marin County, her notebooks were packed with details of landscape and weather, of costumes and customs, all of which when wedded to the historical background absorbed from reading, gave to her California stories such remarkable versimilitude.

Not until Idwal Jones appeared a generation later, with his genre stories and novels of old California, did any writer approach Gertrude Atherton in her mastery of this medium. The first fruits appeared in English magazines and were collected in the volume *Before the Gringo Came*. In 1900 some of the same material, gathered from the De la Guerras, went into the novel called *The Doomswoman*, and still more into *Rezanov* in 1906, both of which were republished in 1915 in a single volume, misleadingly given the same title, *Before the Gringo Came*, of the 1894 volume of stories. No wonder bibliographers have been confused.

Where did *The Splendid Idle Forties* get its title? Toward the end of the 1890's, Mrs. Atherton rewrote her first *succès de scandale, The Randolphs of Redwoods*. The result was published in England in 1899 as *A Daughter of the Vine*, and was roughly handled by the critics, one of whom asked, "Why doesn't Mrs. Atherton give us more stories of the splendid idle forties, instead of harrowing us with the hateful picture of a female drunkard?"

At that moment—it was the year 1902—her American publisher had in press a new and enlarged edition of the stories which had originally appeared in *Before the Gringo Came*. Quickly she got a letter off to New York, "Change book's title to *The Splendid Idle Forties*." *Et voilà*.

Among the sources she used for background, Mrs. Atherton did not overlook *Two Years Before the Mast*, as we read in her autobiography, particularly Dana's account of social activities in Monterey and of the Robinson-De la Guerra wedding in Santa Barbara. Festive balls and weddings fascinated her, attentive as she always was to social happenings, and especially the dance known as *El Son*. We find it appearing in each of her California books.

She did not shy away from describing the cruelty of the Latin people, particularly to animals. The grisly climax of her story, "The Head of a Priest," is worthy of Maupassant. Ambrose Bierce she knew, and she tells wickedly of putting him in his place when he tried to kiss her in public.

I have heard it claimed that the only somewhat less prolific Irving Stone invented the literary form known as the biographical novel. This claim must yield to Mrs. Atherton's priority. In *The Conqueror*, a biographical novel of Alexander Hamilton, she entered this field as far back as 1902. It was one of her greatest successes, and is the only one of her books that has remained in print to this day. The even earlier *Rezanov*, and the later *Immortal Marriage* and *The Jealous Gods*, are other examples of her pioneer work in the biographical novel.

"Nothing in life is so absorbing as writing an historical novel," she declared, "recreating an era and living in it. In no other mental work—save no doubt in poetry—is the imagination fully liberated, does the writer enjoy the divine sensation of having everything his own way."

Three of her books give Mrs. Atherton a respected place among the authors of non-fiction Californiana. Two of them on the Bay region, already mentioned, were written in her very old age. Earlier she wrote *California, An Intimate History*, a one-volume introduction which can still be read with interest and profit. She was a skilled and disciplined writer, setting herself right to the last a minimum of a thousand words a day, writing for four hours every morning, first in longhand, and then retyping and revising each page at least twice.

She preferred to work at home. "I dislike taking notes in public libraries," she wrote, "an emanation of death and decay seems to come from those thousands of old books, many of them bound in aged calf slowly rotting, and makes me feel as if I were in a mortuary, airless and stifling." Things are better now in public libraries.

She never lost her power to write sharp character vignettes. Here, at nearly ninety, is how she described Mary Austin, one of her few peers in California literature:

"She was a born essayist, but less successful with fiction. Later she went to New York to live and there fell in with a group striving to become super-intellectuals (which they were not) and lost her early simplicity and distinction of style found in *The Land of Little Rain* and *The Flock*. Nevertheless her intellect continued to develop. She was immensely flattered and run after. H. G. Wells praised her, and as she was but mortal, her ego became somewhat inflated. 'Of course,' she said to me one day, '*I* am the greatest woman writer living.' 'The hell you are, Mary,'

113

I replied. But she did not smile. There was no room in that massive intellect for humor."

When Gertrude Atherton died, on the threshold of her splendid active nineties, she was the dean of California's writers. Because of that one inspired volume of stories, *The Splendid Idle Forties*, her place in the pantheon remains secure.

Reading List

GERTRUDE ATHERTON (1857-1948)
  The Splendid Idle Forties. New York, Macmillan, 1902.
  Adventures of a Novelist. New York, Liveright, 1932.
  Before the Gringo Came. New York, Tait, 1894. Enlarged edition, New York, Stokes, 1915.
  The Doomswoman. New York, Continental, 1901.
  Rezanov. New York, Authors & Newspapers Assn., 1906.
  California, an Intimate History. New York, Harper, 1915.
  My San Francisco, a Wayward Biography. Indianapolis, Bobbs Merrill, 1946.
  Golden Gate Country. New York, Duell, 1945.

JAMES D. HART, editor
  My First Publication; Eleven California Authors Describe Their Earliest Appearances in Print. San Francisco, Book Club of California, 1961.

Photograph of Gertrude Atherton, courtesy Bancroft Library.

114

Up and Down California in 1860-64

WILLIAM H. BREWER

10

IF THERE IS one thing to be learned in reading California classics, it is that there is no common denominator for their variety, other than the power of the Californian scene to inspire them. *Habent sua fata libelli*, the Roman wrote, meaning that books, as well as people, have their fates. None was more strange, long-deferred, and unlikely than that of William H. Brewer's *Up and Down California in 1860-64*. It did not appear until seventy years after it was written, and twenty years after its author's death in 1910.

As a book, it was not even written by Brewer, and it owes its being to a God-sent editor, one who was a kind of spiritual descendant of the original writer.

From 1860 to 1864 William Henry Brewer was the field leader of the first California Geological Survey, headed by Josiah Dwight Whitney. During those four years he came to know the state as no one before him (and few since) had ever known it, going not only up and down the coast, over mountains, and through valleys, but also back and forth across California, on foot and on mule and by stage. He was endowed with the same determination and stamina that enabled the Spanish padres, Kino, Garcés, and Serra, to triumph over nature as they did.

During this protracted, arduous, scientific odyssey, Brewer amassed the voluminous data needed for mapping hitherto uncharted terrains, collected thousands of botanical and mineral specimens, wrote a daily journal; and to top it all, he expanded his journal in frequent letters to his brother in their native New York state, letters which were fated to survive the perils of place and time, and eventually form a western travel book with few peers.

How do Brewer's letters compare with those of Dame Shirley? The chief difference is in the writers' intentions. Shirley wrote to her sister, a decade earlier, with an eye on a wider audience. She also wrote with such artifice as to appear artless. Each of her letters home was copied by her and given to a San Francisco periodical for publication therein.

Brewer had no such literary ambition or intention. He was a dedicated scientist, trained in the basic disciplines at Yale and in German and French universities. He was nevertheless an unwitting literary artist, capable of writing a vigorous, flowing prose similar to Dana's in *Two Years Before the Mast*. If Brewer had been motivated, as Dana was, to recast his journal-letters in literary form, the result might have had an equally immediate and wide success, for his description of California in the early 1860's is unmatched by any other in its variety, fidelity, and human interest.

Brewer was a humanistic scientist. The people he encountered interested him as much as the scientific phenomena. We meet in him a whole man, capable of responding in the same letter to the nobility of Mount Shasta and the beauty of an Indian squaw.

Yet letters home, whatever their interest, do not in themselves make a book, much less a classic. To survive, art must have form. How was it that Brewer's letters came eventually to achieve literary immortality, to the extent of their having appeared thus far in the three editions of 1930, 1949, and 1966?

Brewer left California in 1864 to become a professor in the Sheffield Scientific School of his alma mater, and there for thirty-eight years he pursued a distinguished career as a man of science. Literature as such never beckoned him, as it did Dana. His letters home remained in the family, and after his death, were eventually transcribed by his sons, hopefully for publication. They made a large and formidable typescript. None of the scholars to whom they were shown was willing or able to undertake the task of editing them for publication.

Finally, the fate that had carried them across the plains by Pony Express and Overland Stage, and by ship, and had preserved them from the loss and destruction that overtakes most family treasures, brought them to the one man supremely fitted by training, temperament, and experience, to effect their transformation into book form.

This man was Francis Peloubet Farquhar of San Francisco, a native of Massachusetts, graduate of Harvard in the class of 1909, who had come to California in 1910 and worked first as an advertising copywriter for the Bancroft-Whitney lawbook publishing company, and had gone on to become one of the West's leading certified public accountants.

Such was his vocation. His avocation was mountaineering. It was Francis Farquhar who introduced rope-climbing into California, after having mastered the art in the Canadian Rockies. He was the longtime editor of the Sierra Club *Bulletin*, president of both the Sierra Club and the California Academy of Sciences, user and patron of research libraries, a man possessed of an encyclopedic knowledge of the history and natural sciences of his adopted state. He was an unusual blend of economist-writer-explorer-conservationist, ideally prepared to cope with the challenging Brewer typescript.

Francis was one of three Farquhar brothers, all of whom became distinguished Californians. The others were Robert, architect of the California Club and the William Andrews Clark Memorial Library, two of Los Angeles's most beautiful buildings; and Samuel, the scholarly printer who transformed the University of California Press from a routine printing office into one of the country's foremost academic publishing houses.

It was a California friend of Brewer's sons, Mrs. Alfred McLaughlin, who served as the link between the letters and their western editor. When Farquhar first saw them, he responded with excitement and enthusiasm, perceiving instantly the inter-

118

est and importance of Brewer's reports as prime Californiana of a period hitherto not adequately illuminated. He entrained at once for Connecticut to meet Brewer's sons. Then, with their blessing, he went to President Charles Seymour and Printer Carl Purington Rollins and contracted with the Yale University Press to publish the edited volume.

This saw Farquhar's work really begin, five long years of it. The letters had to be fashioned into book form, overlapping duplication and family trivia removed; chapter grouping and headings devised, the sections articulated; notes, chronology, illustrations, index, and finally an introduction provided.

All of this meticulous scholarly procedure was carried out in Farquhar's free time from 1925 until publication in 1930. The result was an editorial achievement to rank with that of Bolton's on the Anza expeditions. Like Bolton, Farquhar brought first-hand topographical knowledge to inform and illuminate his editorial work. The Sierra Nevada he had long made his own, having climbed every 14,000 foot peak in the range, thus becoming a charter member of the Fourteen Thousand Club, whose motto, *Altiora Pedimus*, might be loosely rendered as *Feet are Tops*. He had written the authoritative *Place Names of the High Sierra* and was destined eventually to write the definitive *History of the Sierra Nevada*. His friendship with John Muir dated from 1912. He had met his wife, Marjory, while they were roping their way up a crag during a Sierra Club outing. Yes, this man Farquhar was rocky, rugged, and ready.

Up and Down California was an immediate success, but unfortunately the New England press let it go out of print. Californiana was not their "cup of tea." Constant demand for the book led finally to Yale's transferring publishing rights to the University of California Press, which has twice reissued the book with the editor's up-dated notes.

Farquhar's refinement of Brewer's ore was basically one of rearrangement and elimination, not of rewriting or making additions. The content of the book is Brewer's, the form Farquhar's, constituting a perfect symbiosis.

Form is the advantage Dana has over Brewer. *Two Years*

Before the Mast divides organically into three parts: the voyage out, the arrival and stay in California, the voyage home. Brewer's journeys up and down and across California lack climaxes of comparable dramatic effect, although ascents of Shasta, Lassen, and Diablo, and even of the Temescals in southern California, culminating in the final reconnaissance of the Sierra Nevada, are the book's highest points in a double sense.

We live in a time of vast changes, both social and geographic. Our cities grow at the expense of countryside, San Francisco-Oakland toward San José, and Los Angeles toward San Diego, while Bakersfield-Fresno-Sacramento threaten eventually to urbanize the entire Great Valley. Even our hills and mountains are no longer safe from the assaults of earth-moving machines.

For those who are nostalgic to view the land as it was before man began to raise cities and raze mountains, Brewer's book provides a faithful statewide panorama. Preceded only by Dana on the coast, Brewer visited and described those locales destined to be the settings of many subsequent California classics. The Southern California of Helen Hunt Jackson and Horace Bell, the shoreline of J. Smeaton Chase and Robinson Jeffers; the valleys of Robert Louis Stevenson, Frank Norris, John Steinbeck, and Idwal Jones; the foothills of Bret Harte and Mark Twain; the mountains of John Muir and Clarence King; and the desert of Mary Austin—are to be seen in pre-literary state, described by Brewer with his clear and sensuous vision.

And with vitality, great vitality. How else could Brewer have done what he did, have led his band of men and mules up and down the rough and rugged land, camping in all kinds of weather, climbing range after range, and always lugging his heavy barometer and other instruments and botanical specimens box? His letters abound with triumphs, fatigue, and recuperation, are packed with details of clothes and equipment, food and drink, and their travel and camping routines.

Brewer's response to the beauties of California's landscapes never dulled. Each day he perceived the terrain with fresh vision and renewed intensity. Thus the book's interest never flags. It is sustained by the vitality with which he transfused his prose.

Although it is tempting to illustrate this with numerous extracts, one will have to suffice, that of his response to that part of Monterey County lying between what came to be the Jeffers and the Steinbeck lands:

"Yesterday I climbed the ridge southwest of camp. I ascended about 3,000 or 3,500 feet, a hard climb, and had a good view of over a hundred miles of the Salinas Valley from the Bay of Monterey to above where we last struck it, or over the extreme limits of about 130 to 150 miles, with the successive ridges beyond. *Four thousand to seven thousand square miles* must have been spread out before me. I have never been in a land before with so many extensive views—the wide valley, brown and dry, the green belt of timber winding through it, like a green ribbon, the mountains beyond, dried and gray at the base, and deep green with chaparral on their sides and summits, with ridge after ridge stretching away beyond in the blue distance. Then to the north, a landscape I had not seen before, with the whole Bay of Monterey in the northwest. To the west and south of me was the very rugged and forbidding chain of mountains that extends from Monterey along the coast of San Luis Obispo and there trends more easterly—the Sierra Santa Lucia."

We can go behind the letters to their sources in the Bancroft Library and there examine Brewer's field notebooks and the journals from which, about once a week, he elaborated the missives to his brother. It was Francis Farquhar who persuaded the Brewer sons to return these valuable originals to California. The original manuscript letters are in the Yale University Library, as are Brewer's scientific papers subsequent to 1864.

I spent a long day in the Bancroft with the Brewer papers, leafing through the leather-bound pocket books which contain his pencilled notes of field data, facts and figures and drawings, interspersed with occasional jewels such as

"Twixt women and wine, man's lot is to smart;
'Tis wine makes his head ache, woman his heart."

William H. Brewer was a genial man and a magnetic leader. Although Whitney headed the Geological Survey, it was Brewer's authority in the field, his gift for detail, and his ability to organize his data, that contributed greatly to the Survey's results. He was always ready after a day's work to relax around the campfire and share a keg of lager with his crew, or when in the city to accept a bottle of chilled champagne from a pretty young lady. Among the Survey drawings made by Charles Hoffman, the official topographer, is a delicate one of a beer keg, supported by a steer skull.

Brewer came west in 1860 upon Whitney's call, determined to assuage the sorrow he was suffering from loss of wife and infant in childbirth. He had applied earlier to join the Gunnison expedition as a botanist. It was his good fortune that a letter of application did not arrive in time for him to be considered, for most of the members of the Gunnison survey were massacred by the Indians.

Toothache was the worst thing suffered by Brewer during those years of the roughest kind of life. The constant flow of energy that had to be maintained came from a high protein diet of meat—beef or venison—three times a day. His notes reveal that the price for range beef was ten cents a pound. The only time Brewer bowed to one of greater energy was when the young Clarence King joined the survey party and began the climbs that resulted in his *Mountaineering in California.*

Although natural history—trees, plants, flowers, animals, and birds—is constantly noted, Brewer also had an eye for people, for characters encountered—ranchers, drovers, quicksilver miners, hermits, town ruffians, drunks, even Governor Downey, met in passing on a dusty road in the Santa Cruz mountains. The Survey party went armed against bandits and grizzlies, but suffered no serious confrontations. Brewer had both respect and affection for their trusty mules, more sure-footed than any horse. "To put a load of baggage on a mule," he wrote, "and make it stay there, and at the same time not hurt the mule, is a great art."

Brewer's passion was for mountains, the tops of mountains from where he could obtain accurate mapping data by measuring barometric pressure. His pages abound with panoramic descriptions. St. Helena, Diablo, Lassen and finally Shasta, are surmounted. Years later, in an address to the Appalachian Mountain Club, Brewer reported thus on his ascent of California's noblest mountain:

"When we got to the top of Shasta we found that people had been there before us. There was a liberal distribution of "California conglomerate," a mixture of tin cans and broken bottles, a newspaper and a Methodist hymn book, a pack of cards, an empty bottle, and various other evidence of a bygone civilization."

Each year the survey party wintered in San Francisco. Here is how Brewer reacted to such confinement: "To sit down in the office, write, compare maps, make calculations, and plot sections, is harder work than mountain climbing. I began to long for the field again."

Whitney ran a tight ship. On November 19, 1861, he wrote to Brewer about his winter office schedule. "As far as possible, the forenoon should be kept uninterruptedly for writing, and miscellaneous business attended to in the afternoon. The hours from 3 to 5 p.m. will be reserved as far as is necessary for attending to out of door business, receiving calls, and answering questions relating to private business."

Yet there was never any conflict between them; they formed an excellent team. Brewer found time nevertheless to socialize. His journal contains accounts of convivial affairs, as well as of the death and funeral of the time's greatest preacher-orator, the Reverend Thomas Starr King, who shares with Padre Junípero Serra the honor of being California's representatives in the Hall of Fame in the nation's capital. He also did some critical window gazing, as revealed in this journal entry:

"In a shop window are three paintings by three California artists. It is interesting to criticize them. They are respectively taken from Yosemite, Santa Clara Valley and Lake Tahoe. All have skies flecked with cumulous clouds! All have trees none of which are at all characteristic, and all of them have all the colors a landscape painter may use, save those which are so eminently characteristic of the regions they pretend to represent."

The most vexing aspect of the project was the state's precarious financial condition during the Civil War. Although the Whitney Survey was funded originally by an appropriation of $20,000, the legislature made no regular provision for its continuance. Members of the party went for months without expenses or salary. Whitney had to borrow privately to keep it going. Yet such was their probity as devoted public servants that in no instance would Whitney, Brewer, and the others accept the commissions and emoluments constantly offered them by mining interests. Apart from the Secessionists, Brewer found the greatest threat to the state's stability to come from clouded Spanish land-grant titles. No one could be certain of his property.

During his final year with the survey, Brewer accepted appointment as professor of chemistry in the College of California, the precursor of the University of California. On Tuesday, February 9, 1864, he wrote in his journal, "Went over to Oakland and commenced my lectures there. The first use of the new building and the room not yet finished. Had class of about twenty. The place looks lovely. Back by last boat."

In the following summer Yale called Brewer home as professor of agriculture, and for the next four decades he was associated with Yale and Connecticut in a variety of scientific services. He also made expeditions to Greenland and Alaska. On the former, after being shipwrecked within the Arctic Circle, the party was rescued only after the greatest of hardships. Brewer bore a charmed life. As a member of the United States Forestry Commission, he led in the conservation movement. He also pioneered agricultural experiment work in Connecticut and was the president of the state's Board of Public Health.

In the summer of 1869 he was reunited with Whitney on a field trip to the Rocky Mountains, accompanied by four Harvard graduate students of geology. In the *Life and Letters of Josiah Dwight Whitney* we read of their mission in these words:

"There were rumors in geographical circles of eighteen-thousand foot peaks in central Colorado, at the culminating point in the Rocky Mountains; of peaks therefore, which certainly rivaled, and which might surpass, the high places of the Sierra

124

Nevada and the great volcanoes of the Pacific Coast. During the winter and spring of 1869, Whitney took his four apprentices into his study, to struggle under his practical guidance with the discordant evidence of travelers' tales and government reports. After they had learned all that was to be had from books, they were to attack the problem on the ground."

From this field trip Brewer wrote letters to his second wife that rival those from California to his brother. In 1896 he annotated them for possible publication, but it was not until 1930, when Francis Farquhar (into whose hands the typescript had come), generously turned it over to the Colorado Mountain Club of Denver, that it was finally published as *Rocky Mountain Letters, 1869*. I do not know why Brewer himself never finished the project, or why he did not likewise annotate his California letters.

He returned to California in 1875, 1896, and 1907, primarily to visit Charles Hoffman, his closest companion on the Survey. Because of the infirmities of age, he was unable to return a last time in 1910 to attend the Fiftieth Anniversary of the founding of the College of California and to receive an honorary Doctorate of Laws from the University of California. In the university archives I found the story, told in an exchange of correspondence between Brewer and President Benjamin Ide Wheeler:

"Your early connection with the intellectual life and endeavor of California," Wheeler wrote, "make it for us a matter of opportunity and pride to confer upon you such honour as we can on a significant occasion."

In regretting his inability to be present, Brewer replied,

"The early interest I had in the College; my connection with it in 1863-64, until the graduation of its first class; the emotions that were stirred by its later history and that of its child, the University; the Anxiety as well as Faith and Hope with which I watched the growth of the university through the period and perils of its childhood; the Joy, and may I say, Pride, with which I have seen its triumphant success,—all tend to make my regrets of declination akin to sadness, that I cannot be with you on the anniversary."

Then, for one of the very few times in its history, the University of California conferred the degree *in absentia*. Brewer died soon thereafter in his 83rd year.

Similar recognition came, long after, to Brewer's editor. Although his 80th birthday was near, Francis Farquhar journeyed to UCLA in 1967 to receive the honorary degree of Doctor of Humane Letters. Chancellor Franklin D. Murphy's citation indicated the versatility of this Yankee turned Californian:

"Born and educated in New England, he has shamelessly led a double life since coming to California. On the one hand he is a highly successful certified public accountant; on the other he has won fame as a writer, historian, and conservationist. For his valuable contributions to the art of illuminating western history, and for his vigorous efforts to preserve California's natural heritage, we confer upon him honorary membership in the University of California."

After my day's work on the Brewer archives in the Bancroft Library, I spent an evening with the Farquhars in their home at the foot of the Berkeley hills. Although handicapped by failing eyesight, the still sturdy man was able to lay hands on items among his great collection of mountaineering books. His own publications fill a long shelf. When I asked which was his favorite among them, he pulled down a naval construction cost-accounting study made as a naval reserve officer during World War I, saying, "It has probably had more readers and more results than anything else I ever wrote!"

"What next?" I asked.

Farquhar sadly shook his head. "Too late. If my eyes hadn't given out, it would have been a book on Drake in California. I am convinced that Drake did indeed sail into the Bay of San Francisco and careen the *Golden Hind* on the beach at the mouth of Corte Madera Creek."

"Isn't that where his plate of brass was found?" I asked, referring to the relic nailed to a post by Drake when he claimed New Albion for his queen, and which was given to the Bancroft Library.

"Precisely. And I believe it was discovered at the very place where Drake placed it, fallen, of course, and long since covered by rocks and rubble."

"You could call the book *Up and Down the California Coast in 1579!*"

"I shall leave the material I've gathered to the Bancroft," he replied. "It will help someone someday to write the book."

What great good fortune it was that finally brought Brewer into Farquhar's ken.

Reading List

WILLIAM H. BREWER (1828-1910)
Up and Down California in 1860-1864. Edited by Francis P. Farquhar. New Haven, Yale University Press, 1930; reissued in 1949 and 1966 by University of California Press.
Rocky Mountain Letters, 1869. Denver, Colorado Mountain Club, 1930.

EDWIN T. BREWSTER
Life and Letters of Josiah Dwight Whitney. Boston, Houghton Mifflin, 1909.

FRANCIS P. FARQUHAR
History of the Sierra Nevada. Berkeley & Los Angeles, University of California Press in Collaboration with the Sierra Club, 1965. Paperback edition, 1969.

Photograph of William H. Brewer, courtesy of Bancroft Library.

Mountaineering in the Sierra Nevada

CLARENCE KING

11

"THE GREAT American poet," wrote Clarence King, a hundred years ago, "it may confidently be predicted, will not book his name from the Sacramento Valley." King was a mountain lover who looked down (in a double sense) on all valleys, the San Joaquin, the Sacramento, the Salinas and the Owens. It was a mountain that first drew him to California; not one of the Sierra Nevada which he was destined to celebrate in his only literary book, but rather a more northern pinnacle, that volcanic monolith, California's noblest mountain, Shasta.

This is how it came to pass. William H. Brewer was in his third year as field deputy for Josiah D. Whitney's California Geological Survey, writing home letters that eventually formed *Up and Down California in 1860-64*. In addition to family letters, Brewer wrote also to his former colleagues at Yale where, in 1863, Clarence King was a student in the Sheffield Scientific School.

At twenty-one, the blue-blooded Rhode Islander was a star athlete and outdoorsman, on the threshold of graduation and uncertain of what career to follow. Then, by chance, he heard one of his professors read a letter from Brewer, in which the botanist-geologist told of his ascent of Mount Shasta. "That settles it," King exclaimed, and with a classmate for companion

128

he headed for California, proceeding on horseback from St. Joseph, Missouri.

After a lodging-house fire in Nevada cost them their possessions, including money and a letter of introduction to Professor Whitney, they earned a stake by working in a quartz mill, then made it over the Sierra Nevada to Sacramento, where they boarded a river boat to San Francisco.

How cunningly Fate rules the lives of her chosen ones! Also a passenger on that paddle-wheeler was William H. Brewer, whose Shasta letter had lured King to California. Let King's companion, James H. Gardiner, tell what happened. In a letter home, the young man wrote,

"The steamboat was crowded with people from the mines. Many rough, sunburned men in flannel shirts, high boots, belts, and revolvers were around me, but among them one man attracted my attention. There was nothing peculiar about him, yet his face impressed me. Again and again I walked past him, and at last, seating myself in a chair opposite, pretending to read a paper, I deliberately studied this fascinating individual. An old felt hat, a quick eye, a sunburned face with different lines from the other mountaineers, a long weather-beaten neck protruding from a coarse gray flannel shirt and a rough coat, a heavy revolver belt, and long legs, made up the man; and yet he is an intellectual man—I know it. I went to Clare and told him the case, and showed him the man. He looked at him, and, without any previous knowledge to guide him in the identification, said, from instinct, 'That man must be Professor Brewer, the leader of Professor Whitney's geological party.' "

Whereupon Clarence King introduced himself, and within three days of their arrival in San Francisco, he was appointed Assistant Geologist of the Whitney Survey. As such, he accompanied Brewer on his second reconnaissance of the Sacramento Valley, eventually bearing northeast from Red Bluff to climb Lassen Peak. King's exuberant manner of mountain climbing, inspired by a reading of Tyndall on Alpine glaciers, was here first manifested. Brewer told of King's descent in a bruising *glissade*.

130

Shasta was next, that magnetic mountain then believed to be the highest in the United States. Its summit was for King a kind of journey's end. When he came to write of it in *Mountaineering in the Sierra Nevada*, he was moved to ecstatic, even tumultuous prose:

"When I ask myself today what were the sensations on Shasta, they render themselves into three—geography, shadows, and uplifted isolation. . . . A singularly transparent air revealed every plain and peak on until the earth's curve rolled them under remote horizons. The whole great disk of world outspread beneath wore an aspect of glorious cheerfulness. The Cascade Range, a roll of blue forest land, stretched northward, surmounted at intervals by volcanoes; the lower, like symmetrical Mount Pitt, bare and warm with rosy lava colors; those farther north lift against the pale horizon-blue solid white cones upon which strong light rested with brilliance. It seemed incredible that we could see so far toward the Columbia River, almost across the State of Oregon; but there stood Pitt, Jefferson, and the Three Sisters in unmistakable plainness. Northeast and east spread those great plains out of which rise low lava chains, and a few small, burned-out volcanoes, and there, too, were the group of Klamath and Goose Lakes lying in mid plain glassing the deep upper violet. Farther and farther from our mountain base in that direction the greenness of forest and meadow fades out into rich, mellow brown, with warm cloudings of sienna over bare lava hills, and shades, as you reach the eastern limit, in pale ash and lavender and buff, where stretches of level land slope down over Madelin plains into Nevada deserts. An unmistakable purity and delicacy of tint, with transparent air and paleness of tone, give all desert scenes the aspect of water-color drawings. Even at this immense distance I could see the gradual change from rich, warm hues of rocky slope, or plain overspread with ripened vegetation, out to the high, pale key of the desert."

The circumstances of his departure for California and union with Brewer indicate Clarence King's character—responsive, bold, perceptive, and dynamic. A veritable prodigy, he went on to ever higher achievements, culminating in his founding and directing the United States Geological Survey. Then, at the peak of his scientific career, he left government service and embarked on a vain search for private wealth to support his hedonistic tastes. He died worn out in 1901, short of his sixtieth birthday.

As man, scientist, and writer, Clarence King is one of the most brilliant, puzzling, and disappointing figures in our history. It is nearly a century since his classic work appeared in 1872, the first on what has come to be a long shelf of western mountain literature. It is the work which seemingly inspired John Muir's *The Mountains of California*, published twenty-two years later.

A rereading of King's book led me to King's scientific writings, then to Thurman Wilkins's definitive biography of 1958, and finally to a perusal of the King papers in the James D. Hague collection at the Henry E. Huntington Library. This reading and research culminated in a revelation, documented by Professor Wilkins, that the aristocratic New Englander, renowned scientist and member of exclusive clubs and learned societies, was for the last fourteen years of his life secretly married to a Negro woman, a former housemaid, who bore him five children. No casual affair, it was a marriage of meaning and warmth to both man and wife which, if disclosed, the conventions of the age would not have condoned.

The tension of having to hide his union with the woman he loved, exacerbated by financial disaster suffered in the panic of 1893, drove King out of his mind and hastened his early death. The Bloomingdale asylum to which he was self-committed for a year was located on Morningside Heights, and gave way to what became Columbia University. Just before he was discharged, in December 1894, King wrote to Henry Adams, "I shant like it so well a few months hence when Columbia College moves in here and displaces these open, frank lunatics with Seth Low and his faculty of incurables, so I better go now."

Mountaineering in the Sierra Nevada was the child of King's love affair with California which lasted the three years, 1863-66, he was with the Whitney Survey. His writing during that time was of the kind practiced by Brewer—penciled scribblings in field notebooks, preserved in the Huntington Library.

As a letter writer he was no match for his mentor. The chapters which compose his book were not written until several years after he had left the California survey and was heading one of his own, the renowned United States Geological Survey of the Fortieth Parallel, embracing a hundred mile strip from eastern Colorado to the California line. The idea for it came from Whitney, but the execution, involving first the most adroit Washington lobbying, followed by the recruitment of a brilliant corps and its leadership in the field, was carried out by the bold young King.

Bret Harte was King's literary sponsor. In 1870 the *Overland Monthly* published King's essay on the Shoshone Falls of Idaho's Snake River. Their relationship failed to flourish. Harte renigged on paying King for the contribution. Worse than that, when he went east in a triumph that ended miserably, Harte abused King's credit to run up bills that the younger man had eventually to pay.

It was the *Atlantic Monthly* that encouraged King to write a series of California essays which were then gathered in book form. The volume's success was stimulated by a sensational occurrence in 1873 which gave the author wide publicity. As the leading American geologist, King was responsible for exposing the Great Diamond Hoax, a fantastic scheme which had salted a Utah site with diamonds and rubies and paved the way for a vast international swindle. King's expert knowledge and swift action revealed the plot and made him a hero in the financial centers of San Francisco, New York, and London.

A revised edition of his book in 1874 could have been successfully followed by others on the West, and by stories and novels, for Clarence King was gifted with a colorful style. His interest was in people as well as in science and scenery. He became the idol of the eastern cultural establishment, whose arbiters would have puffed his books to great heights.

And yet, except for a single *jeu d'esprit*, a letter from Spain that was published in *Century* magazine as "The Helmet of Mambrino," King wrote no more in the field of belles lettres. In science also he left a single monument, his *Systematic Geology*, the opening volume of the massive seven-volume set of publications that came from the work of the Fortieth Parallel Survey.

Can we account for this? Why is King remembered, with Dana, as the author of a single youthful classic? What stopped their flow of fine prose? Dana was imprisoned in New England gentility and could never again open the vein that had disclosed the pure gold of *Two Years Before the Mast*. King's self-imposed literary restraint was more complex. Except for its mountains, he did not like California. He was contemptuous of the host of travel writers about the Golden State. "I always go swiftly by this famous point of view," he wrote of Yosemite's Inspiration Point, "feeling somehow that I don't belong to that army of literary travellers who have planted themselves and burst into rhetoric. Here all who make California books dismount and inflate." Did he have Bayard Taylor in mind?

Compared with New England, he found California wanting. "The men and women are dull, unrelieved; they are all alike," he wrote of the Sacramento Valley. "The eternal flatness of landscape, the monotony of endlessly pleasant weather, the scarcely varying year, the utter want of anything unforeseen, and absence of all surprise in life, are legible upon their quiet uninteresting faces. They loaf through eleven months to harvest one."

King's California essays were, he admitted to a friend, only experiments to see if natural history could be made into popular reading. The warm reception given them apparently satisfied him. He was thirty years old when the book appeared. He lived as many years again, years of scientific and social activity and travel, rich in friendship and love, and also of crumbling financial security. His forsaking first literature, then science, in a search for wealth as an international mining entrepreneur, were fatal turns that led to frustration, failure, and death.

Readers are incorrigible in demanding ever more of writers. We are not alone in wanting more of Clarence King. His contemporaries had great expectations of him as a literary man. Upon his death his colleagues in the Century Club of New York published a memorial volume, consisting of his Spanish story,

"The Helmet of Mambrino," and tributes by such great contemporaries as Henry Adams, John La Farge, John Hay, William Dean Howells, and others. They remembered King as a fabulous raconteur, a Yankee Sheherezade, who talked away a whole library of books. Hay testified "to the literary treasures he squandered in his daily and nightly conversation," how King "poured out in inexhaustible profusion his stores of fancy and invention. There were scores of short stories full of color and life, sketches of thrilling adventure, not less than half dozen complete novels, boldly planned and brilliantly wrought out—all ready for the type or the pen; which now—an infinite pity!—are only the stuff that dreams are made of."

Howells, the dean of American letters, came to the heart of it when he wrote, "King was above everything indifferent to literaary repute. He would have preferred not to own the things he wrote, and kept only for his reward the aesthetic delight he had in doing them. I believe that he always vaguely meant to write a great work of fiction, although I do not believe he ever would have done it. He was supposed to have by him the beginning of a novel, and perhaps he had, but it was rather something to bluff his inquiring friends with, to dream over and to fancy finishing, rather than ever really to expect or intend finishing."

Does the shade of Howells ever wander west as far as San Marino? I hope so, for there in the Huntington Library is that fragment of a novel, only a few pages, heavily revised, laid on shipboard in the Caribbean, setting forth the conversation of Negro cabin stewards and a glimpse of a forty-year-old New England spinster, tantalizing in its brevity and promise. Although the manuscript is undated, it was probably written in the 1890's, after King's recovery from mental illness, when he and Henry Adams voyaged to Cuba.

My explanation of why Clarence King never developed as a literary writer is that he was too gregarious. Creative writing is a solitary occupation. Family, friends, and society are the natural enemies of the writer. He must be alone, uninterrupted, and slightly savage, if he is to sustain and complete an undertaking. There are exceptions. D. H. Lawrence was a notable one, a writer who could work in the midst of a crowd. King was a magnetic talker around whom people always congregated. Even on that last trip to Cuba, Adams reported how King became sociably involved with the islanders on various levels, and was never alone and contemplative.

King was a gifted writer, a feeling for words apparent even in the most formidable of his productions such as the huge monograph, *Systematic Geology*, of 1878. When I called for the entire set of the Fortieth Parallel Survey to be brought from the library's basement stacks, the girl on duty ruefully held out her slender arms and said, "Our page is off today and I'm afraid I can't lift those books. Would you mind going down to the basement and using them there?"

"Delighted," was my reply, having always preferred cafeteria libraries.

I saw what she meant when I found the set with its even larger atlases, books that were obviously playing a part in holding up the building. I carried the King volume to a table, and there turned its 801 pages, marvelling at the chromo-lithographs by Julian Bien, and the black and white illustrations after photographs by T. H. O'Sullivan. Finally my eyes were held by this paragraph, written by one who was ever moved by land that culminated in mountains to write his finest prose:

"The method of this volume is historical. It is an attempt to read the geology of the middle cordilleras, and to present the leading outlines of one of the most impressive sections of the earth's surface-film. Over this area is a sky of liquid but cold blue, singularly vaporless for many weeks of the year. Clouds, when they come, gather round the mountain summits or drift over the plain at low elevations, sailing against the hill-slopes to break up and dissolve in the dry air. In the aspect of the country the most conspicuous features are, the pale tones of the plains— light golden green in summer, russet in autumn, and white in winter; the deep blue-green of the forest-covered heights always in view, looming over a plain; and, perhaps most characteristic of all, the cool but dazzling brilliance of the sunlight."

136

When the wheel stops turning, the payoff is to what a writer did, not to what critics wish he had done. Clarence King's reputation as a geologist is now only historical, his work superseded by later research. As a talker, no faint echo is heard. As lover, husband, and father, his story can never be fully known, for his white kinfolk are said to have destroyed the evidence that was in their hands. We have only a few of the love letters he wrote to Ada, his wife, which appeared in a court transcript thirty years after his death, letters of strong feeling and passionate expression. "Ah, my dearest, I have lain in my bed and thought of you and felt my whole heart full of love for you. It seems to me often that no one ever loved a woman as I do you. In my heart there is no place for any other woman and never will be. My whole heart is yours forever."

It was King's only marriage.

So what we begin and end with is *Mountaineering in the Sierra Nevada*, the book that keeps his name alive. The first edition of 1872 was followed by two reprints, and then in 1874 a fourth edition contained a new preface and additional pages on King's climb of Mount Whitney. His first ascent, in blinding weather, was actually of neighboring Mount Langley. When his error was bitingly corrected in print by a later climber, King characteristically rushed west and climbed the true peak.

The preface to the fourth edition constitutes King's farewell to literature. "There are turning-points in all men's lives which must give them both pause and retrospect. In long Sierra journeys the mountaineer looks forward eagerly, gladly, till pass or ridge-crest is gained, and then, turning with a fonder interest, surveys the scene of his march; letting the eye wander over each crag and valley, every blue hollow of pine-land or sunlit gem of alpine meadow; discerning perchance some gentle reminder of himself in yon thin blue curl of smoke floating dimly upward from the smouldering embers of his last camp-fire. With a lingering look he starts forward, and the closing pass-gate with its granite walls shuts away the retrospect, yet the delightful picture forever after hangs on the gallery wall of his memory. It is thus with me about mountaineering; the pass which divides youth from manhood is traversed, and the serious service of science must hereafter claim me."

In 1889 King bought the book's plates and suppressed its further publication, the reason apparently being the complaints of a character described by him in one of the chapters. After King's death, Scribners reissued the book in 1902. The most desirable modern edition is the one edited with an introduction and bibliography by Francis P. Farquhar, illustrated from photographs by Ansel Adams. In 1963 Thurman Wilkins contributed an introduction to a photo-reprint of the first edition.

What are some of its excellences? Foremost is its vitality, a necessity for a book's survival as readable literature. King transfused his prose with the same vigor which marked his life. The high point is his description of the ascent and descent of Mount Tyndall, an expedition which he and Dick Cotter volunteered to carry out as an offshoot of the Brewer survey party. Whatever their embellishments and exaggerations, these two chapters are at the summit of mountaineering literature. King and Cotter were the first to climb the highest Sierra. However comparatively easy it has become to do, with the aid of the accumulated generations' experience, the pioneer effort was altogether heroic. These chapters rise and fall in crescendo and diminuendo, sweeping the reader along to the welcome relief of the final paragraphs.

"At last, faintly curling above the sea of green tree-tops, a few faint clouds of smoke wafted upward into the air. We saw them with a burst of strong emotion, and ran down the steep flank of the moraine at the top of our speed. Our shouts were instantly answered by the three voices of our friends, who welcomed us to their camp-fire with tremendous hugs."

"After we had outlined for them the experience of our days, and as we lay outstretched at our ease, warm in the blaze of the glorious camp-fire, Brewer said to me, 'King, you have relieved me of a dreadful task. For the last three days I have been composing a letter to your family, but somehow I did not get beyond, 'It becomes my painful duty to inform you.' "

Another excellence is King's gallery of characters, such as the miserable hog ranchers, those early-day Joads called the Newtys of Pike, a chapter worthy of Bret Harte and anticipatory of Al Capp and Little Abner.

Imagination was a hallmark of both Clarence King's life-style and prose-style. Although an examination of the Brewer-King field notebooks reveals no such events as chronicled by King in the chapter, "Kaweah's Run," we can only admire the story-teller's art in transforming a routine horseback ride from Visalia to Mariposa into a thrilling escape from Mexican bandits. It is a vivid glimpse of the novelist *manqué*.

An even more persuasive one is in that Spanish tale, "The Helmet of Mambrino." King employed the form of a letter to a friend in San Francisco in telling of his discovery of Don Quixote's golden helmet, which was actually a barber's brass basin. While in Spain, King journeyed to La Mancha, the Don's natal region, and there searched out a battered utensil and had it shipped, with the covering letter, to his crony in California. There it remained a cherished keepsake during the man's lifetime, then it was lost. Today one like it hangs on a wall in the Century Club in memory of their charming King.

The tale was reprinted in 1938 by the Book Club of California, with an introduction by the indefatigable Francis Farquhar. It is a miniature masterpiece of imagination and expression. No wonder his contemporaries wanted more.

Although John Muir's *Mountains of California* is a more graceful and unified book than King's, it followed a blazed trail. Clarence King was the first to climb the Sierra Nevada, and the first to write of the range in sunlight and storm. The poet in him who lent beauty to his prose was suppressed by the scientist, who in turn was forsaken by the seeker of worldly goods and pleasures. King's life became increasingly sad, and finally tragic.

How would he view his beloved range today, he who foresaw what civilization would mean to the wilderness? "It was not until a week after [the ascent of Mount Tyndall] that I realized we had felt none of the conventional sensations of nausea, head-ache, and I don't know what all, that people are supposed to suffer at extreme altitudes; but these things go with guides and porters, I believe, and with coming down to one's hotel at evening there to scold one's picturesque *aubergiste* in a French which strikes upon his ear as a foreign tongue; possibly all that will come to us with advancing time, and what is known as 'doing America.' They are already shooting our buffaloes; it cannot be long before they will cause themselves to be honorably dragged up and down our Sierras, with perennial yellow gaiter, and ostentation of bath-tub."

By 1901 King knew that he was dying. Whereupon he arranged to send Ada and their children to Canada, where the prejudice against colored people was less severe. He also revealed to her his true identity, and made provision with a friend for a fund to support her and their children after his death. Then he went west for the last time, seeking a cure for the tuberculosis that had wasted his sturdy frame, first to Prescott and Pasadena, and finally to Phoenix. In vain. His case was hopeless.

Wilkins records that King's sense of humor did not desert him. "During a lucid moment in his delirium he heard the doctor say that the heroin must have gone to his head. Many a heroine, King murmured, had gone to better heads than his was now." He died in his sleep, the day before Christmas. His brother-in-law came and returned the body to Newport for burial.

Not only his book keeps his name alive. There is Mount Clarence King, elevation 12,909, one of the most majestic of the Sierran peaks. Few are they who are remembered by both a book and a mountain.

Reading List

CLARENCE KING (1842-1901)
Mountaineering in the Sierra Nevada. Boston, J. R. Osgood, 1872; revised & enlarged edition, Scribner, 1874; edited by F. P. Farquhar, Norton, 1935; facsimile of 1872 edition, edited by Thurman Wilkins, 1963.
Systematic Geology. Washington, Government Printing Office, 1878.
The Helmet of Mambrino. Introduction by Francis P. Farquhar. San Francisco, Book Club of California, 1938.

CENTURY ASSOCIATION, NEW YORK
Clarence King Memoirs. The Helmet of Mambrino. New York, Putnam's, 1904.

THURMAN WILKINS
Clarence King, A Biography. New York, Macmillan, 1958.

Photograph of Clarence King, courtesy of Bancroft Library.

12

FROM THE AIR, California is a land of mountains. Except for the Central Valley, the state has hardly any continuous flat lands, and even the great valley itself is narrowly constricted by the Coast and the Sierra Nevada ranges. The old-fashioned flat map gives no true concept of the enormous irregularity of the state. Ideal are the new plastic relief maps, reproducing the contours, from Mt. Whitney to Death Valley.

I keep one of these maps on my study wall as a reminder that California is one of the great mountain states of the world; and furthermore that its settlement and development cannot be understood without a recognition of what the mountains have done and do for its people.

One of my earliest memories is of a framed motto that my parents hung on the wall of the room where I took my afternoon nap. Handsomely printed, with a single decorative initial, it read, "Climb the mountains and get their good tidings. Nature's peace will flow into you as sunshine flows into trees. The winds will blow their freshness into you, the storms their energy, while cares will drop off like the autumn leaves."

It mattered not that no author was given. I took it for gospel. Years passed before I learned that it was by John Muir, from his book *Our National Parks*.

His *The Mountains of California* was among the books inher-

142

ited from my parents. As a boy I knew it only from its tan-colored binding, stamped on the back with the head of a mountain sheep and on the cover with a wreath of pine branches. I never thought of reading it. Mountains were to climb, not to read about.

Then in the Depression years, when I experienced a rediscovery of California upon homecoming after several years' absence, I first read Muir's book, and with great joy. The title is misleading. It should be called *The Sierra Nevada of California*, for its chapters, except for one on "The Bee-Pastures," are entirely on that great range. First published in 1894, its essay chapters had appeared in magazines during the two previous decades. This was Muir's first book, and it remains his best.

There are two ways of viewing the Sierra Nevada. Seen from the east, from the Land of Little Rain, the range rises vertically as a wall of granite, named by the Spanish the Sierra Nevada, the saw-toothed, snowy range. Ansel Adams's photographic edition of Mary Austin's classic pictures this eastern viewpoint.

The view from the west is more subtle and mysterious. It is the view John Muir first had of the Sierra Nevada, newly arrived in California in 1868, a footloose Scot of thirty. He could truly say, as Robinson Jeffers said half a century later upon first seeing Carmel, that he had come without knowing it to his inevitable place.

Here is how Muir described this first view: "Along the eastern margin [of the San Joaquin Valley] rises the mighty Sierra, miles in height, reposing like a smooth, cumulous cloud in the sunny sky, and so gloriously colored, and so luminous, it seems to be not clothed with light, but wholly composed of it, like the wall of some celestial city. Along the top, and extending a good way down, you see a pale, pearl-gray belt of snow; and below it a belt of blue and dark purple, marking the extension of the forests; and along the base of the range a broad belt of rose-purple and yellow, where lie the miner's gold-fields and the foot-hill gardens. All these colored belts blending smoothly make a wall of light ineffably fine, and as beautiful as a rainbow, yet firm as adamant."

"When I first enjoyed this superb view, one glowing April

143

day, from the summit of Pacheco Pass, the Central Valley but little trampled or plowed as yet, was one furred, rich sheet of golden compositae, and the luminous wall of the mountain shone in all its glory. Then it seemed to me the Sierra should be called not the Nevada, or Snowy Range, but the Range of Light."

Today the freeway through Pacheco Pass finds cars speeding along too fast for contemplative viewing. If one can find a safe turn-out on not too hazy a day, he will see much of what John Muir saw just a century ago. Although the Central Valley has been trampled and plowed, the Range of Light is still the all-determining overlord of the heartland. Its peaks still milk the Pacific storms of the moisture that falls as snow, whose spring melt and run-off make the Central Valley the world's greatest fruit orchard.

The timelessness of Muir's book derives from its faithful interpretation of Sierran splendors. Chapters are devoted to the passes, the glaciers, meadows, forests, storms, floods, squirrels, birds, and mountain sheep. These are the unchanging characteristics which remain what they were when Muir fell in love with them in the 1870's. Whereas much of California's coast, valleys and foothills, and above all, its cities, is changed since Muir's time, the Sierra Nevada remains indomitable.

No man was more influential than John Muir in preserving the Sierra's integrity. If I were to choose a single Californian to occupy the Hall of Fame, it would be this tenacious Scot who became a Californian during the final forty-six years of his life. It was John Muir whose knowledge wedded to zeal led men and governments to establish the National Park Service. Yosemite and Sequoia in California, the Petrified Forest and the Grand Canyon in Arizona, and the glacier wilderness of Alaska are what they are today largely because of this one man, in whom learning and love were co-equal. More than any other, he was the answer to that call which appears on the Courts Building in Sacramento: *Give me men to match my mountains.*

John Muir lost only one conservation battle, that with the city of San Francisco over the damming of the Tuolumne River and the subsequent flooding of Hetch Hetchy, a Sierran glacial valley nearly as remarkable as its neighboring Yosemite. It was a defeat comparable to that suffered by Mary Austin in her struggle to prevent Los Angeles from making her Land of Little Rain even more arid.

From the time of his first book's appearance in 1894 until his death at Los Angeles in 1914, John Muir was in the forefront of the nation-wide movement to preserve our national resources from destruction by private interests. Of *The Mountains of California* Muir's biographer, Linnie Marsh Wolfe, wrote, "It met with immediate and far-reaching success. It rallied and solidified the conservation sentiment of the entire nation, leading directly to a new upsurge of determination to preserve the forests." The book followed by two years Muir's equally momentous founding of the Sierra Club. That heroic story has been told by Holway R. Jones in *John Muir and the Sierra Club: the Battle for Yosemite*.

If one has not read *The Mountains of California*, the foregoing might lead to the assumption that it is a tract for conservation, disguised as nature writing. Not so. There is no arguing in it, no special pleading. Muir simply describes the grandeur of the Sierra Nevada, with an eye also for the details of the great canvas. "The Douglas Squirrel" and "The Water Ouzel" are examples of Muir's felicitous way of picturing wild life. The latter essay is probably the best loved of all writings on American birds. Here is a sample:

"He is a singularly joyous and lovable little fellow, about the size of a robin, clad in a plain waterproof suit of bluish gray, with a tinge of chocolate on the head and shoulders. In form he is about as smoothly plump and compact as a pebble that has been whirled in a pothole, the flowing contour of his body being interrupted only by his strong feet and bill, the crisp wing-tips, and the up-slanted wren-like tail. . . . No cañon is too cold for this little bird, none too lonely, provided it be rich in falling water. Find a fall, or cascade, or rushing rapid, anywhere upon a clear stream, and there you will surely find its complementary Ouzel, flitting about in the spray, diving in foaming eddies, whirling

145

like a leaf among beaten foam-bells; ever vigorous and enthusiastic, yet self-contained, and neither seeking nor shunning your company."

One need not go as far as the Sierra Nevada to see water ouzels. The higher canyons of Southern California's mountains are graced by this lively little bird.

My favorite chapter is "A Wind-Storm in the Forests," Muir's description of the tempest from a perch in the top of a hundred-foot Douglas spruce. Here is no sedentary botanist's technical paper, but rather an on-the-spot broadcast:

"Never before did I enjoy so noble an exhiliration of motion. The slender top fairly flapped and swished in the passionate torrents, bending and swirling backward and forward, round and round, tracing indescribable combinations of vertical and horizontal curves, while I clung with muscles firmly braced, like a bobolink on a reed." Re-reading this essay on the Sierra wind, I recalled Dana's description of the storm-tossed ship and sea from the top of the mast.

It was John Muir who first declared Yosemite Valley to be glacial in origin. This was counter to State Geologist Josiah D. Whitney's thesis that Yosemite was created by a geologic cataclysm, a claim supported by Clarence King whose book preceded Muir's by two decades. Muir they dismissed as a mere sheepherder and ignoramus. Alas for them, it was the self-taught Scot who proved to be right. His theory was confirmed as fact. In 1950 the Sierra Club collected Muir's original glacial papers from the *Overland Monthly* of 1874-75, and published them as *Studies in the Sierra*, with a foreword by the distinguished Caltech geologist, John P. Buwalda.

More books came from Muir's pen, but none has the power, the style, and the charm of his first. It is his single classic. In a lesser work, *The Yosemite*, published in 1912, Muir pondered the problem of whether automobiles should be allowed in the Park. What would he say of today's congestion on the Valley floor?

There is much writing about him, from the official *Life and Letters*, edited by William F. Badé, to the standard biography,

147

Son of the Wilderness, by Linnie Marsh Wolfe. A fine anthology, drawn from his various books, is *The Wilderness World of John Muir*, edited by Edwin Way Teale, himself a superb writer on natural history. Ansel Adams, greatest of the Sierra's photographers, has memorably embellished Muir's prose in *Yosemite and the Sierra Nevada.*

The oddest book in the literature of these mountains and John Muir is a novel, written by a wandering English noblewoman, Thérèse Yelverton, the Viscountess Avonmore. She arrived in the Valley soon after John Muir did, and proceeded to fall in love with him. At that stage of his life, Muir's love of nature did not include women; he was in his forties before he married and fathered two daughters. Unrequited love led the ardent woman to make Muir the hero of *Zanita, a Tale of the Yo-Semite*, published in 1872. This rare book can be read today, when found, only by the most ardent Muiriac.

Perhaps its chief value lies in this first-hand description of the wild young Scot: "His open blue eyes of honest questioning, and glorious auburn hair might have stood as a portrait of the angel Raphael. His figure was about five feet nine, well knit, and bespoke that active grace which only trained muscles can assume. Truly his garments had the tatterdemalion style of a Mad Tom. The waist of his trousers was eked out with a grass band, a long flowery sedge rush stuck in the solitary button-hole of his shirt, the sleeves of which were ragged and forlorn, and his shoes appeared to have known hard and troublous times."

John Muir is not without honor in his adopted state. Schools, a mountain, and streets are named for him. Muir Woods is a virgin redwood grove on the shoulder of Mt. Tamalpais, which guards the northern approach to the Golden Gate. The most fitting memorial, however, and the one that would please him the most, is the John Muir Trail, a pathway for walkers that stretches one hundred eighty-five miles along the western crest of the Sierra Nevada, from Yosemite Valley to Mt. Whitney.

If you would seek John Muir's ghost, look for it along this trail, the restless spirit of a visionary Scotsman. He travelled light, nourished on hard bread, sugar and tea. Tied to the belt of this

148

bearded mountain man, who rarely wore a coat even in winter, were his notebook and pencil.

That John Muir was able to see, to sense, and to say—for he possessed the essential Three S's of literature—is why we have the book that is his immortality, a book to re-read in the different stages of our lives. We change and go; it abides.

I had the paperback with me on two trips to the Sierra Nevada, and re-reading it there was a transcendent experience, with literature and landscape in perfect register.

In May the runoff from a record snowfall filled the canyon of the Merced with thunder and flying spray. I imagined what it was like in the springtime of John Muir's first visit, a century before: no roads, no cars, no people; only the sombre masses of gray green granite and the glory of falling water. In September the Valley was quieter, the waterfalls diminished, the people gone. I stared up at El Capitan and its beetling Muir Wall, beautiful almost beyond reality; then I took the road on up to Tioga Pass, climbing from ponderosa and sequoia to red fir, sierra juniper, and the highest lodgepole pine; and paused there on the granite backbone of the range, the naked rock shining like satin, before descending Lee Vining Canyon to the domain of Mary Austin.

As the pressure of land use and development increases in the nation's most populous state, *The Mountains of California* will become increasingly meaningful and precious. It is one man's testament to the glory of the Sierra Nevada, that radiant Range of Light. By the act of reading, book and range become ours. Such is the power of a classic.

Reading List

JOHN MUIR (1838-1914)
The Mountains of California. New York, Century Co., 1894; Doubleday Natural History Library, Anchor Books, with Foreword by Jack McCormick, 1961.

The Yosemite. New York, Century Co., 1912. Doubleday Natural History Library, Anchor Books, with Foreword by F. R. Grunsky, 1962.

WILLIAM FREDERIC BADE
Life and Letters of John Muir. Boston, Houghton Mifflin, 1924. 2 vols.

HOLWAY R. JONES
John Muir and the Sierra Club. San Francisco, Sierra Club, 1965.

LINNIE MARSH WOLFE
Son of the Wilderness; the Life of John Muir. New York, Alfred A. Knopf, 1945.

Photograph of John Muir, courtesy of William F. Kimes.

Two Years Before the Mast

RICHARD HENRY DANA, JR.

13

READING AND falling in love are similar in that their impact depends upon when they occur in life. Youthful reading and young love are fresh and wide-eyed. They are also brief and shallow in intensity. As one ages and acquires standards of measurement, the two acts take on duration and depth.

Thus it was that my first reading of *Two Years Before the Mast* was like young love—a sweet interlude of excitement, a quickly unravelled yarn of the sea. I must have been about fifteen when my parents gave me an illustrated edition of Dana's book. All it meant to me then was an adventure story and nothing more.

Years passed, and I came upon Dana's book in another edition, a reprint whose pages were turning brown and brittle. I reread it, and then by magic, a boy's book became a man's book, possessed of the power to move me deeply.

This happened in London, soon after a chance reading of another California book, Mary Austin's *Lands of the Sun*, had brightened a rainy day in Paris and made me homesick for my faraway golden state. So there I was in England, tempted to seek work and remain abroad, when that rediscovery of Dana made me more than ever determined to go home and see California with new vision gained from reading him and Austin.

Growing up in California, I had taken it for granted, unimpressed by the fact that it had deserts, mountains, valleys, and seacoast, that it was a world in itself, a commonwealth of diversity and abundance. Needed was absence and perspective, and others' eyes, to enable me clearly to see the glory of those physical features. If Mary Austin revealed the valleys and hills, it was Dana who showed me the seacoast, the western wall of America, seen from offshore, looking landward.

How different the Pacific coast is from the Atlantic shore! On the eastern sea frontier the land lies low, broken by bays, inlets and estuaries. When it becomes the rugged coast of Maine, it is even more different from California's, for the reason that there is found no long line of breakers rolling in to crash against the shore. In the farthest northeast deepwater comes to the granite cliffs where the waves explode suddenly rather than break gradually.

It was January 1835 when the brig *Pilgrim*, five months out of Boston via Cape Horn, dropped anchor in eleven fathoms of water three miles off Santa Barbara. "It was a beautiful day," Dana wrote, "and so warm that we wore straw hats, duck trousers, and all the summer gear. As this was midwinter, it spoke well for the climate."

After describing a fire that had swept the mountains back of Santa Barbara and driven the town's inhabitants to the beach for three days, Dana continued.

"I shall never forget the impression which our first landing on the beach of California made upon me. The sun had just gone down; it was getting dusky; the damp night wind was beginning to blow, and the heavy swell of the Pacific was setting in, and breaking in loud and high 'combers' upon the beach. We lay on our oars in the swell, just outside the surf, waiting for a good chance to run in."

Then Dana described the running in. Nothing has changed since the young Yankee came ashore for the first time. A small boat is still beached by the same means. If one doubts this, he should go to Zuma Beach in southern California when the lifeguards are training for their annual dory race, and watch them take a heavy rowboat out and in through the surf. They could be acting out Dana's script.

152

Two Years Before the Mast was the first, and it remains the greatest book of maritime California. It is a seacoast book, ranging from San Francisco to San Diego, with shore leaves at Monterey, Santa Barbara, and San Pedro. The purpose of the *Pilgrim's* voyage was to gather hides in exchange for its cargo of Yankee goods.

Listed on the brig's manifest were spirits in casks, teas, coffee, sugar, spices, raisins, molasses; hardware, crockeryware, tinware, cutlery; clothing, boots and shoes from Lynn, calicoes and cottons from Lowell, crepes, silks, shawls, scarves, necklaces, jewelry and combs; furniture, Chinese fireworks, and English cartwheels with iron tires.

These were traded for bullock skins that were roughly cured on the California beaches, then packed down in the hold of the returning ship to the total of 40,000 in one trip. Carried back to Boston, they were tanned and made into shoes and other leather goods. Shoes (Dana observed) which were brought back to California and worn out in the pursuit of more cattle and the curing of more hides. A profitable cycle.

Until the drought of the 1860's wiped out the herds of "cattle on a thousand hills" and gold became the cornerstone of the new state, this cycle of trade—hide-droghing, it was called—constituted California's prime economy. Dana came at its height, and in describing it he also pictured coastal California with clear vision, deep feeling, and precise prose.

Few other books of Dana's time—*Two Years Before the Mast* was published in 1840—have remained constantly in print and are read today. His was an immediate success. Ten thousand copies were sold in the first year. Numerous translations followed. Many imitations appeared in the succeeding decade, none of which is known today, except by literary historians. Melville's *Moby Dick*, published a decade later, drew on Dana for some details, and yet it was not one of the imitators. Dana encouraged Melville in the writing of his epic of whaling. Although there is no evidence that Dana read Melville's masterpiece, I find it hard to believe that he never did.

What was the part played by what I have called the Three S's

154

of literature in the success of *Two Years Before the Mast?* Consider the first one, the power to see. What gave this New England youth such lucid vision? He was only nineteen when he came to California, and yet he saw the lay of the land, the weather and the gray whales, the settlements and inhabitants, with keen perception.

We can only call upon a trite phrase to explain this power: it was God-given. He was born able to see things clearly, to see things as they are, the opposite of the distorted and cloudy vision with which many of today's writers in prose and poetry view the outer world.

Dana saw the coast in that halcyon time before the people came. He foresaw the rise of San Francisco; he responded to the charm of Monterey and its absence at San Pedro. He recognized the strategic placement of Point Conception, which he called "the dividing line between two different faces of the country. As you go to the northward of the point, the country becomes more wooded, has a richer appearance, and is better supplied with water; while to the southward of the point, there is very little wood, and the country has a naked, level appearance, though it is still fertile."

Dana also noted the wind-made ways of California's weather: the autumn norther called the Santa Ana, curse of the dry fire season; the winter south-easterly that brings rain from January to April; the prevailing summer westerly that blows from noon until sundown and air-conditions the coastal plain.

In their ignorance of topography, winds and weathers, I would fear to question a class of young people on the local phenomena of the coast, even though they were native sons. In their bondage to national media and rush toward outer space, they have lost the power of knowing and loving what is near and dear. Stroboscopic light and amplified sound lead to blindness and deafness to sunset and surf.

Of the coastal points described by Dana, none is better known today than the one that bears his name. Dana Point is a community and is also the conglomerate headland from which the hides were thrown to the beach below. His telling of it illustrates how his prose rose to the level of literature:

"Down this height we pitched the hides, throwing them as far out into the air as we could; and as they were all large, stiff, and doubled, like the cover of a book, the wind took them, and they swayed and eddied about, plunging and rising in the air, like a kite when it has broken its string. As it was now low tide, there was no danger of their falling into the water; and, as fast as they came to ground, the men below picked them up, and, taking them on their heads, walked off with them to the boat. It was really a picturesque sight: the great height, the sailing of the hides, and the continual walking to and fro of the men, who looked like mites, on the beach. This was the romance of hide-droghing!"

Today there is a little park and belvedere at the top of Dana Point, and the state has erected Historical Landmark Monument No. 189, which commemorates the young sailor's having been there in 1835.

Without the power to sense, that is for responding sensitively and sensuously to what he saw, Dana's visually keen and accurate narrative would have been so much dead prose, mere journalism, form without spirit. He brought to all he saw and did a sympathetic awareness of his fellow men. A good example is his account of the flogging aboard the *Pilgrim*. A sailor lost overboard also evokes a passage on the meaning of death at sea. His nursing of the sick Kanaka on the beach at San Diego, and a vignette of the black cook's attachment to a pet pig, are further examples of Dana's compassion.

The majesty of the Californian coast never failed to move him, as in this passage when he came ashore at San Juan Capistrano and lingered alone on the beach at the foot of what is now Dana Point:

"There was a grandeur in everything around which gave a solemnity to the scene, a silence and solitariness which affected every part. Not a human being but ourselves for miles, and no sound heard but the pulsations of the great Pacific. And the great steep hill rising like a wall, and cutting us from all the world but the 'world of waters.' I separated myself from the rest, and sat down on a rock, just where the sea ran in and formed a fine spouting horn. Compared with the dull sand beach of the rest of the coast, this grandeur was as refreshing as a great rock in a weary land. It was almost the first time that I had been positively alone since I had left home. My better nature returned strong upon me. Everything was in accordance with my state of feeling, and I experienced a glow of pleasure at finding that what of poetry and romance I ever had in me had not been entirely deadened."

Dana's feelings were not limited to landscape. He was responsive to women's charms, as later evidence shows. One speculates what his life would have been if he had followed the example of other Yankees, married a Californian and remained on the coast. If he enjoyed romancing in Monterey or Santa Barbara, no evidence of it is in his narrative, and the detailed journal from which the book was drawn was lost upon Dana's return to Boston. Surviving among the Dana papers, however, is an ironical letter to him from a shipmate after reading *Two Years Before the Mast*, which twits him for saying nothing about "The beautiful Indian Lasses, who so often frequented your humble abode in the hide house, and rambled through those splendid groves attached thereto, or the happy hours experienced rambling over those romantic hills, or sitting at twilight on those majestic rocks, with a lovely Indian Girl resting on your knee."

If Dana had dared hint of such delights, they would have surely been eliminated by the publisher, who employed the proper poet William Cullen Bryant to give the manuscript a fatherly reading.

Although upon his return to Massachusetts, Dana settled into the conventional mould of husband, father, and lawyer, there was a sensual animal in him that was never completely tamed. He had a strange practice while on lecture tours of disguising himself as a sailor and visiting brothels, apparently only to lecture the women on their wicked ways. Even stranger was his confessional practice of reading to his wife such entries in his journal. A quarter century after his first voyage, Dana went off alone on a health-seeking trip around the world. Through it all his eyes were drawn to feminine beauty, and in Bombay he was smitten by the water-bearers. "No duchess that I ever saw walked so well," he wrote in his journal, "I cannot keep my eyes from them."

If Dana had sailed to the South Seas as Melville did a few years later, instead of to California, we might have had another *Typee*, Melville's romantic narrative of his love for the Polynesian maiden called Fayaway.

Which brings us to the third S, the power to say, that is to communicate vision and feeling by the means of strong and supple prose. How came this youth to such a command of language? Partly it was in the genes. His father was a writer. Young Dana was brought up on the King James Bible and other classics of English style.

His prose cost him no sweat or tears. When soon after his return his full journal was carelessly lost by his cousin, leaving only an original 20 pages of skeleton entries to work from, Dana sat down o'nights, after long days spent as a law student at Harvard, and in six months wrote out *Two Years Before the Mast* in a single virtually uncorrected draft.

The book's power comes from an accumulation of specific incidents. It also gains impact from its threefold form—The Going, The Staying, The Return—thus satisfying the reader's desire for symmetry, whether it be in art or architecture, poetry or prose. What might have been anti-climax, the return voyage, reached new heights in the struggle to round Cape Horn in the dead of winter. Those pages, Melville declared, seemed to have been written with an icicle.

Dana was an artist in the way he rearranged his experiences in order for them to have maximum impact on the reader. His book was no artless effusion. He was able to overlay experience and observation with exact prose, so that there was no blur between them. Life and language thus came into perfect register.

Dana could work magic in a sentence or two, as in this description of the putting to sea when a southeasterly blew in on the roadstead at Santa Barbara: "While sheeting home, we saw the *Ayacucho* standing athwart our hawse, sharp upon the wind, cutting through the head seas like a knife, with her raking masts, and her sharp bows running up like the head of a greyhound. It was a beautiful sight. She was like a bird which had been frightened and had spread her wings in flight."

Here we see knife, greyhound, and bird—images of sharpness, speed, and grace—artfully arranged in a simple composition.

When necessary, Dana could swell his prose in organ-music passages, such as those describing the iceberg in southern waters, or of the ship under full sail in the halcyon night after rounding Cape Horn, the more serene and moving for its following the storm scenes.

We have noted the immediate success of *Two Years Before the Mast*. It sold 20,000 copies in the first ten years. Did it make its author rich? It did not. Dana unfortunately accepted $250 from Harper's in exchange for all rights in the book. The publisher made $50,000, and would not concede a dollar to Dana beyond the initial payment. It is one of the shabbiest episodes in American publishing. Even the English publisher, Moxon, who pirated the book, voluntarily sent Dana $500.

After twenty-eight years when the copyright reverted to him, Dana issued another edition—with another publisher, need I say—to which he added a chapter, "Twenty-Four Years After." This is a nostalgic account of his return to California in 1859, en route around the world. In 1964 a scholarly edition, edited by John H. Kemble and illustrated from early photographs and from drawings by Robert Weinstein, restored Dana's complete text, which Harper's had somewhat altered and which Dana didn't bother to replace in his Author's Edition.

The only other travel book Dana wrote was *To Cuba and Back*, an undistinguished work lacking in feeling and style. In 1873 at the age of 57, Dana wrote to his son, "My life has been a failure compared with what I might and ought to have done. My great success—my book—was a boy's work, done before I came to the Bar."

Apart from his two greatest sea voyages, Dana had no genius for living. A career as a writer was inconceivable to such a staunch member as he was of the Boston aristocracy. His marriage, though fruitful with six children, was not a happy one. Although he finally prospered as a lawyer, specializing in maritime cases, he wore himself out in the drudgery of courtroom preparation and appearances. He was badly beaten when he ran for Congress. His appointment as Ambassador to the Court of St. James was rejected by the Senate. The truth is, Dana hardened into a Tory and a snob, losing his youthful awareness of how he affected those around him. He aged ungracefully.

Looking back, we see that his tragedy was in not having followed the sea. He would have quickly risen to Mate and Master, and because of his intelligence and ability, his feeling for marine life, and the very authoritarian manner which caused his political defeats and rebuffs, he would have triumphed in the command of seagoing vessels. His volume, *The Seaman's Friend*, published soon after his masterpiece, became a standard handbook for mariners.

Dana was not blind to having taken the wrong way. In 1859 while on his world trip, he wrote to his wife, "The truth is I was made for the sea. It suits me and I am always content when on it. I believe I was intended for a sailor. My life on shore is a mistake." A maritime existence would also have allowed him outlets denied by his family and professional life for what was obviously a strongly sexed nature.

Another time while away on a lecture trip, he wrote these words to his wife, in which is summed up the sadness of a life which, in the end, Dana believed to have been a failure: "We ought to have been travellers; had no profession and no home, and roamed over the world together, like two civilized and refined gypsies."

His final years, spent in Europe, retired from the law and with no fixed abode, were a fulfillment of that secret desire for freedom from convention and responsibility. Reconciliation had taken place between him and his wife, his children were established, he had inherited ample means, all of which cast a sunset glow. Italy drew him finally, and in 1881 he wrote to a friend at home,

"This is the land of vines, olives, figs, oranges and lemons, of beauty in nature and art, in human form and movement and voice, in the blue islands, the blue wave, and the violet hillsides. It is a dream of life." And a vision not unlike the one he had once had of the newfoundland of California, half a century before.

Racked by pleurisy and pneumonia, Dana died a year later in Rome. In the previous spring while walking with her husband in the Protestant Cemetery over the grass star-scattered with anemones and violets, with the shades of Keats and Shelley hovering near, Sarah Dana had asked him, "Is this not the spot where one would like to be forever?" And he had replied, "Ah yes, it is indeed."

And so she buried him there by the graves of the two English poets, their friend Trelawney, and Shelley's little boy. The erstwhile Yankee sailor's gravestone bears these words:

RICHARD HENRY DANA
OF BOSTON
UNITED STATES OF AMERICA
Born August, 1, 1815
Died in Rome January 6, 1882

Reading List

RICHARD HENRY DANA, JR. (1815-1882)
Two Years Before the Mast; A Personal Narrative of Life at Sea. New York, Harper, 1840; new edition with subsequent material by the author, Boston, Houghton Mifflin, 1869 and reissued in 1911, Houghton, with added chapter by R. H. Dana III & illustrations by E. Boyd Smith; Modern Library, 1936, with foreword by James D. Hart; edited from the original manuscript by John H. Kemble and original drawings & photographs by Robert H. Weinstein, Los Angeles, Ward Ritchie Press, 1964, 2 vols. The New American Library Signet Classic, Afterword by Wright Morris, 1964, reprints the 1869 edition.
The Seaman's Friend. Boston, Little & Brown, 1841. Subsequently titled *The Seaman's Manual.*

To Cuba and Back, A Vacation Voyage. Boston, Ticknor & Fields, 1859; abridged by C. H. Gardiner, Carbondale, Southern Illinois University Press, 1966.
The Journal. Edited by Robert F. Lucid. Cambridge, Belknap-Harvard University Press, 1968. 3 vols.

CHARLES FRANCIS ADAMS
Richard Henry Dana, a Biography. Boston, Houghton Mifflin, 1890. 2 vols.

SAMUEL SHAPIRO
Richard Henry Dana, Jr., 1815-1882. East Lansing, Michigan State University Press, 1961.

Photograph of R. H. Dana, Jr., courtesy of Massachusetts Historical Society.

ROBERT LOUIS STEVENSON

14

WHAT BROUGHT people to California in the 19th century? Furs and hides, gold, land, sunshine and health. It was none of these classic lures that attracted Robert Louis Stevenson from Europe. Something even more magnetic brought the 29-year-old Scot to California in 1879. A woman. Stevenson had met her three years earlier in France. Her name was Fanny Van de Grift Osbourne. She was then 39, a native of Indiana, married for nineteen years and the mother of two children; disillusioned and separated from her philandering husband who had remained in California.

Fanny was no ordinary woman. Small, dark, passionate, with black eyes, Stevenson said, like those of one sighting a loaded pistol; eyes, their friend Colvin said, "full of sex and mystery." Stevenson took one look at her through an open Dutch door in a provincial tavern, and was hers for life.

Gradually she became everything to him—mistress, manager, nurse—and their marriage, which took place at San Francisco in 1880, lasted until his death fourteen years later in Samoa. She outlived him twenty years, the high priestess of a Stevenson cult and the matriarch of a large clan.

Sound romantic? It was. Few marriages can match it. D. H. Lawrence and Frieda, Robinson Jeffers and Una, are comparable in their triumphing over the obstacle of a previous marriage, in the passionate nature of the women and the creative inspiration they gave their men.

Stevenson spent a year in California, long enough to win his bride and improve his health, culminating in a short honeymoon on the shoulder of Mount St. Helena. From that year came a book, *The Silverado Squatters*, his transmutation of their sojourn at the abandoned Silverado mine in Napa County, and essays on Monterey and San Francisco which are some of the best things ever written about those places.

In the Monterey and Silverado regions, Stevenson also found the setting and atmosphere that served later for *Treasure Island*. Everything was grist to his mill. His stepson, Lloyd, went along on the honeymoon to Silverado. The average man would have resented this. Not Stevenson. He included the boy in the circle of affection, wrote verses for him to print on his handpress; and most important of all, created *Treasure Island* for him, to the everlasting joy of all boys and men.

Stevenson was a writer both born and made. Although he came near death in California from the hardships of the journey by emigrant ship and overland train, he never stopped writing, although he usually did it propped up in bed.

Nurse Fanny was also a good listener. Although she has been accused of marrying Stevenson for the money she would inherit after his expected early death—and she *was* a bit of an adventuress—she prolonged his life and excited his work.

His feelings about her were ambivalent. Time and again, in prose and poetry, he paid tribute to her. "Teacher, tender, comrade, wife," are his words for her, graven eventually on their tomb in Samoa. He also called her a tiger, a swarthy gypsy, his dusky love with golden knee and shoulder.

No writer's triumph over the obstacles of illness, a conventional public, and parental objection to his liaison, is more heroic than Stevenson's. A summary of it should be required reading in all schools of writing. "It's not the first writing that troubles me," he said, "and I don't mind the second; it's the third version of my work that kills me."

In the memoir of his stepfather by Lloyd Osbourne, we read

164

of how Stevenson wrote and rewrote *Dr. Jekyll and Mr. Hyde* in the span of six days, sixty thousand words in all, and on top of that copied out the whole in another two days—no typewriters then—and had it in the mail on the third.

Until recently a reader had to seek in various volumes for Stevenson's Californiana, and then it was not as he first wrote it. His editors and his family prettified him, removing what they regarded as coarse material and expressions. The truth is, Robert Louis Stevenson was a highly sexed, earthy man whose public utterances and image were perverted by the proprieties of the Victorian era.

Thanks to Professor James D. Hart of the University of California we now have a complete edition of Stevenson's American books, *The Amateur Emigrant, Across the Plains, The Silverado Squatters* and other California writings. The text of *From Scotland to Silverado*, edited by Hart, is based on the original manuscripts, many of which are in the greatest of all R.L.S. collections, formed by Edwin J. Beinecke and preserved in the library given by him and his brothers to Yale University.

After eleven days of plains, Rockies, and desert, Stevenson thrilled to the Pacific slope of the Sierra Nevada, describing it with ecstasy similar to that felt by the Joads when they surmounted the Tehachapis and saw the Valley. He went on to Monterey to meet Fanny. They had been separated a year. She was still married to Sam Osbourne.

"The one common note of all this country," Stevenson wrote of Monterey, "is the haunting presence of the ocean. A great faint sound of breakers follows you high up into the inland cañons; the roar of waters dwells in the clean, empty rooms of Monterey as in a shell upon the chimney. The woods and the Pacific rule between them the climate of this seaboard region. On the streets of Monterey, when the air does not smell salt from the one, it will be blowing perfumed from the resinous tree-tops of the other."

Forest fire and lumbering and the resulting denudation of the land Stevenson saw as the greatest threat to California. "California has been a land of promise in its time, like Palestine; but if the woods continue so swiftly to perish, it may become, like a

Palestine, a land of desolation." He lamented the destruction of the two noblest indigenes, "redwoods and redskins."

He was also dismayed by the ruin into which the Carmel Mission had fallen. For the *Monterey Californian* he wrote an article, appealing for funds to restore the church, which concluded, "A fine old church, a fine old race, both brutally neglected; a survival, a memory, a ruin. The United States Mint can coin many million more dollar pieces, but not make a single Indian; and when the Carmel church is in the dust, not all the wealth of all the States and Territories can replace what has been lost."

He also took a dim view of the Hotel Del Monte which had just opened in Monterey. "Alas for the little town! it is not strong enough to resist the influence of the flaunting caravanserai, and the poor, quaint, penniless native gentlemen of Monterey must perish, like a lower race, before the millionaire vulgarians of the Big Bonanza."

Stevenson was wrong. They did not perish. They withdrew to "Tortilla Flat" to await the coming of John Steinbeck.

In spite of its effect on his weak chest, Stevenson was enchanted by the sea-fog, and his description of it has never been bettered:

"At sunset, for months together, vast, wet, melancholy fogs arise and come shoreward from the ocean. From the hill-top above Monterey the scene is often noble, although it is always sad. The upper air is still bright with sunlight; a glow still rests upon the Gabelano Peak; but the fogs are in possession of the lower levels; they crawl in scarves among the sandhills; they float, a little higher, in clouds of a gigantic size and often of a wild configuration; to the south, where they have struck the seaward shoulder of the mountains of Santa Lucia, they double back and spire skyward like smoke. Where their shadow touches, colour dies out of the world. The air grows chill and deadly as they advance. The trade-wind freshens, the trees begin to sigh, and all the windmills in Monterey are whirling and creaking and filling their cisterns with the brackish water of the sands. It takes but a little while till the invasion is complete. The sea, in its lighter order, has submerged the earth. Monterey is curtained in for the night in thick, wet, salt, and frigid clouds, so

166

to remain till day returns; and before the sun's rays they slowly disperse and retreat in broken squadrons to the bosom of the sea. And yet often when the fog is thickest and most chill, a few steps out of the town and up the slope, the night will be dry and warm and full of inland perfume."

Stevenson moved to San Francisco where in the winter months he found more sunshine. He was also closer to Fanny who had gone there to persuade her husband to grant a divorce. This was no ordinary triangle; in fact it resembled a *menage à trois*, for at one point, when Osbourne lost his job, poor Louis found himself the sole support of them all.

No wonder he collapsed and had his first hemorrhage. In spite of what the neighbors might say, Fanny took him into her Oakland cottage and nursed him back to health. Through it all he kept writing. Her divorce was finally granted, and they were married at San Francisco on May 19, 1880. The essay Stevenson wrote thereafter on San Francisco is nearly as good as the one about Monterey. Again it reveals his acute perception of place. The opening sentence tells us that he had read an earlier California classic:

"The Pacific coast of the United States, as you may see by the map, and still better in that admirable book, *Two Years Before the Mast*, by Dana, is one of the most exposed and shelterless on earth." He went on to picture the fantastic development of the city from sandy waste to seaport metropolis:

"Choose a place on one of the huge throbbing ferry-boats, and, when you are midway between the city and suburb, look around. The air is fresh and salt as if you were at sea. On the one hand is Oakland, gleaming white among its gardens. On the other, to seaward, hill after hill is crowded and crowned with the palaces of San Francisco; its long streets lie in regular bars of darkness, east and west, across the sparkling picture; a forest of masts bristles like bulrushes about its feet; nothing remains of Drake but the faithful trade-wind scattering the smoke, the fogs that will begin to muster about sundown, and the fine bulk of Tamalpais looking down on San Francisco, like Arthur's Seat on Edinburgh."

168

He sensed the geological insecurity of the peninsula, anticipated the earthquake of 1906, and referred to the Indian legend that San Francisco once rose out of the sea and would sink again. This recalls Jeffers's prophecy, "Someday this coast will dip and be clean."

Their honeymoon took Louis and Fanny above the fog-line in Napa County, north of San Francisco, 2400 feet up on the southeastern slope of Mount St. Helena. There they found an abandoned cabin at the site of what had once been the Calistoga Gold and Silver Mine. It was a mess into which they moved. Water had to be carried up a steep trail. Poison oak grew up through cracks in the floor. Buzzing rattlesnakes encircled the place. Fanny came down sick. The reality is in a letter to his mother in Edinburgh:

"This life takes up all my time and strength. By the time I have had my two sun baths and my two rubs-down with oil, and given Sam (his stepson Lloyd) his lessons and written a bit of diary, I have no stomach for more."

Here's the clue to *The Silverado Squatters*. *A bit of diary.* Each day this writer of genius took the pulse of their life and fixed it in words to be fashioned into the finished book. It was written over the next two years in Switzerland and France, painfully drafted by Stevenson propped up in bed, fighting the tuberculosis which had become active.

In spite of illness, this was his zenith of creativity, from which he wrote *Silverado*, *Treasure Island*, and *A Child's Garden of Verses*. After they left France because of Fanny's fear of cholera, his mounting popular success was accompanied by heavy family responsibilities, culminating in the exotic Samoan experience and his death from a cerebral hemorrhage.

When her publisher called for more books like *The Land of Little Rain*, Mary Austin replied that it took her at least a dozen years to absorb the essences of a place and distil them in literature. Stevenson worked faster. Like D. H. Lawrence, whom he resembled as writer and man, Stevenson thrust down roots the moment he came to a place. Volumes and libraries have been written about California, and yet none holds more essential truth

169

than Stevenson's few pages. His account of their sojourn in Napa County is the classic account of that place and time.

The journal kept at Silverado is the book's first draft. As a gift from Edwin J. Beinecke, the original manuscript is in the Huntington Library. In 1954 the Book Club of California published *The Silverado Journal*, edited and introduced by John H. Jordan. We are thus able to enter the workshop of Stevenson's mind and see what he retained, added, and omitted.

The finished work, *The Silverado Squatters*, first appeared in *Century* magazine for November and December 1883, for which Stevenson received $200. The second installment was followed immediately in the same issue by Helen Hunt Jackson's Los Angeles essay, "Echoes in the City of the Angels," which preceded *Ramona* by a year.

Stevenson's book was published at London in 1883 in an edition of 1000 copies. A second edition of 6000 copies in 1886 indicated the rising star of his popularity. The work's opening paragraph establishes the dominance of Mount St. Helena in a rather matter of fact presentation of locale. It took a few pages for Stevenson to warm up. Then he writes this paean to the time of year, the place, and the mountain, capturing the quintessence of California the mountainous:

"Calistoga was a pleasant place to dwell in; beautifully green, for it was then that favoured moment in the California year, when the rains are over and the dusty summer has not yet set in; often visited by fresh airs; now from the mountain, now across Sonoma from the sea; very quiet, very idle, very silent but for the breezes and the cattle-bells afield. And there was something satisfactory in the sight of that great mountain that enclosed us to the north; whether it stood robed in sunshine, quaking to its topmost pinnacle with the heat and brightness of the day; or whether it set itself to weaving vapours, wisp after wisp growing, trembling, fleeting, and fading in the blue.

"The tangled, woody, and almost trackless foothills that enclose the valley, shutting it off from Sonoma on the west, and from Yolo on the east—rough as they were in outline, dug out by winter streams, crowned by cliffy bluffs and nodding pine-trees—were dwarfed into satellites by the bulk and bearing of Mount St. Helena. She over-towered them by two-thirds of her own stature. She excelled them by the boldness of her profile. Her great bald summit, clear of trees and pasture, a cairn of quartz and cinnabar, rejected kinship with the dark and shaggy wilderness of lesser hill-tops."

Those who do not understand the ways of a man with a pen, and who are unaware of the alchemy whereby a writer transmutes something common into something precious, will be puzzled by the discrepancy between the reality of daily life and the idyll Stevenson made of it. It was a fulfilment of what he had expressed in *Travels with a Donkey*, his French book lived and written during the year before he rejoined Fanny in Monterey. There he said it simply: "To live out of doors with the woman one loves is of all lives the most complete and free."

Warm and dry above the fog, he gazed down and wrote "The Sea Fogs," one of the book's finest chapters. He gave the entire Silverado experience a pungent sensuality that reflects his joy at recovering his health, at least temporarily, and in winning the woman he loved.

The Silverado Squatters is more than an arcadian adventure; it is peopled, as his earlier books are not, with creatures of flesh and blood. It marks his coming of age, the end of his youth and bachelorhood. In the decade of life left him, Stevenson moved closer to the greatness that was denied him by early death and the limitations of his time. "If as a writer or an artist you run counter to their narrow notions," he said of the Victorian bourgeoisie, "they simply and silently withdraw your means of subsistence."

He was also faced with the need to earn large sums to support the establishment that grew up around him in Samoa, and he was restricted by Fanny's over-protectiveness. His writing, especially in the *Fables*, took him farther and farther from the public image she had fashioned of him. Here is how he described her toward the end of his life:

"She runs the show. Infinitely little, extraordinary wig of grey curls, handsome waxen face like Napoleon's, insane black eyes, boy's hands, tiny bare feet, a cigarette, wild blue native dress, usually spotted with garden mould. Hellish energy; relieved by fortnights of entire hibernation. Can make anything from a house to a row of houses. Doctors everybody, will doctor you, cannot be doctored herself. A violent friend, a brimstone enemy. Is always either loathed or slavishly adored—indifference impossible. Dreams and sees visions."

California has not been unappreciative of Stevenson. Before Hart established the definitive texts, Professor George R. Stewart wrote his master's thesis at Berkeley on "Stevenson in California, a Critical Study." Two later books by Anne Roller Issler expand this subject: *Stevenson at Silverado* and *Happier for his Presence: San Francisco and Robert Louis Stevenson* are essential Stevensoniana. The best biography is *Voyage to Windward* by J. C. Furnas. The best memoir is *An Intimate Portrait of R.L.S.* by his stepson Lloyd Osbourne, who was with him to the end. Here is a sample from it:

"He was never willing to coddle himself. He would say, 'O, hell, what does it matter? Let me die with my boots on.' It has always been a satisfaction to me that he did. Unlacing them as he lay dead, that reiterated remark of his came back to me very poignantly. Intrepid to the end, he had had his wish, which was symbolic of so much more."

His sister-in-law, Nellie Van de Grift Sanchez and his step-daughter Isobel Strong Field, wrote their memoirs of Louis. Fanny never did. Her biography was written by Margaret Mackay.

In the two decades that Fanny survived him, she grew rich, monolithic, and matriarchal, far different from the tawny bohemian of yore. She generously provided for Jules Simoneau, the Frenchman at whose restaurant Stevenson ate and drank during his months in Monterey, and for Cummy, Stevenson's old nurse to whom he dedicated *A Child's Garden of Verses*. Henry James was fascinated by her. He called her "barbarous and instinctive, a grizzled old lioness."

Fanny died at Santa Barbara in 1914, also from a cerebral hemorrhage, and her ashes were placed with Louis in Samoa. Gelett Burgess designed their tomb, bearing Stevenson's *Requiem*, first drafted in San Francisco when he thought he was going to die:

> Under the wide and starry sky,
> Dig the grave and let me lie.
> Glad did I live and gladly die,
>   And I laid me down with a will.
>
> This be the verse you grave for me:
> *Here he lies where he longed to be;*
> *Home is the sailor, home from sea,*
> *And the hunter home from the hill.*

The tomb also bears Ruth's speech to Naomi in Samoan; Louis's Scotch thistle, Fanny's tiger lily, and his verses about Fanny quoted earlier.

The Stevenson House in Monterey is maintained as a state museum. In San Francisco Portsmouth Square is graced by the galleon-mounted monument and words from his "Christmas Sermon." In 1968 Mr. and Mrs. Norman H. Strouse founded The Silverado Museum in St. Helena. Therein is to be seen their notable collection of R. L. S. books, manuscripts, and memorabilia. The state has marked the site of *The Silverado Squatters* above Calistoga. There is a zig-zag trail up the steep slope above the Toll House to where the mine cabin once stood. Both are gone. An air of peace is there, in the woods of oak and madrone where the man and woman and little boy once lived.

In 1911 the clubwomen of Napa County erected a monument of Scotch granite on the cabin's site in the form of a lectern with open volume, bearing verses Stevenson wrote in memory of a boy who died at the Swiss sanitorium where *Silverado* was written. The monument is weathering badly. Time has not touched the book.

173

ROBERT LOUIS STEVENSON (1850-1894)
The Silverado Squatters. London, Chatto & Windus, 1883.
Silverado Journal. Edited by J. E. Jordan. San Francisco, Book Club of California, 1954.
From Scotland to Silverado. Edited by James D. Hart. Cambridge, Harvard University Press, 1966.

ANNE ROLLER ISSLER
Our Mountain Hermitage; Silverado and Robert Louis Stevenson. Stanford University Press, 1950.
Happier for his Presence; San Francisco and Robert Louis Stevenson. Stanford University Press, 1949.

J. C. FURNAS
Voyage to Windward; the Life of Robert Louis Stevenson. New York, Sloane, 1951.

LLOYD OSBOURNE
An Intimate Portrait of R. L. S. New York, Scribner, 1924.

MARGARET MACKAY
The Violent Friend; the Story of Mrs. Robert Louis Stevenson. Garden City, Doubleday, 1968.

McTeague

FRANK   NORRIS

15

FRANK NORRIS would have liked Raymond Chandler's Los Angeles novels for their violent reality. A generation earlier, he called
for such a literature in an essay about San Francisco, a prophetic
call which he himself answered in *McTeague*, published two
years later.

"London had her Dickens, New Orleans her Cable, New York
her Davis, Boston her Howells, Paris her Zola," he wrote in 1897,
"but San Francisco still waits for her novelist. Where is the man
that shall get at the heart of us, the blood and bones and fibre of
us, that shall go a-gunning for stories up and down our streets
and dives and along our wharves and into our theatres; yes, and
into the secret chambers of our homes as well as our hearts?"

Before 1899 San Francisco had not lacked novelists, none of
whom, however, met Norris's specifications. Twain, Harte, and
Stevenson had come and gone. Nothing like *McTeague* had been
written—a realistic tale of a brutal dentist and an avaricious
woman, of desire and degeneration, culminating in murder and
flight and death in the desert. From his background, education,
and experience, Frank Norris was the last writer one would have
predicted as the author of such a grim novel.

This unpredictable unlikeliness of the whom, when, and where
of genius is an endless fascination of literature. It is not subject to
the laws that govern the sciences. Everything seemed to point

Norris away from what he eventually achieved; and yet from our vantage point in time, we can see that everything he did before he finally wrote *McTeague* contributed to its writing.

Born at Chicago in 1870, his father a wealthy jeweler, his mother an art-loving clubwoman, Norris came to San Francisco as a boy of fourteen when his father sought a more healthful climate. After an initial stay in the Palace Hotel, the Norrises moved into a palatial home on Sacramento Street, two blocks from the Polk Street shopping district that was to provide the setting for *McTeague*.

When Frank showed promise of becoming an artist, the family took him to Europe for study in Paris, Florence, and Rome. There he developed a passion for medieval arms and armor and wrote an anonymous article on the subject which appeared, as his first published work, in the *San Francisco Chronicle*. He also became a fencer and an opera lover. Of all that he learned in France, the most important thing was the language; this enabled him later to read the naturalistic novels of Emile Zola on which *McTeague* was modeled. Although Norris began to write in Paris, his subject was the Middle Ages, not contemporary San Francisco. It was Zola who hustled him out of the past into the present.

His father took a dim view of Frank's defection from art to literature, and summoned him back to California. Four years at the university in Berkeley taught him less about writing than about the philosophy of evolution, gained in the natural history classes of Professor Joseph LeConte. It was this special view of life that was embodied in his subsequent writing. Membership in the fraternity of Phi Gamma Delta gave him an outlet for high spirits and friendships that endured, as well as models for characters in his novels. He was no aesthetic recluse. He liked poker and girls. A passion for football served him later when, as a San Francisco journalist, he wrote a weekly column on the sport.

A fifth year at Harvard was the springboard that launched him into the stream of literature. In the writing class of Professor Lewis E. Gates he found the encouragement of a master teacher that brought *McTeague* into being. Students were

176

required to submit weekly themes and stories based on life they had observed, not read about. Norris chose the life of the Polk Street neighborhood. Is there another instance in literary history of a masterpiece being created from assignments of an academic classroom?

All of Norris's literary activity continued without his father's approval. His mother was the believer, and it was she who paid for the publication of his first book, a ballad called *Yvernelle*. Frank's parents were divorced and after his father's early death, his money was left to his second wife. Instead of thwarting the son's development, this change of fortune provided impetus for him to earn his own living.

This he proceeded to do as a journalist on *The Wave*, a weekly paper established by the Southern Pacific to boost its Hotel Del Monte in Monterey. He wrote prolifically for it—stories, articles, reviews, and the sports feature. A serialized novel, *Moran of the Lady Letty*, inspired by Stevenson's *The Wreckers*, led to his discovery by a New York publisher, who brought Norris east to become a manuscripts reader for his firm. This in turn led to publication of his own novels and financial independence.

Norris also managed to get to Cuba and to South Africa as a war correspondent, to marry and father a daughter, to form warm friendships, and also to aid the rising young Theodore Dreiser by recommending publication of *Sister Carrie*, another milestone in the development of realistic American fiction.

From all of this varied activity, one might assume that Norris had by now reached middle age. Not at all. He was barely past thirty, his life due to end in 1902 at the age of thirty-two, when a neglected attack of appendicitis ended fatally in peritonitis.

That was a fateful year in California literature, marking the death of Norris and the birth of Steinbeck, the two novelists who were to immortalize the San Joaquin Valley in *The Octopus* and *The Grapes of Wrath*. It was also the year of Bret Harte's death.

It is fruitless to speculate on Norris's achievement if he had lived as long as Steinbeck to age sixty-six. There is no assurance that he would have continued to develop. Steinbeck reached zenith by his 36th year. During the nearly thirty years that fol-

178

lowed his masterpiece, he never regained the height to which he took the Joad family and his readers.

McTeague was Norris's first novel in point of composition, written by the time he had reached 25, and although it was followed by half a dozen more, it remains his best. *The Octopus* and *The Pit*, the two novels he managed to write in his projected trilogy, The Epic of the Wheat, are more ambitious, varied, and conventionally interesting, and yet they lack the concentrated impact of *McTeague.*

Norris had the genius to transmit his own vitality into his writing. I do not find it irrelevant that his mother's favorite poet was Robert Browning, the most dynamic of the Victorians. Norris had no use for the Mauve Decade's versifiers, sonneteers, and fancy writers. He loved Stevenson's adventure stories and Kipling's tales of India. He wanted prose to have guts, and even in Paris when he was obsessed by the Middle Ages, his stories were violent and bloody. "If I had a son who wrote like that," a friend said to Norris's father, "I would put him in a lethal chamber." The elder Norris's reaction to *McTeague* was probably speechless.

Today the book's shock waves have long since passed, and we are only amused when we read that it was attacked in 1899 as a "Study in Stinks," or that another critic cried, "This breed of Norrises must be stamped out." However, William Dean Howells, the foremost critic at the turn of the century, praised *McTeague*, at the same time regretting what he said was an absence of beauty.

I find it something more than beautiful. It is an enthralling view of life, observed with loving careful detail. Norris's early interest in art served him well when he finally became a writer. His scenes and setting are vividly pictorial.

We see San Francisco and the East Bay at the end of the century, as electricity and telephones were coming in and there was still a neighborhood life that ebbed and flowed with the tides of night and day.

"It's the life that we want," wrote Norris in that prophetic essay quoted earlier, "the vigorous, real thing, not the curious weaving of words and the polish of literary finish. We don't want literature, we want life. Kipling saw it here and Stevenson, as they passed through, and they heard the unwritten tales of us as they ran. The tales are there. The public is there. A hundred clashing presses are hungry for you, future young story-writer of San Francisco, whoever you may be. Strike but the right note, and strike it with all your might, strike it with iron instead of velvet, and the clang of it shall go the round of the nations."

Norris struck it surely in *McTeague*, and it is still ringing. All that he knew, felt, believed, plus his own animal vitality, conceived, shaped, and permeated the book. It is deeply felt, precisely observed, and masterfully constructed, the work of a youth, the work of a master. In short, a literary miracle and masterpiece, a California classic.

Since 1964 we have had *McTeague* in paperback and with an Afterword by Kenneth Rexroth, a San Franciscan ideally fitted to write about this greatest of all San Francisco novels. "Clearly defined characters in verifiable relationships with one another, moving visibly toward objective doom; careful attention to the architecture of the narrative; refusal of the narrator to surreptitiously involve himself in his characters—these, I suppose," says Rexroth, "are what distinguish classic from romantic tragedy. Norris is not Sophocles, but he certainly produced a minor classic novel in *McTeague*. He would never do it again. Good as they are, his other novels suffer from tendentiousness. In writing of the great and evil, he could never quite recapture the evenhanded magnanimity that seemed to come to him so easily and naturally in telling the story of these trivial people."

The Octopus is better known than *McTeague*, although it is a lesser achievement as a work of art. The reason for its wider reputation is that it has a broader social theme and significance, the struggle of the San Joaquin ranchers against the Southern Pacific monopoly, culminating in the Mussel Slough massacre, that tragic incident of violence which occurred when the railroad's minions confronted the ranchers. By 1900, Norris was feeling the power of his prime and hearing the call of California. He had a need to undertake an epic. In a letter to Howells we read first of his plan:

"I think there is a chance for somebody to do some great work with the West and California as background, and which will be at the same time thoroughly American. My idea is to write three novels around the one subject of Wheat." And to another critic he wrote, "The Wheat series will be straight naturalism with all the guts I can get into it."

In reading *The Octopus*, I confess to having been moved more by the valley scenes—the first rain and subsequent plowing, the barn dance and fight, the jackrabbit drive, and the panoramic descriptions—than by the conflict between ranchers and railroad, cold potatoes now that the lobbying power of the Southern Pacific is only history. Norris's visions of the valley recall those of Muir and Steinbeck. Fully as much as seacoast, mountains, and desert, the central valley is pure Californian, ever powerful in its effect on life and literature.

Here is one of Norris's pictures of the San Joaquin:

"As he had planned, Presley reached the hills by the head-waters of Broderson Creek late in the afternoon. Toilfully he climbed them, reached to the highest crest, and turning about, looked long and for the last time at all the reach of the valley unrolled beneath him. The land of the ranches opened out forever and forever under the stimulus of that measureless range of vision. The whole gigantic sweep of the San Joaquin expanded titanic before the eye of the mind, flagellated with heat, quivering and shimmering under the sun's red eye. It was the season after the harvest, and the great earth, the mother, after its period of reproduction, its pains of labor, delivered of the fruit of its loins, slept the sleep of exhaustion in the infinite repose of the colossus, benignant, eternal, strong, the nourisher of nations, the feeder of an entire world."

Reading it, we recall that passage in *The Mountains of California* when John Muir stood at the summit of Pacheco Pass and looked across the Valley to the Sierra Nevada; and that equally transcendent page in *The Grapes of Wrath* when the Joads crested the Tehachapis and saw for the first time their promised land; or Mark Twain's view of the Valley upon coming over the mountains from Nevada.

Creative writers take liberties with landscape. Thus did Norris in *The Octopus*. The actual setting in history was Tulare County. Norris did his field work northwest of there in San Benito County, spending two months on the great wheat-raising Rancho Santa Anita near Hollister. The little town of San Juan, the Mission San Juan Bautista, and the Morse Seed Farm, were moved in his imagination to Tulare County where the action takes place. He also transplanted the coast live oak, *quercus agrifolia*, to the habitat of the valley white oak, *quercus lobata*, but who cares? We don't read novels for a botany lesson.

What is supreme in these two best books of Norris, *McTeague* and *The Octopus*, is their undiminished vitality and their clairvoyant vision of California, urban and rural, a land Norris loved till his death. They are realistic without being disgusting.

In the final pages of *The Octopus* occurs another instance of the way writers have been drawn by the mountainous Sur Coast, that stretch of shoreline which has been the heartland to so many. It occurs when the *Swanhilda*, loaded with wheat, has put to sea from San Francisco, headed for famine-stricken India. Toward evening the master points out to Presley, the poet, that they are off Point Gordo and that a line drawn due east would pass through Tulare. "He looked long and earnestly at the faint line of mountains that showed vague and bluish above the waste of tumbling water. Those were the mountains of the Coast Range."

Exiled in New York after publication of *The Octopus*, Norris could no longer resist the pull of the Golden State. From Fanny Stevenson he and his wife planned to buy ten acres of her ranch near Gilroy, enlarge the cabin thereon called "Quien Sabe," and make it their camping base. Above all, he loved San Francisco. "I don't suppose I shall ever feel at home away from there," he wrote to a friend not long before he died, "Indeed I have come to look forward to the time when I shall come back to San Francisco to live for good and all." His last letter was to Fanny Stevenson, in September 1902. A month later he was dead. They buried him in Mountain View Cemetery, Oakland.

It was thirty years after his death before the first biography of Norris appeared, written by Franklin Walker of Mills College. It remains a model work of selectivity, insight, and interpretation. The Book Club of California and the Bancroft Library have furthered Norris's reputation by their publications and their collections of source material. Beginning in 1950, Professor James D. Hart led an international search to recover the manuscript of *McTeague*, a page of which had been included with each set of the Argonaut edition of Norris's *Complete Works*, published in 1928 by Doubleday of New York. About half of the manuscript is now in the Bancroft Library, either in the original or photocopy. The letters and manuscripts kept by Norris's mother and widow were lost in the great San Francisco fire. In addition to the scattered pages of *McTeague*, Hart hunted down valuable Norrisana from a variety of sources.

In 1924 the great German director, Eric von Stroheim, faithfully rendered *McTeague* in film, 42 reels in all, ten hours in length, shooting it on Polk Street and in Death Valley. Jean Hersholt played Marcus, to whose dead body McTeague found himself fatally handcuffed, and he recalled that it was the most grueling role of his Hollywood career, as the director kept the cast in Death Valley for days to shoot the scene over and over and over, with the temperature at 120°.

When M.G.M. would not distribute the marathon film, von Stroheim cut it in half. Still the studio refused. Finally a studio editor cut it even more, and it was finally released as "Greed." It was a failure, the life and the continuity gone, so that audiences were confused because of what it didn't show. Von Stroheim would never view his mutilated masterpiece.

Now with the stamina they have developed to sit through today's interminable double bills, audiences are better conditioned to endure a ten-hour feature, if the original uncut version should have survived the several snippers.

FRANK NORRIS (1870-1902)

McTeague, A Story of San Francisco. New York, Doubleday, 1899; San Francisco, Colt Press, 1941, introduction by Charles G. Norris; New American Library, Signet Classic, with an Afterword by Kenneth Rexroth, 1964.

The Octopus, A Story of California. Garden City, Doubleday, 1901; New American Library, Signet Classic, with an Afterword by Oscar Cargill, 1964.

Frank Norris of "The Wave"; Stories and Sketches . . . 1893 to 1897. Introduction by Oscar Lewis. San Francisco, Westgate Press, 1931.

A Novelist in the Making; a Collection of Student Themes . . . ed. by James D. Hart. Cambridge, Harvard University Press, 1970.

FRANKLIN WALKER

Frank Norris, A Biography. New York, Doubleday, 1932.

JAMES D. HART

"Search and Research; the Librarian & the Scholar." In *College & Research Libraries*, September 1958.

Photograph of Frank Norris, courtesy of Bancroft Library.

Martin Eden

JACK   LONDON

16

FOR YEARS I have carried around a quotation from *Enemies of Promise*, a book of literary criticism by Cyril Connolly, awaiting the time when it would be supremely applicable. At last the time has come, with a rereading of *Martin Eden*, *The Sea Wolf*, *The Call of the Wild*, and a dozen other books by and about Jack London.

First to quote it, then take up the matter of its relevance to the San Francisco-born writer who died a suicide in 1916 on his ranch in the Valley of the Moon, Sonoma County. The English critic wrote:

"Success is bad for a writer because it cuts him off from his roots, raises his standard of living, and so leads him to overproduction, lowers his standard of criticism, and carries with it the germ of its opposite, failure."

In all of American literature there is no more apt an illustration of this dictum than Jack London. His biography should be required reading in writing classes to encourage persistence against the obstacles of poverty and lack of education, as well as to warn against the perils of unbridled success in the form of money and fame.

Enduring literary fame is a lottery, Stendhal declared, in which the winning ticket is not drawn until a hundred years after the writer's death. With the half-way mark passed, Jack London's fame would appear to hold such a ticket. Ironical reversals happen sometimes with the passage of time. What Mark Twain wrote primarily as boys' adventure books—*Tom Sawyer* and *Huckleberry Finn*—have become adult classics. What Jack London wrote as red-blooded, masculine works—*The Call of the Wild, White Fang, The Sea Wolf*—now have more youthful readers than old.

Although I do not intend to write exclusively about *Martin Eden*, for with two-score books in all, Jack London holds more than a single ticket in Stendhal's lottery, yet I believe that *Martin Eden* best illustrates the way in which London refined literature from the raw material of his own life's success and failure. It is a classic example of Connolly's thesis, an anatomy of one writer's rise and fall.

Strangely enough, London's first title for the novel was *Success*. Its publication in 1909 resulted in misunderstanding by London's large following, who regarded him as America's foremost apostle of Socialism. *Martin Eden* portrayed London's own rise from proletarian origins, mounting success as a writer, his conquering of bourgeois society, love affair with an intellectual woman and embracing of Socialism, his literary fame, and then a disillusionment with both love and fame, leading finally to suicide by drowning. Readers of the book accused him of unfaithfulness to Socialism. Not so, London replied, *Martin Eden* was meant to be an exposure of extreme individualism and its negative fruits. He was indignant because his readers failed to perceive his intention, which was an attack on the doctrines of Nietzsche and his philosophy of the superman.

Both readers and writer were wrong. *Martin Eden* is quite simply a strong, autobiographical, confessional work, of the same school, though not as great a book, as Lawrence's *Sons and Lovers*. Its hold on time and the reader comes from the passion which animates it, the skill of its narrative style. At his best, and *Martin Eden* represents London at the peak of his power, he was able to infuse language with the energy he lavished on life. It is a lean book without any padding, and it drives forward without pause.

The writing of *Martin Eden*, with its scapegoat hero, served to extend its author's life, enabling London to carry on for another seven years, before he too chose suicide as the way out of the maze into which an excess of success had led him. Reading it today with our overview of London's violent life, from its rough and humble beginnings to worldly conquest and riches, stirs ambivalent feelings in the reader, of admiration at the triumph, of sadness at the defeat.

Jack London is in the mainstream of American literature, having much in common as man and writer with two, who in some ways were his successors, Steinbeck and Hemingway. As Californians, London and Steinbeck were deeper rooted natives than any other writers of their time. Unlike Steinbeck, who felt compelled to leave his land of origin and could never return, try though he did in *Travels With Charley*, London was unable to stay away, even in the idyllic South Seas to which, like Stevenson, he voyaged with a woman in a search for happiness. He never found it there, nor in Hawaii. Drink and illness drove him back to his ranch, near the setting of *The Silverado Squatters*.

Throughout London's Californian novels and stories, culminating in *The Valley of the Moon*, is embodied a passionate love of his native land. His tragedy was that he was never able to gear a manic-depressive nature to an ordered existence, nor to achieve a single great book of the land with the sustained lyricism and objective power of Steinbeck's masterpieces of the California earth.

London and Hemingway were blood brothers in their celebration of the virile life of hunting, fishing, fighting, and drinking. They were fascinated by their own maleness. Both were drawn, as correspondents, by the violence of war. Hemingway's Cuban *finca* resembled London's Sonoma *hacienda*. Both men were destroyed by success, and both sealed their destruction by suicide, one by gun, the other by poison.

Although *Martin Eden* is autobiographical, it is not to be read as a literal story of its author's life. As yet there is no single source for the whole story. *The Book of Jack London* by his second wife, Charmian; *Jack London, an Unconventional Biography* by Joan London, his daughter by his first wife, Bessie; *Sailor on Horse-*

188

back, a biographical novel by Irving Stone; and other works are valuable for their facts and insights, yet there remains to be written a definitive biocritical account of Jack London and his books. Masses of source material await its writer in the collections of the Huntington Library. Is it not ironical that the great socialist writer's papers are preserved in the great capitalist's library? Time is a great reconciler of opposites.

When London's first story was accepted by the *Atlantic Monthly*—he was to follow the route of Bret Harte into print: debut in the *Overland Monthly*, leading to Boston's prestigious *Atlantic*—the editor asked if "Jack London" were a pseudonym. Although it was not, neither was it the author's natal name. His father was a wandering, Maine-born, Irish astrologer, Professor William Chaney, an erudite man, equally magnetic as lecturer and philanderer. His mother was Flora Wellman, a black sheep Middle Westerner of Welsh descent. They were never married.

Before John Chaney was born, in San Francisco on January 12, 1876, his father had left Flora, and the boy never laid eyes on him. Flora then married a widower, John London, and it was his stepfather's name that Jack London carried to fame. When he was still a boy, the family moved across bay to Oakland, Alameda, and Livermore, which were then countryside.

An influential person in London's early life was the Oakland city librarian, the poet Ina Coolbrith, Bret Harte's faithful devotée. It was she who widened the boy's horizon to encompass the world of books. Years later when queried by a Wisconsin library school instructor, seeking in her words "to cross fertilize boys and books," London replied, "Two wonderful things happened to me when I was a small boy that practically directed the entire course of my life, and I doubt if neither of these things had happened to me that I should ever have become a writer."

The first was his coming upon a tattered copy of Ouida's novel *Signa*. "It put in me an ambition to get beyond the skylines of my narrow California valley and opened up to me the possibilities of the world of art." The second was the kindness shown him by Miss Coolbrith. "It was this world of books, now accessible, that practically gave me the basis of my education."

These cultural counterbalances helped bring London through the hazards of his youth as a waterfront rough, oyster pirate on the bay, sailor on a seal-hunting expedition to the Siberian islands, and finally as an Alaska gold hunter. Through all of this violent experience books were his talismans.

It was the Alaskan adventures that led to his rise as a writer, a swift rise but not an instantaneous one, as the painful progress is telescoped in *Martin Eden;* and it is for his stories of the Far North that he is best known and most read today. Beginning with *Son of the Wolf*, published in 1900, London wrote several more books about Alaska. His literary models were Bret Harte and Rudyard Kipling.

The Call of the Wild followed in three years. It is generally held to be the best dog story ever written. Why it is also the best of the scores of stories London ever wrote is not answerable. We only know that it is, that it marks zenith on the arc of his craft. In March of 1903 he wrote to his publisher, George P. Brett of Macmillan, "The whole history of this story has been very rapid. On my return from England I sat down to write it into a 4000-word yarn, but it got away from me and I was forced to expand it to its present length." He finished it in thirty days of sustained writing.

For its serialization in the *Saturday Evening Post*, London received $2000, and quickly spent it. Although Brett feared it would prove too realistic for the public taste in animal stories as formed by the sentimental tales of Ernest Thompson-Seton, he paid London $2000 for all rights to the long story. His fears were unfounded. The bibliography of Jack London, published in 1966, takes ten pages to list the editions of *The Call of the Wild*, which have never ceased to appear in many languages.

London's devotion to Socialism led to the most unusual of his books, *People of the Abyss*, a valid sociological study of the city of London's East End slums. Disguised as a derelict, London lived there for three months, gathering the material for his book. It and *The Iron Heel*, a prophetic novel of a future dictatorial age, as well as his adventure stories, are responsible for London's lasting popularity in the Soviet Union. Lenin's death-bed reading was an essay by Jack London.

When we come to *The Sea Wolf*, published in 1904, we find it to be even more pertinent than *Martin Eden* in illustrating Connolly's pronouncement about success as an encouragement to overproduce and to lower standards. The reason for this is to be found in what occurred after the financial rewards of *The Call of the Wild*.

London's standard of living soared. He married, had two daughters, and at his home in Piedmont he held constant open house for Bay region intellectuals. He bought a small yacht, the *Spray*, to use as a workshop for writing the novel that became *The Sea Wolf*. He also installed his family in summer camp at Glen Ellen in Sonoma County. There he met Charmian Kittredge, an aggressive woman who replaced Bessie in his affections and became his second wife.

The Sea Wolf was based on London's adventures as a seal-hunter, and up to a point, it is one of the best of all sea stories, shelvable next to *Two Years Before the Mast* and *Moby Dick*. Then, with the entrance of a woman character, it degenerates into a preposterous, sentimental romance.

The reason for this was that half way through writing the book, London ran out of money. In order to sell serial rights to *Century* magazine, he had to promise the editor that the man and woman characters, when shipwrecked alone on an island, would do nothing to offend the subscribers. Offered $4000 on those terms, London telegraphed the editor that he could blue pencil as much as he wished, and that he was "absolutely confident the American prude could not be shocked by the second half of the book."

He was right. The only ones to be shocked were the critics. When they properly ridiculed the woman, London rose to the defense of his model, Charmian Kittredge. "I was in love with a woman, and I wrote her into my book, and the critics tell me that the woman I love is unbelievable."

So there it is in sad brevity: overproduction to meet a soaring standard of living and a consequent lowering of artistic standards when blinded by emotion and the need for cash. This continued, and by the time of his death in 1916, London was earning $75,000 a year and spending $100,000. Writing for the big money of "the slicks" was no better for his genius than it was for Hemingway's. In a pitiful sales letter to an editor, intended to justify a substantial advance for a planned book, London wrote,

"Three characters only—a mighty trio in a mighty situation, in a magnificently beautiful environment. Each of the three is good; each of three is big. It will be a winner. It is all sex, from start to finish—in which no sexual adventure is actually achieved or comes within a million miles of being achieved, and in which, nevertheless, is all the guts of sex, coupled with strength. . . . As I go over this novel, I am almost led to believe that it is what I have been working toward all my writing life, and now I've got it in my two hands."

Alas, no writer was ever more self-deluded. *The Little Lady of the Big House*, London's final novel, is his worst.

His last books include the powerful *John Barleycorn*, subtitled *Alcoholic Memoirs;* and *The Star Rover*, a strange novel of a San Quentin prisoner reliving previous reincarnations while confined in a straightjacket. The most Californian of them is *The Valley of the Moon*, a story about an Oakland teamster and his bride, their flight from the city and return to the land in a search for an ideal place, a valley in the moon. On this book London lavished his love of pastoral California. His young couple range from the Big Sur to Oregon and back to his beloved Sonoma Shangri La, their journey made by team and wagon in that idyllic era before the advent of the automobile. It was this same premechanical time that produced J. Smeaton Chase's California travel classics.

One is tempted to free the descriptive passages from the now embarrassing slang speech London gave his prize-fighting teamster hero and which badly dates the book, and print them separately as a travel essay. And yet it is a passionate book, its characters sharply drawn, and it is purely Californian. Over the land from Mission Carmel to Mt. Shasta, London lovingly passes, seeking his valley of the moon, to find it finally at Glen Ellen. His marriage with that Sonoman region is as absolute as that of Jeffers and Steinbeck with the coast and valleys of Monterey County, of Norris with the San Joaquin Valley, of Muir with Yosemite. In their wanderings in search of their ultimate place, the couple were drawn first by the Big Sur hinterland, but rejected it because of its remoteness from farm markets.

The Valley of the Moon, and indeed London's very life, culminate in this passage which describes the discovery and end of the quest:

"Ahead and toward the right, across sheer ridges of the mountains, separated by deep green canyons and broadening lower down into rolling orchards and vineyards, they caught their first sight of Sonoma Valley and the wild mountains that rimmed its eastern side. To the left they gazed across a golden land of small hills and valleys. Beyond, to the north, they glimpsed another portion of the valley, and, still beyond, the opposing wall of the valley—a range of mountains, the highest of which reared its red and battered ancient crater against a rosy and mellowing sky. From north to southeast, the mountain rim curved in the brightness of the sun, while Saxon and Billy were already in the shadow of evening. He looked at Saxon, noted the ravished ecstasy of her face, and stopped the horses. All the eastern sky was blushing to rose, which descended upon the mountains, touching them with wine and ruby. Sonoma Valley began to fill with a purple flood, leaving the mountain bases, rising, inundating, drowning them in its purple. Saxon pointed in silence, indicating that the purple flood was the sunset shadow of Sonoma Mountain. Billy nodded, then chirruped to the mares, and the descent began through a warm and colorful twilight."

Jack London was a vital part of the literary history of his time in California. He wrote of and was written about by his creative peers—George Sterling, Ambrose Bierce, Edith Wharton, Gertrude Atherton, Mary Austin, and Upton Sinclair. He praised Frank Norris's *Moran of the Lady Letty* and his posthumous *Vandover and the Brute*, but what he thought of Norris's masterpiece, *McTeague*, I do not know. London's last summer in Carmel with George Sterling was in the year before Robinson Jeffers arrived there in 1914. London regarded Sterling as America's finest poet. I believe that he would have been even more moved if he had lived to read Jeffers's mature verse.

In *The Valley of the Moon* London portrayed the Carmel literary colony, and in *Martin Eden* the San Francisco intellectuals, including George Sterling as Brissenden, figure in several scenes. He did not like *The Silverado Squatters*, although his comments on it, in letters to his friend Cloudesley Johns, were written before he had discovered his own neighboring sanctuary.

Among the London manuscripts in the Huntington Library is an unpublished introduction to *Two Years Before the Mast.* It is one of the finest tributes ever written to the truth and the power of Dana's classic.

Although London eventually resigned from the Socialist Party, his Glen Ellen ranch remained a haven for ex-convicts and other unfortunates. The ranch's huge overhead drained his financial resources. He lost $46,000 alone on a vast planting of eucalyptus trees. His return to the land was more than a pastoral retreat. He regarded himself as a practical agrarian. Here is how he expressed it in a letter written only a month before his death:

"I have no countryside home. I am a farmer. It is because I am a farmer that I live in the country. I am that sort of farmer who, after delving in all the books to satisfy his quest for economic wisdom, returns to the soil as the source and foundation of all economics. What am I doing? In few words, I am trying to do what the Chinese have done for forty centuries, namely, to farm without commercial fertilizer. I am rebuilding worn-out hillside lands that were worked out and destroyed by our wasteful California pioneer farmers. I believe the soil is our one indestructible asset, and by green manures, nitrogen-gathering crops, animal manures, rotation of crops, proper tillage and drainage, I am getting results which the Chinese have demonstrated for forty centuries."

His dream was to found a landed dynasty—a dream like Joseph Wayne's in *To a God Unknown*—but neither of his wives bore him a son. He erected Wolf House, a noble structure of stone and redwood; it was destroyed by arson before completion, and London never sought to rebuilt it. The ruins stand today as part of the Jack London State Historical Monument.

The woman who did the most to ease the burdens and tensions of his open-handed way of life was not his "mate woman" Charmian, but rather his devoted step-sister, Eliza London Shepard. It was she who nursed him at the end when, his body burned out by alcohol, a self-administered overdose of morphine took his life. She saw to it that his ashes were placed where he wanted them to be, atop a knoll on the ranch. There she set the big red lava rock London called "the stone the builders rejected."

Although success destroyed him body and soul and damaged much of his writing, so abundant was Jack London's talent, so enduring the vitality with which he transfused his best work, that time has dealt lightly with those classics, *The Call of the Wild*, the first half of *The Sea Wolf*, *Martin Eden*, and his love of California as expressed in *The Valley of the Moon*. At his best he realized what Martin Eden strove for, "an impassioned realism, shot through with human aspiration and faith."

Reading List

JACK LONDON (1876-1915)
The Call of the Wild. New York, Macmillan, 1903. New American Library, Signet Classic, with Foreword by Franklin Walker, 1960.
Martin Eden. New York, Macmillan, 1909; Penguin, 1967; Vol. 3 of Bodley Head Jack London, Edited by Arthur Calder-Marshall, London, 1965.
The Sea-Wolf. New York, Macmillan, 1904. New American Library, Signet Classic, Afterword by Franklin Walker, 1961.
The Valley of the Moon. New York, Macmillan, 1913.
Letters. Edited by King Hendricks and Irving Shepard. New York, Odyssey Press, 1965.

CHARMIAN K. LONDON
The Book of Jack London. New York, Century Co., 1921. 2 vols.

JOAN LONDON
Jack London and his Times, an Unconventional Biography. Seattle, University of Washington Press, 1968.

JOSEPH NOEL
Footloose in Arcadia; a Personal Recollection of Jack London, George Sterling & Ambrose Bierce. New York, Carrick & Evans, 1940.

IRVING STONE
Sailor on Horseback, the Biography of Jack London, Boston, Houghton Mifflin, 1938.

CYRIL CONNOLLY
Enemies of Promise. Boston, Little, Brown, 1939.

Photograph of Jack London, courtesy of Bancroft Library.

J . S M E A T O N   C H A S E

17

I DO NOT claim the status of genius for J. Smeaton Chase. He is a
minor writer. Yet a book need not be of major importance to be
a classic. Minor classics, with which literature abounds, are sometimes more comfortable to live with than those rare works of
heroic stature which demand great effort to read and comprehend.

Born at London in 1864, Joseph Smeaton Chase came to California in 1890. He lived first "on the flank of Cuyamaca," a
triple-peaked mountain northeast of San Diego known as Old
Queer Mack. It is not known for sure what brought the young
man of twenty-six to California. Probably it was a quest for
health, wealth, and happiness. He found them all in modest
proportions, and he left a short shelf of books to the lasting enjoyment of readers.

Chase was forty-seven when his first book appeared, and then
during the last decade of his life—he died at Banning in 1923—
he wrote five and co-authored a sixth. His work appeared earlier
as essays and articles in English and American periodicals. Little
is known of his life, apart from what he tells us in his books. We
do know that he came from a literary line; his father, Samuel
Chase, was a publisher; his brother worked in a London bookstore.

Chase appears in the Los Angeles directories from 1893 on.

He lived for some time with a wealthy family on their ranch in the San Gabriel Valley, where he tutored their sons. When by 1921 he had arrived in *Who's Who in America*, we read in his own words that he was "interested in sociological work in California; a settlement resident, Bethlehem Institutional Church, Los Angeles, for many years." In other words he was a social welfare worker, for an agency located at 510 North Vignes Street (near today's Union Station), that concerned itself with laborers and their families. It was headed by Dr. and Mrs. Dana W. Bartlett. Later he worked in a camera store on 5th street near Main.

Chase's books, however, were not on social themes. They were about the natural wonders of his adopted state, its seacoast, valleys, mountains, and desert. No writer since Brewer ranged wider in southern, central, and northern California. Why is it that his books are more readable than most of the hundreds, even thousands, of volumes of California topography and travel? The answer is to be found in their indefinable charm, in a quality of style implicit in what he saw and how he said it. It is Chase's personality, his character, that comes through in his prose and make his books of enduring interest.

Smeaton Chase's first work, *Yosemite Trails*, appeared in 1911. It is a blend of guide book and nature essays, based on three journeys through the Sierra Nevada roundabout Yosemite. Its dedication reveals something of its origin:

"To Frederick Oliver Popenoe of Altadena, California, at whose suggestion the expeditions of which this volume is the result were undertaken, this adventure of a first book is by the author cordially inscribed."

Popenoe owned a nursery which stocked subtropical fruits He sent his son Paul to Algeria to import date palms. It was the Popenoes who introduced date growing into the Coachella Valley. In a letter to me, Paul Popenoe recalls Chase's passion for mountains, desert, and seacoast, and of how his father encouraged Chase to write about them.

Yosemite Trails takes a place on the shelf of Sierra Nevada literature not too far below Muir's *The Mountains of California*, to which Chase pays tribute. It shows the author in possession of

a mature and fluent style, and also to be a botanist of considerable learning.

The same year marked the appearance of Chase's second book,
Cone-Bearing Trees of the California Mountains, "prepared not
by a botanist for botanists, nor by a botanist for students, but by
a tree-lover for tree-lovers, and aims simply at enabling anyone
going into our California mountains to distinguish the pines, firs,
and other coniferous trees he may meet."

This handbook is as useful now as it was then, for trees are
not given to change. It is also an attractive work because of photographs, mostly by Chase himself, and line-drawings by Carl
Eytel, the German artist long identified with Palm Springs. The
book is now scarce, though not expensive when found in a sec-
ondhand-books store.

Of all the books written by Smeaton Chase, his third, *California Coast Trails*, is the best, perhaps because his imagination
was excited more by the seacoast than by the other physical
features of the state. Our shore is a unique feature. Other states
have valleys, mountains, and deserts, but only California has a
coastline of such length and variety.

It inspired Chase to write his finest book, the narrative of two
horseback rides he took, the first in 1910 from El Monte through
Laguna Canyon and down coast to San Diego; and then in 1911,
May to November, from El Monte again to the coast at Malibu
and on north to the Oregon border. *California Coast Trails* is one
of the few California travel books to approach *Two Years Before
the Mast* as literature.

By literature, I mean prose of more than factual value; prose
with perspective in time and place, with historical background
and overtones, as well as precise observation of the immediate
present. Chase rode with Cabrillo, Drake, Serra, Dana, and
Stevenson at his side. He had a constant sense of the past.

And of the future. That was a fateful year, 1911, as men took
to the sky. It moved Chase to these words:

"The shore here, as all along this mountain-walled coast, is
bold and scenic, fringed everywhere with islets about which the
water coils and lurches in unceasing turmoil. I cannot imagine

a more alluring yachting ground than this hundred-mile reach of lone water, with its barrier of summer gold or winter emerald; and in the coming era of air travel one of the inducements held out to tourists by the Pacific Coast Aerial Transportation Co. will certainly be 'the unrivalled panorama of the Santa Lucia chain of mountains, rearing its glowing rampart from the isle-gemmed empire of the sea to the azure vault of the empyrean.' "

Today's plane flights between Los Angeles and San Francisco are more over land than sea. Once, however, my plane was routed over water all the way. Flying a mile high and a few miles off-shore, I saw the coast of Chase's vision. The time was spring, and the hills were at once emerald and gold, as the new grass was overlaid with flowering mustard; and along the Sur coast the mountains came plunging down just as Cabrillo, Dana, Chase, and Jeffers described them.

Chase also foresaw the changes that would be wrought by the automobile. He saw progress approaching and he didn't like it. His book is permeated with nostalgia for California Pastoral. Reading it today half a century later, the jets going over in a parade of planes and the automobile become our master, we are thankful that he rode and wrote when he did.

In his choice of a horse as travelling companion, Chase certainly had in mind Stevenson's *Travels with a Donkey*. Two horses figure in Chase's narrative. First was Chino who made it as far as the Jolon Valley, then Anton (named for Mission San Antonio), a former Forest Service animal who proved his mettle clear to Oregon, where man and beast took the steamer home from Crescent City.

In Chase's time when those equine motels known as livery stables were still to be found in every town, a horse could be cared for when its rider wanted a soft bed. Most of the nights however were spent in the open, on the beach or in the forest. There were perils too, as when Chase and Chino were nearly swallowed by quicksand.

I went by automobile one autumn over Smeaton Chase's coast trails, following him as best I could. In parts of the back country the landscape remains as he described it. Great stretches of coast-

200

land have been removed from public access by the needs of the armed forces, at Camp Pendleton above San Diego, at the Point Mugu Missile Range, and at the Vandenberg Air Force Base seaward from Lompoc.

An area that he found posted "No Trespassing" is open today. When Chase rode down Topanga Canyon to the coast, he encountered the fenced land of the Rancho Topanga Malibu Sequit. "I knew that public right of way through the ranch had long been contested by the owners, and I had been warned that I might find my way disputed by their myrmidons with shotguns. But there was nothing except the passive placard to prevent my entering."

He camped that night at the mouth of Trancas Canyon, under "a great tent-like sycamore." That very tree stands today in the field between the creek and the country store. "I was up at four o'clock and broke camp early," Chase wrote, "the breeze was strong and keen, and an inexhaustible freshness was in the air, as if the world had been created within the week." I live today near where Smeaton Chase camped many years ago, and I can report that the weather has not changed.

On up coast he went, with detours whenever one of the missions lay inland. At Santa Barbara he visited with Father Zephyrin Engelhardt, the Franciscan historian. He ascended Refugio Pass to gain Mission Santa Ynez, and beyond San Simeon he rode up San Carpoforo Creek to crest the range and reach Jolon and Mission San Antonio.

Although his botanical knowledge was considerable, Chase's book is not a catalog of trees and flowers. Every lighthouse encountered called for a visit to the keeper and his staff. The lights at Point Conception, Piedras Blancas, Point Sur, and Pigeon Point are still there, with posted visiting hours.

The social worker is revealed in his interest in the humble people he encountered and in the vignettes of backwater characters. His fluency in Spanish made him welcome when *frijoles* were on the table. "The reader will no doubt notice," he writes, "that the California Spaniards and Mexicans enter more into my narrative than their numerical strength in the population of the

201

state would render natural. The reason is partly that my purposes led me much into those out-of-the-way districts where they still form a large element in California life, and partly that I have a genuine liking for them. I confess to having no sympathy with the slighting regard in which they, especially the Mexicans, are held by the great majority of people in the West."

Before the area commandeered by Vandenberg had expanded to the north, it was possible to reach the coast from Casmalia, then cross over the headland of Point Sal to the dunes below Pismo Beach. I found the road closed by a locked gate. Approaching it I overtook a traveller the sight of whom gave me a start. He was a booted man, leading a saddle horse laden with camping gear. He did not look up when I passed. Was it the ghost of Smeaton Chase?

One reason for *California Coast Trails'* excellence is its sense of form, rising like a wave to crest, then breaking over and receding. The journey's high point is that stretch of coast which returns again and again into our consideration of California literature. Here is how Chase approached it:

"On leaving Morro I found myself entering that little-known stretch of mountain country which borders the Pacific closely for a distance of about a hundred miles. For most of that distance there are no roads and few settlers, while the trails are rough, steep, and often so little travelled as to be difficult to follow. Further, no maps of the region were to be had. Many persons had told me that I should never get through without a guide."

Chase left the coast below the Big Sur and struck inland through what was then the Hearst Rancho Piedras Blancas and is now the Hunter Liggett Military Reservation. After inspecting the Mission San Antonio, then unrestored, he returned to the coast over the Nacimiento summit. From there he looked down on the great panorama described years later by John Steinbeck in *To a God Unknown.* Chase's description is typical of his way of wedding what he saw with how he said it:

"That morning's trail was the most delightful I had experienced on the trip, winding down the forested mountain-side among yellow-pines, oaks, and madroños. The ground was all ashy rose with the fallen leaves of the last-named tree, and was like one of those wonderful old Persian rugs. Across the cañon the mountains rose in steep slopes of faded gold, laced here and there with the dark files of timber; and beyond, the distant back ranges receded in varying tones of blue. The fog was slowly drawing out to sea, and suddenly, as if a curtain were partly lifted, I could look beneath the sheet of dazzling cloud and see the crinkled water a thousand feet below, leaden in the shadow of the dense vapor. A short distance up the coast Cape San Martin stood sharply out, a line of surf marking where the great shoulder of mountain plunged into the ocean."

Chase met a hermit such as one described by both Jeffers and Steinbeck. In an essay contributed to the *Overland Monthly*, differing in detail from the chapter in the book, he wrote of encountering two tenderfoot hikers who were jettisoning their overload of equipment, and of coming on a pile of their discards, including a blank notebook. This he eagerly retrieved, for his own had been filled. If these travel diaries survive, I have yet to find them. They account for the wealth of detail and precise observation which characterizes his finished writing.

North of San Francisco, Chase quickened his pace, as October presaged the rainy season. Weather, topography, and flora all changed. The Spanish influence disappeared. He paid homage to Drake, and in Eureka to Bret Harte whose newspaper career began there. This is, Chase observed, the capital of northern California, as San Francisco is of central, Los Angeles of southern. He accurately delineated California as tri-, not bi-partite.

California Coast Trails was published in 1913 in both American and English editions. Two years later Chase collaborated with Charles Francis Saunders in *The California Padres and Their Missions*, which is good history and good literature. Saunders wrote the historical chapters, Chase the interludes of legend and lore; and in *The Penance of Magdalena*, the scarcest of Chase's books, he extracted his parts dealing with five of the southernmost missions.

In 1915 Smeaton Chase moved to Palm Springs where two years later he married Isabel White, one of the three White sisters

204

who were destined to play leading roles in the history of the desert community. *California Desert Trails* appeared in 1919. Here again his travelling companion was a horse, named Kaweah in honor of Clarence King. A burro, Mesquite, was rejected because of her innate stubbornness.

Although the automobile and air conditioning have opened the desert to city living, and Palm Springs is not what it used to be, Chase's book is not out of date. The seacoast has changed more than the mountains and the desert. Desert flora and fauna and weather have changed not at all. His range is from 29 Palms to Borrego, with a side trip to Warner's Ranch in the Laguna Mountains; then via El Centro and Brawley and the dunes to Yuma and up the Colorado to Blythe. His prose gains unity from the river, as it did from the coastline. The complexity of the desert somewhat disperses the thrust of his book. The earlier coast book is monothematic and thereby more powerful.

And yet *California Desert Trails* ranks with *The Wonders of the Colorado Desert* as a masterpiece of descriptive writing about California's southeastern corner. A night march moved Chase to the same wonder that possessed him as he rode along the Pacific shore, with only water between him and China:

"Hour after hour went silently by while Kaweah kept up his steady pace. Sometimes I checked him while I let the silence and solitude possess me. In the great indefinite space and under the full half-sphere of sky glittering with stars from zenith to horizon, I might have been the sole inhabitant of the planet. The faint, momentary breeze seemed to come from infinite distance; was born perhaps in Ceylon, and had ranged over starlit oceans and untrodden Asian peaks to pass me here, then roam on, and on, and die, maybe, among the snows of Spitzbergen. Geography took on a vital meaning. Ahead I seemed to look over the plains of Texas to the eastern seaboard, the Bermudas, the Canaries, Europe with its struggling, staggering nations. I felt the draw of my own land, the lodestone till death of every Briton. Behind was the vastness of the Pacific, the welter of awakening China. There lay the frozen tundra, and there, under friendly Polaris, the no longer defiant North Pole."

Chase's last book, a coda to the symphonic *California Desert Trails*, followed a year later in 1920. *Our Araby* is a booster book for Palm Springs. Valuable as early history, it will also be read today with nostalgia by those who remember the village before it became a city.

Smeaton Chase never lost his identity as an Englishman. *California Coast Trails* was dedicated "To my brothers, whose lot it has been to remain in the old home land." *California Desert Trails* bears this dedication: "To my Aunt in the little red town among the rainy Cumberland mountains, this uncommonly dry volume is affectionately inscribed."

I journeyed to Palm Springs to see what evidence remains of Chase's residence there half a century ago. In the grassy cemetery at the foot of Mt. San Jacinto wherein the Murrays, the Coffmans, and other less notable pioneers are buried, I found his grave, guarded by sentinel palms. Buried with him is his wife, Isabel, who survived him nearly forty years. Most moving of all, however, was a scrap of paper found in the fragmentary archives of Mrs. Chase, preserved in the former home of her sister, Cornelia, which now houses the museum of the Palm Springs Historical Society. In Chase's flowing hand I read these words:

"Out of that strong love I bear to my dear native land I ask that, subject to the equal claims of my brothers, my name might be put on the gravestone of my father and mother in old Bexley Churchyard, Kent, England. There is space, I think, for only one name to be added. I should like to think that though my body will—as I now expect—lie in California ground, there will be the slight record of my name as an Englishman remaining in an English churchyard."

That his wish was carried out by his widow is evidenced by a photograph, also in the archives, of the Bexley gravestone. There at the bottom, beneath the names and dates of his parents, is carved his name and dates of birth and death, thus linking him forever with England and California.

Reading List

J. SMEATON CHASE (1864-1923)
Yosemite Trails. Boston, Houghton Mifflin, 1911.
Cone-Bearing Trees of the California Mountains. Chicago, McClurg, 1911.
California Coast Trails. Boston, Houghton Mifflin, 1913.
The Penance of Magdalena. Boston, Houghton Mifflin, 1915.
California Desert Trails. Boston, Houghton Mifflin, 1919.
Our Araby; Palm Springs . . . Pasadena, Star-News, 1920.
"Exploring the Santa Lucia Sierra of California," in *Overland Monthly*, December 1913, & reprinted in Emil White's *Big Sur Guide*, 1955.

CHARLES F. SAUNDERS and J. SMEATON CHASE
The California Padres & Their Missions. Boston, Houghton Mifflin, 1915.

W. W. ROBINSON & LAWRENCE CLARK POWELL
The Malibu. Los Angeles, Dawson's Bookshop, 1958; Paperback edition, Ward Ritchie Press, 1970.

Photograph of J. Smeaton Chase, courtesy of California State Library.

Give Your Heart To The Hawks

ROBINSON JEFFERS

18

THE BIG SUR coast of Monterey County had a long wait for its laureate. Nearly four centuries elapsed between the time when its discoverer, Juan Rodriguez Cabrillo, saw it from sea and when its poet, Robinson Jeffers, saw it from land.

Although the log of Cabrillo's voyage along the coast in 1542 has not survived, a contemporary chronicler records the discoverer as declaring, "All the coast passed this day is very bold; there is a great swell and the land is very high. There are mountains which seem to reach the heavens, and the sea beats on them; sailing along close to land, it appears as though they would fall on the ships."

After a plan aborted to take his bride of a year and live in Europe, Jeffers wrote to his publisher, "The August [1914] news turned us to this village of Carmel instead, and when the stagecoach topped the hill from Monterey, and we looked down through pines and seafog on Carmel Bay, it was evident that we had come without knowing it to our inevitable place."

In the centuries between Cabrillo and Jeffers others had come, stayed briefly, written, and left. Dana was thrilled by the social life of Monterey in the 1830's. Stevenson was too ill to venture far beyond the Carmel Mission. A camping trip into the nearby Santa Lucia mountains nearly killed him. He managed nevertheless to write a few essays about the region which are timelessly true. If Mary Austin had remained and been less ego-centric, she could have done for the region what her *Land of Little Rain* did for the desert east of the Sierra Nevada. She left a few years before Jeffers came, never to return. George Sterling's gifts were dwarfed by the grandeur of the coast, although he did write one memorable poem to the abalone. His death in 1926 was commemorated by Jeffers in a moving elegy.

Now we can look back over the more than half century since Jeffers first saw the coast at Carmel, and perceive the inevitability of his becoming the region's laureate. Everything conspired to make it so. He was young—only twenty-seven—and strong; he was passionately wedded to a woman of rare beauty and intense nature; he was highly educated in travel, classics, literature, and science; he was a poet from boyhood and youth in Europe and Southern California; and he had a small income which afforded the leisure needed for writing something other than journalism. Poetry written on an empty stomach makes lean food for readers.

In 1914 Carmel was only a village. South to the Sur the coast remained as Cabrillo saw it. A wagon-road lurched as far as the canyon of the Big Sur River. Beyond that a horse-trail clung to the high cliffs.

Then it was that the time, the place, and the poet coalesced in one of those rare conjunctions that produce enduring litera-ture. With poem after poem, book upon book, Robinson Jeffers built his monument, from *Californians* in 1916 to *The Beginning and the End* published a year after his death in 1962 at the age of seventy-five. In this half century of achievement he rose to supreme eminence, a Shasta among poets. No other bard of his time other than Yeats, approached the power and the glory, the strength and tenderness, or the prophetic vision of Jeffers. He towered too high for most to see the full bulk of him. Only now are we beginning to perceive him in perspective.

Now we are being given books which enable us to understand the growth and the meaning of his life and work: Melba Berry Bennett's biography, *The Stone Mason of Tor House* and Ann N. Ridgeway's *The Selected Letters of Robinson Jeffers*; a paper-back of *Selected Poems*; the Sierra Club folio, *Not Man Apart*, lines of Jeffers illustrated with photographs of the coast. Books, pamphlets, theses, articles, and reviews are increasing in number. Several religious figures have written about Jeffers—a Jesuit, a Dominican, an Episcopalian, a Catholic nun. This is not astonishing, for Jeffers is a religious poet.

He has been translated into European languages, including the Czech. Hopefully there will be a collected edition of his poetry to include his long narrative poems and his adaptations of Greek tragedies. He was unfortunate in his two chief publishers, the first going bankrupt, the other letting most of his books go out of print.

Until he entered the magnetic field that was to hold him in Carmel until his death, Jeffers's future was cloudy and uncertain. His father, an eminent theologian, had hopes for his son to become a professional man, a minister or a doctor. His younger brother, Hamilton, became an astronomer at the University of California's Lick Observatory.

Robin, as he was called, graduated from Occidental College in 1905, then studied medicine at the University of Southern California, although he never received the M.D. At both schools he contributed poetry to student magazines. He also wrestled and was on the track team, and climbed two of the best Southern California had to offer in the way of mountains: San Antonio and San Gorgonio. He resembled other young bohemians then and now, in being devoted to wine, women, and sports. The poems he wrote of nature and love were merely conventional.

Then in a German class at U.S.C., he met his fate in a glance, just as Stevenson met his when he first saw Fanny Osbourne. It was an encounter as decisive as the subsequent one with the coast at Carmel. Jeffers's fate was a woman in her early twenties, taking her M.A. in English. "She was very beautiful," Jeffers recalled years later, "capable of intense joy and passionate resentment, little of stature, dowered with great blue eyes and heavy bronze hair. It was no wonder that she was married at seventeen."

Una Call Kuster was indeed a married woman, and there ensued several years of troublesome and passionate delay, including a trial separation, before her husband granted a divorce.

Robin and Una were married at Tacoma in 1913. Their children were twin sons, Donnan and Garth, born three years later—and his poems.

"My nature is cold and undiscriminating," Jeffers wrote, "she excited and focused it, gave it eyes and nerves and sympathies. She never saw any of my poems until they were finished and typed, and yet by her presence and conversation she has co-authored every one of them. She is more like a woman in a Scotch ballad, passionate, untamed, and rather heroic—or like a falcon—than like any ordinary person."

The Jeffers lived first in a cabin in the Carmel pinewood. Then in 1919 they bought land on Mission Point, south of the village, and there built a stone house. Because the mason needed a helper, Jeffers worked in this role at $4.00 a day. Thus his fingers learned the art, he said, of marrying stone with stone. He went on alone to build Hawk Tower, also of sea-granite, and to plant several thousand cypress and eucalyptus trees for privacy and protection from the sea-wind.

House and tower stand to this day. All but a few of the trees, however, have been felled to make room for houses on the land the Jeffers were eventually forced to sell to pay rising taxes and assessments. Hindsight enables us to see what an unusual state park could have been made of the original acreage, trees, house, and tower. The timing was wrong. Now it is too late. The only thing time has not touched is the poetry. As well as his stone work, Jeffers knew what he had lastingly wrought: "a few poems stuck in the world's thought."

Anyone writing of great poetry is confronted at last by mystery. This is true of Jeffers's work. We can say that it was the fruit of his double marriage, to a woman and to a land, and that it was fertilized by his heritage and education; and yet we do not know what were the precise or the subtle things that changed him from a good poet to a great poet.

His first book, *Flagons and Apples*, published at Los Angeles in 1912 and sponsored by John Steven McGroarty, the Mission Play poet, is composed of ordinary love lyrics, written mostly to Una in the years of their stormy courtship. His second book,

Californians, contains transitional nature poetry, with both Southern California and Big Sur settings. Healed of his lovesickness, Jeffers turned to the splendors of the natural world and wrote objective narratives, often on tragic themes. The form and the diction of his verse remained traditional, and the influence of Milton, Wordsworth, and Shelley is omnipresent.

Eight years passed before his third book, *Tamar and Other Poems*, lit the heavens like a sun. His verse was no longer conventional in form, diction, or subject. Sex had become a major theme. His voice was prophetic, his world-view somber. Critics were moved to high praise. Readers were attracted. Publishers bid for him. He became famous as a poet, legendary as a recluse.

What happened in those eight years to effect such radical changes? Here is the mystery, one similar to the transformation of Walt Whitman from a hack journalist to the author of *Leaves of Grass*. Jeffers himself seemed puzzled by the change. In writing of the year 1917 he said, "Great men have done their work before they were thirty, but I wasn't born yet."

Was it the war that destroyed his inherited Christian idealism? Was it the death of his father and the birth of his sons which occurred in 1916? Or the building of Tor House in 1919? Could it have been an emotional experience outside of marriage? From the beginning Una held him on a choke-tight rein. He was ever attractive to women. Described as a Greek god in youth, he aged nobly, illustrating the truth of his verse, "The heads of strong old age are beautiful beyond all grace of youth; they have dealt with life and been atempered by it."

Clues to the mystery are scattered throughout his work. In 1938, after he and Una had weathered a crisis in their marriage involving another woman, and he found himself exhausted and temporarily written out, Jeffers wrote an anguished letter to Una: "I believe I'll have a new birth in the course of time—not willing yet to grow old at fifty like Wordsworth, and survive myself—something will happen—and *live through this hell come home to me*—something will change, something will happen.

"It is a little like my extravagances of 1917 to '19, except that

I was uncritical then, and able to keep myself fairly quiet by not writing a lot of foolishness. (Now I know too much). After that we began to make Tor House—*and that was worth while,*—quite aside from the accidental birth of my own mind."

A strange letter, both revealing and concealing. Among the four hundred letters in the Ridgeway volume, it is the only one which is not crystal clear. It was obviously written under intense emotional stress.

Another clue to Jeffers's miraculous maturity is found in the Introduction he wrote for the Modern Library edition of *Roan Stallion, Tamar, and Other Poems* (1935), in which he tells of his wish to become original and yet not be eccentric, and of meditating on his literary future one day in 1914 on a walk he and Una took in the Carmel pinewood:

"The seafog was coming up the ravine, fingering through the pines, the air smelled of the sea and pine-resin and yerba buena, my girl and my dog were with me . . . and I was standing there like a poor God-forsaken man-of-letters, making my final decision not to become a 'modern.' I did not want to become slight and fantastic, abstract and unintelligible.

"I was doomed to go on imitating dead men, unless some impossible wind should blow me emotions or ideas, or a point of view, or even more rhythms that had not occurred to them. This book began to be written three or four years later. I was past my green-sickness by that time, and did not stop to think whether the verses were original or followed a tendency, or would find a reader. Nor have I ever considered whether they deserved to find one."

A reading of Jeffers' letters reveals the ambivalent feelings he had about the isolation from society and rigid work-schedule Una held him to—writing in the morning, stone-work and tree-planting and watering in the afternoon. He had a gregarious side to his nature and a magnetism for women, both of which threats to his creative routine Una ruthlessly curbed.

Consider this confession by Jeffers, in a review he wrote of a fellow poet's book:

"A poet is a specialist highly developed in some few issues and

214

deficient or at least repressed in others; the energy that informs this book will perhaps not content itself with words and ideas. These are something, but they are such a little part of life;—as if a lover should be satisfied with fondling the hair or admiring the hands. Strong natures do not willingly concentrate on poetry, they need some exile or blindness to shut them up to it." Jeffers had Una.

Now is it clear what brought this poet to genius? Not to me.

What *is* clear is that from 1924 to 1933 Jeffers's creative arc rose to zenith in a fiery trajectory of great books that established his fame. *Tamar, Roan Stallion, The Women at Point Sur, Cawdor, Dear Judas, The Loving Shepherdess, Thurso's Landing,* and finally, the volume on which this essay is based, *Give Your Heart to the Hawks.* In the long narratives and short lyrics which comprise these volumes of his prime, we find the poet at his finest.

Other books followed, including more narratives and lyrics and the Broadway triumph of *Medea,* an adaptation of Euripides, actually more Judith Anderson than Jeffers. The money it earned was sorely needed. Among other expenses, the Jeffers were assessed $6000 for a sewer district they did not need.

History dealt roughly with Jeffers. The second World War was shattering. As a strong young man he survived the shock of the first, but the conflict which began in 1939 hit him at age fifty, and he never recovered from it. His tragic view of humanity deepened, as he saw civilization destroying itself. The atomic bomb was the final blow. His last verses, except for a few tender family pieces, are bleak and often strident with prosaic reiterations of his doomful philosophy.

To add to his metaphysical sorrow, personal grief became nearly unbearable with the death of Una from cancer in 1950. Their life had been lived upon the assumption that she would survive him to write his biography. It would have been a great one, for Una Jeffers was a gifted writer. Her letters pulse with life. Robin bore her death like the stoic he was. He survived her by a dozen years, lovingly cared for by his son Donnan and his daughter-in-law Lee, comforted with grandchildren by them and by the other twin, Garth and his German wife. It was nevertheless a kind of death in life. To compound misery his publisher neglected his books and a new generation of academic critics scorned his verse.

Which brings me finally to *Give Your Heart to the Hawks and Other Poems*. My choice of it is arbitrary, for its two predecessors, *Cawdor and Other Poems* (1928) and *Thurso's Landing and Other Poems* (1932) are also works of his creative apogee. The scale tips in favor of *Hawks* for the reason that, in addition to the title poem, the volume also contains the only group of poems Jeffers wrote about places outside of California. The several summers the Jefferses spent in Taos as guest of Mabel Dodge Luhan produced only a single poem.

In *Descent to the Dead* Jeffers composed a sequence of lyrics on the British Isles, where he and Una and their sons lived during part of the year 1929. Although published also as a separate volume, this sequence is more readily found as part of *Give Your Heart to the Hawks*. These are poems peopled by the ghosts of the early Britons and Celts, rich with legend and lore. The Irish poems are among the best ever written about that haunted island.

Give Your Heart to the Hawks is the tragedy of a ranch family on the Sur coast, doomed by sex and violence to destruction. It is the story of Cain and Abel in modern dress, of crime and conscience, of a strong man destroyed by a passionate woman, and of the woman's survival with the man's unborn child within her. It is marked by Jeffers's almost pathological abhorrence of cruelty, his sensitivity to pain and suffering, and by his compassion for all who suffer, be they hawks or humans.

This painful narrative is made bearable by the grandeur and beauty of the natural setting, and by the final act which frees the hero from his pain. When Lance Fraser leaps from the high cliff to death on the rocks below, we feel relief and are purged, for we have experienced what the Greeks called *katharsis*, the purification of our own emotions by identification with others' troubles.

"The story that heaps emotions or complexities and makes no thoroughfare," Jeffers once wrote in defense of his choice of violent themes, "is a weakening story and so I should think an

216

immoral story; but the story that through whatever passes attains significant release will influence its reader in the same sense, and this is good for him, it is normal. It is a 'happy ending,' for something happens, whether marriage or escape or sudden death, a lysis, a freeing of some sort; and a settlement, an adjusted balance."

When Mary Austin wrote to Jeffers to protest his choice of sexual themes, his reply was characteristic of the gentleness with which he always responded to criticism:

"You are right of course about the unessentialness of sex as a motive in literature, but practically it's a great help to have violent emotion of some sort; and fear, hunger, and so forth are rather narrowing, ambition likely to be too technical,—oh well, we have to use what we can manage. But I agree with you in sum."

When I wrote my thesis on Robinson Jeffers, as a student in France forty years ago, I had been on the Monterey coast only once, in 1929 at the time the Jeffers family was in Ireland, and then only for a week; and yet it was long enough for me to see and to sense the inseparable relationship between his poetry and the landscape. My eventual book included a map of the coast showing the settings of his poems, drawn by M. F. K. Fisher, a fellow student in Dijon.

Upon my return to California I visited the Jeffers for the first time. It was a thrilling experience for me, a very young man at the threshold of a literary career, and their kindness and encouragement were decisive and helpful.

Robin and Una drove me down coast as far as the road then went, to a point beyond the canyon of the Big Sur River. There were books and maps in the car with us, and many a sudden stop for animated discussion. As a result, the American edition of my book contained a fuller map drawn by Ward Ritchie, and which has since served literary pilgrims to the Jeffers country.

Time and again I have returned to that enchanted coast, always with a volume of Jeffers on the seat beside me. His poetry is moving wherever it is read, but read there in the setting which it exalts, it is supremely so. However high his soaring vision takes

217

us—and fifty years ago Jeffers foresaw our colonization of outer space—his poetry remains rooted in earth. He viewed the coast and the mountains with the eyes of a scientist. His work can be read with joyful recognition by botanist, ornithologist, geologist, meteorologist, and astronomer. Flowers and trees, birds, rocks, weather, the stars, all are woven into the texture of his verse, lending it reality.

Thanks to such good citizens as architect Nathanael Owings and his wife Margaret, writer Nicholas Roosevelt, and former State Senator Fred Farr, the coast road, State 1, was declared a Scenic Highway and the zealots in Sacramento restrained from widening it. The road *is* narrow, winding, precipitous, most certainly hazardous, and in storm impassable. Let it remain so, world without end. Our Portuguese discoverer would not be slighted if it were to be renamed the Cabrillo-Jeffers Highway.

As for the way in which Tor House and Hawk Tower have been surrounded by Carmel's creeping growth, Jeffers's was the long view of the visionary poet, seeing far beyond the disappearance of his handiwork. Here is what he wrote in the poem called *Tor House:*

> But if you should look in your idleness after ten thousand years,
> It is the granite knoll on the granite
> And lava tongue in the midst of the bay, by the mouth of the Carmel
> River-valley, these four will remain
> In the change of names.

And the poem, *Post-Mortem*, ends with these poignant lines:

> Though one at the end of the age and far off from this place
> Should meet my presence in a poem,
> The ghost would not care but be here, long sunset shadow in the seams of the granite, and forgotten
> The flesh, a spirit for the stone.

218

Reading List

ROBINSON JEFFERS (1887-1962)
Give Your Heart to the Hawks. New York, Random House, 1933.
The Beginning and the End. New York, Random House, 1963.
Selected Poetry. New York, Random House, 1938.
Selected Poems. New York, Random House, Vintage paperback, 1963.
Cawdor and Medea. Intro. by William Everson (Brother Antoninus), New York, New Directions paperback, 1970.
Selected Letters. Edited by Ann Ridgeway, with Foreword by Mark Van Doren. Baltimore, Johns Hopkins Press, 1968.

MELBA BERRY BENNETT
The Stone Mason of Tor House; the Life & Times of Robinson Jeffers. Los Angeles, Ward Ritchie Press, 1966.

LAWRENCE CLARK POWELL
Robinson Jeffers, the Man & His Work. Los Angeles, Primavera Press, 1934, photoreprint, New York, Haskell House, 1966; updated edition, Pasadena, San Pasqual Press, 1940.

BROTHER ANTONINUS
Robinson Jeffers, Fragments of an Older Fury. Berkeley, Oyez, 1968.

FREDERIC I. CARPENTER
Robinson Jeffers. New York, Twayne, 1962.

EDITH GREENAN
Of Una Jeffers. Los Angeles, Ward Ritchie, 1939.

SIERRA CLUB
Not Man Apart; Lines from Robinson Jeffers, Photographs of the Big Sur Coast. Edited by David Brower. San Francisco, Sierra Club, 1965. Paperback edition, 1969.

Photograph of Robinson Jeffers by Edward Weston, courtesy of Occidental College Library.

To A God Unknown

JOHN STEINBECK

19

THEY SAY that lightning never strikes twice in the same place. This is not true of literary lightning. Twice within the same generation genius struck the same one of California's fifty-eight counties—Monterey. That beautiful segment of the state which includes the Carmel-Big Sur coast, the Santa Lucia and the Gabilan ranges and the Salinas Valley, was the site of our first capital, the seacoast town of Monterey. I regret that it was ever moved from there. Let Sacramento have its claim as the political heart of California, Monterey County is supreme in a literary sense, for it nurtured and brought to fruition our greatest poet, Robinson Jeffers, and our greatest novelist, John Steinbeck.

Because of the different mediums they wrote in and because their literary terrains were separate, the two were neither competitive nor repetitive. Unless another writer comes with equal or superior genius, he had better choose one of the other counties to write about. Monterey is theirs by virtue of the classics they created from its landscapes and seascapes, its people, their history and lore—what an English poet called "inscapes."

If Jeffers and Steinbeck ever met, it was only in passing. Neither was a joiner, a speaker, a holder of press conferences. Jeffers came to the county in 1914 and stayed until he died, half a century later. Steinbeck was born in 1902 at Salinas, the county seat, went to school there, and attended Stanford University off and on during the years 1919-1925. Later he was a day laborer in New York. He returned on a freighter through the Panama Canal, lived as a caretaker at Lake Tahoe and there wrote his first novel, *Cup of Gold*. He settled next in Pacific Grove and Monterey, then at Los Gatos in nearby Santa Clara County, until in 1939 the rocketing success of *The Grapes of Wrath* orbited him worldwide, to land finally at Sag Harbor, Long Island, and New York City where he died in December, 1968.

In the decade before he left California, John Steinbeck wrote those books about his native county and state which established his fame. While the harsh decade of the Thirties, the Depression years, starved many an embryonic writer, it made Steinbeck, gave him theme, sinew, and song. Jeffers rose in the decade and a half before, then declined in the Thirties. Steinbeck entered the period in the prime of life. He had the stamina not only to survive but to thrive. In that single epoch, in the face of economic and literary obstacles, he persisted in writing book after book, eight in all, culminating in *The Grapes of Wrath*. For this cumulative achievement he received the Nobel Prize in 1962.

In the thirty years after his great novel of the migratory Joad family appeared, he wrote books about Mexico, Norway, Russia, and Long Island, all of which, in my judgement, represent a literary decline. Every writer has his creative arc, beginning at nadir, rising to apogee, then descending, sometimes in an abrupt fall, often more slowly. Steinbeck's was the latter. His leaving California was the beginning of the descent, and yet he had no choice. The golden vein was worked out.

From the Atlantic shore he looked back in nostalgia and wrote several more California books—*The Wayward Bus, Cannery Row, Sweet Thursday, East of Eden*—each progressively inferior to his best work, just as Jeffers's poetical narratives after the culmination of *Give Your Heart to the Hawks* echo his greatness.

Whereas *East of Eden* is the most ambitious of Steinbeck's novels, it is a contrived epic, a book without a soul, that leaves a bitter taste in the reader's mouth. Unlike the earlier books written in his idealistic prime, *East of Eden* is disillusioned, sombre, and hopeless. I lay this partly to the horrors and cruelties of

World War II, in which Steinbeck served overseas as a newspaper correspondent, partly to the blind alleys into which he had been led by success. The best thing in the book is the opening description of the Salinas Valley, the author's beloved Long Valley, his native heath, which embodies the *genius loci* of his work, just as the seacoast embodies Jeffers's.

Posthumous publication of the journal kept by Steinbeck during the writing of *East of Eden* reveals a basic difference between its composition and that of *The Grapes of Wrath*. Whereas the latter came with a rush, almost faster than the writer could cope with, *East of Eden* came slowly and deliberately. "But I think the energy core is kind of worn down," Steinbeck wrote in his journal. "I think, since I have done so much so far, that I will let it go for the day. I don't want to get too tired. I want to take enough time so that I will avoid the rather terrible exhaustion of the Grapes of Wrath."

His great valley novel was written by an almost solitary creative man, with only the company of his first wife, Carol, "hutched up," as he called it in a card he wrote to me near the end of the book, in their little house at Los Gatos. *East of Eden* was written "in a pretty little house" on New York's 72nd street, with another wife, two sons, amidst the distractions and demands of café and theater society.

His journal is embarrassingly self-conscious, even coy, and sad to read.

The coda to Steinbeck's divorce from California is found in *Travels With Charley in Search of America*. Whereas Stevenson made a book out of his travels with a donkey, Steinbeck's pal was a poodle. In one of the saddest passages he ever wrote, he describes the disillusion of his return to Tortilla Flat and Cannery Row. Afterward he and Charley climb Frémont's Peak, highest point of the Gabilan range that separates the Salinas from the San Joaquin valley, and there he looks down a last time on the land of his boyhood. As for his dog, "Charley, having explored the area, sat at my feet, his fringed ears blowing like laundry on a line. His nose, moist with curiosity, sniffed the wind-borne pattern of a hundred miles."

In his last book, *America and Americans*, essays to accompany photographs by various craftsmen, Steinbeck gave eloquent voice to his tenacious faith in his country. Did it presage a revival of his creative genius? We will never know. Two years later he died.

It was with *To a God Unknown* that I discovered Steinbeck and his other early books. The credit is not mine. We rarely discover a book on our own. We read about it, or are told of it by a friend, a librarian, a bookseller, or a reviewer. Help is needed to discern the pearls of literature in the trash-heap of our age of permissive print.

It was the year 1935. I was working in Jake Zeitlin's bookshop on Los Angeles's downtown West Sixth Street, then the street of secondhand bookshops, evicted later by banks, savings and loan, and airline offices. Steinbeck's fourth book, *Tortilla Flat*, had just been published. Our sales were not equal to Zeitlin's enthusiastic order. I was filling the store window with the overstock. It was Wednesday afternoon, the time of our weekly visit from Paul Jordan-Smith, literary editor of the *Los Angeles Times*, who the week before had given *Tortilla Flat* a rousing review. Los Angeles has never had a book evangelist to equal P. J. Smith. When he beat the drum and blew the bugle, the glory sounded clear to Cucamonga.

So there I was crouched in the store window, dressing a display of *Tortilla Flat*, as the rangy critic came striding up Sixth Street from the *Times* office where he had "put to bed" the Sunday book page. When he saw through the glass what I was doing, his face lit up, he gestured and began talking. A crowd gathered on the sidewalk, whereupon he herded them into the shop, still talking, and soon our overstock of *Tortilla Flat* was sold.

"Powell," Jordan-Smith lectured me, when he and Zeitlin and I were at last having coffee in the back room, "you wrote a book about Robinson Jeffers. Now read Steinbeck's *To A God Unknown*, published two years ago. It's Jeffers in prose."

"I'm willing," I said, "but I've never seen a copy."

"I'll tell you why," the critic continued, "because it was a flop.

Its publisher went broke and orders for it were returned unfilled. Talk about your unlucky writers! If Salinas John didn't have the strength of a young bull, he would have gone under long ago. His first novel, *Cup of Gold*, a pirate story, came down in the stock market crash. His next, *The Pastures of Heaven*, stories about a tiny valley between Monterey and Salinas, also drew a bankrupt publisher. And do you know, young man, that *Tortilla Flat* was turned down by half a dozen houses before Pascal Covici took it?"

At this point Zeitlin interrupted Jordan-Smith's lecture. "And do you know who told Covici about it? It was Ben Abramson, the Chicago bookseller, the man who got me into bookselling, bless him."

"Well and good," I agreed, "but where can I get hold of *To A God Unknown?*"

P. J. chuckled, rubbed his hands together, strode the length of the store and back, then declared, "From me, sir, from me. I'll bring you my copy next Wednesday."

And so he did, and I read it in a gulp. He was right. It *was* a kind of prose Jeffers, that is, a powerful narrative of sex and religion, love of the fertile earth and its death by drought and rebirth by rain. Whereas Jeffers wrote of ranchers in the coastal canyons south of Carmel, Steinbeck's tale was of the Jolon Valley at the eastern base of the Santa Lucias, separated by hills from the longer Salinas Valley. Mission San Antonio de Padua stands at one end of the smaller valley. Near there Gertrude Atherton lived as a bride on one of the family's ranches. The Mission appears occasionally in Jeffers's verse, although he rarely crossed the mountains for his settings. He and Steinbeck made an unconscious division of Monterey County for their separate purposes. Dominant tree of the Jolon Valley is the coast live oak, *quercus agrifolia*, a noble specimen of which is central in *To a God Unknown* as a kind of Golden Bough or sacred tree.

Steinbeck wrote this book at the peak of his youthful power. It is a lyrical hymn to earth. Although I lack evidence, my belief is that Steinbeck was influenced by Jeffers, particularly by the poet's longest narrative poem, *The Women at Point Sur* (1927). The hero of each book, an Old Testament prophet figure, lies down and dies at the end, convinced that the earth's immortality requires the individual's death by self-sacrifice.

Steinbeck respected Jeffers's monarchal rights to the seacoast. Only once does he gain the Nacimiento crest of the Santa Lucias and, as Smeaton Chase did before him, look down on the coast below. This is one of the climactic scenes in *To a God Unknown*. When drought—and Steinbeck shares Jeffers's revulsion for the dry seasons—threatens the ranch and its livestock, Joseph Wayne and his brother ride to the ridge, and then comes this passage:

"The trail went into a pass of shattered granite, and the next moment the two men looked down on a new fresh world. The downward slope was covered with tremendous redwood trees, and among the great columned trunks there grew a wild tangle of berry vines, of gooseberry, of swordferns as tall as a man. The hill slipped quickly down, and the sea rose up level with the hilltops. The two men stopped their horses and stared hungrily at the green underbrush. The hills stirred with life. Quail skittered and rabbits hopped away from the path. While the men looked, a little deer walked into an open place, caught their scent and bounced away. Thomas wiped his eyes on his sleeve. 'All the game from our side is here,' he said. 'I wish we could bring our cattle over, but there isn't a flat place for a cow to stand.' "

Then they meet a mad hermit, a character found in several of Jeffers's poems. Each night at sundown he sacrifices one of his little caged animals and birds to the setting sun. "I am the last man in the western world to see the sun," he exults, "after it is gone to everyone else, I see it for a little while. I've seen it every night for twenty years. Except when the fog was in or the rain was falling, I've seen the sun set."

To a God Unknown is not a perfect novel. Despite faults of overwriting and stereotyped characters, Steinbeck's remains a living book, lit with passion for his native earth. No book about California, unless it be *The Vineyard*, contains deeper feeling for and fidelity to its landscape, seasons, and weathers, its history and lore.

226

In succeeding books Steinbeck cast off into the socio-economic stream. *In Dubious Battle* and *The Grapes of Wrath* are novels about agricultural California in the valleys of the Salinas and the San Joaquin. They grew out of his experiences and observations in the Depression, and they represent a challenge to idealistic youth to work for social betterment. Great literature comes from passion and matching control. *The Grapes of Wrath* was a culmination of Steinbeck's social zeal and literary power in the same way that *Ramona* brought Helen Hunt Jackson to fulfillment as a writer. She created it and died. Steinbeck's effort nearly cost him his life.

In the autumn of 1938 while living in Los Gatos, he was on the home stretch in writing his dust-bowl classic, wracked by rheumatism and sciatica. "I am desperately tired," he wrote to his agents in New York (in a letter very much like the one Mrs. Jackson wrote to Col. Higginson) "but I want to finish. And mean. I feel as though shrapnel were bursting about my head. I only hope the book is some good. Can't tell yet at all. It is a slow plodding book but I don't think it is dull."

The Grapes of Wrath is anything but dull. Its worldwide reception, hailed abroad and reviled at home, left Steinbeck physically exhausted, and also the victim of that worst of all enemies, success.

"I'm so busy being a writer," he complained, "that I haven't time to write. Ten thousand people have apparently put aside all other affairs to devote themselves to getting me to speak. And I'm so increasingly afraid in crowds that I do not talk comfortably to a pair of dice any more."

Steinbeck resembled Jeffers in his dislike of personal publicity. He never went the way of Hemingway to pose as a hard-boiled hero. If he sometimes wrote badly, at least he never wrote cynically nor merely for money.

When the California State Library asked him to fill out a questionnaire for their biographical file on Californian writers, his jesting answers were characteristic of his attitude toward any invasion of his personal privacy:

Name: John Ernst Alcibiades Socrates Steinbeck
Born: Lesbos, Magna Graece, 1902
Father: Herodotus Xenophon Steinbeck
Mother: Chloe Mathilde Lopez
Married to: Jo Alfreda Jones, in Tia Juana
Writings: The Unstrung Harpie, 1906
        Taxgiversating Tehabedrous. MacDougall,
        1927
        Barnacles (Ballinadae). Monograph. 2 vols.
        Stanford University Press
        Bugs, a Critical Study. Morbide Press

Monterey County is *the* place to read and re-read Jeffers and Steinbeck. One should go first up State 1—past San Simeon and along the cliff-face road to the Big Sur and on to the Carmel River. The paperback of Jeffers's poems will serve as guide to this still wild and beautiful seacoast.

In Monterey Steinbeck is gone, but his books are there. No use looking for an actual place called Tortilla Flat; there is none. Cannery Row, however, is real, is there. Doc Ricketts, the marine biologist whose personality and philosophy moulded the young Steinbeck, is dead. He was memorialized by his pupil in "About Ed Ricketts," a preface to *Log from the Sea of Cortez*. With money from *The Grapes of Wrath*, Steinbeck funded a biological expedition to the Gulf of California. The resulting *Sea of Cortez* includes Ricketts's scientific classification of specimens and Steinbeck's narrative log. The book is a marvelous hybrid.

That earliest bohemian Montereyite, Robert Louis Stevenson, is evoked by Steinbeck in a short story called "How Edith McGillicuddy Met R.L.S." It and other vintage Steinbeckiana are found in the *Viking Portable Steinbeck*. Hard to find is the first critical book about the writer, *The Novels of John Steinbeck*, by Harry Thornton Moore, a onetime UCLA student. It contains a map of the Steinbeck Country, locating the settings of his books up to 1939.

The reading traveller should next turn inland to Salinas, where Steinbeck's father was the County Treasurer. The son's early manuscripts were written in blank ledger books in a minuscular hand which enabled him to set down a large number of words in a small space. His mother was a school teacher. Then the route follows the Long Valley, the hundred-mile Salinas, but not via U.S. 101. A better way is the parallel road to the west which ankles in and out of the arroyos of the Santa Lucias. There the travelling reader should pull over and re-read "The Red Pony," one of the boyhood stories in *The Long Valley*.

Nearing King City the road bears west southwest. There "El Camino Steinbeck" leaves the Salinas, climbs a low pass and enters the Jolon Valley, the setting of *To A God Unknown*. Much of it is now a part of the Hunter Liggett Military Reservation. Beware of manoeuvring tanks! This is the *cor cordium*, the heart of hearts of the Steinbeck country.

The road proceeds to ascend the Nacimiento River, climbing up and out of the valley, rising high and deep into the Santa Lucias. It was once a wagon road to the coast, and although it has been graded and widened, it still requires careful driving.

That eastern slope of the Santa Lucias, now protected as a part of Los Padres National Forest, is fair virgin land, uncut and unburned, watched over by the guard station on Junipero Serra Peak (elevation 5844), the highest point of the range. Its forest is blended of madrone, bay, walnut, sycamore, oak, and the native incense fir. No redwoods grow on the landward side, for *sequoia sempervirens* likes salt fog in the air.

At the summit, high point also of *To A God Unknown*, the vista is back on forest and valleys, east to the Sierra Nevada. Below in the west are the redwoods, the ocean; and the sound of the surf, a muted boom of breakers, followed by the sullen backwash of boulders, that immemorial music of sadness which has haunted poets from Homer to Jeffers. Here is a viewpoint unique in our literature. By their genius a poet and a novelist possessed this double landscape. By the alchemy of art, the magic of literature, their possession is now shared forever by all who read.

JOHN STEINBECK (1902-1968)

The Pastures of Heaven. New York, Brewer, 1932.

To a God Unknown. New York, Ballou, 1933.

Tortilla Flat. New York, Covici, Friede, 1935.

In Dubious Battle. New York, Covici, Friede, 1936.

The Long Valley. New York, Viking Press, 1938.

The Grapes of Wrath. New York, Viking Press, 1939.

Journal of a Novel; the East of Eden Letters. New York, Viking Press, 1969.

The Log From the Sea of Cortez. New York, Viking Press, 1962.

Travels With Charley in Search of America. New York, Viking Press, 1962.

America and Americans. New York, Viking Press, 1966.

The Portable Steinbeck. Selected by Pascal Covici. New York, Viking Press, 1946.

HARRY THORNTON MOORE

The Novels of John Steinbeck, a First Critical Study. Chicago, Normandie House, 1939.

Photograph of John Steinbeck, courtesy of Viking Press.

California and the West

C H A R I S   A N D   E D W A R D   W E S T O N

20

WHICH CALIFORNIA CLASSIC best describes the Golden State in its entirety? Brewer's *Up and Down California in 1860-64* would be chosen by many. That rugged scientist covered nearly all of the state. Human nature also interested him almost as much as natural phenomena. In the century since his time, few books have offered such a wide-lens view of California.

California and the West by the Westons is one that does. I use "wide-lens" deliberately, for Edward Weston was a photographer. His companion, Charis, kept a prose log of their travels, and in their book it is beautifully married to his photographs. In the course of 35,000 miles of travel, they ranged the entire state, from Anza-Borrego to Crescent City, and from Oceano to Inyo.

Edward Weston was more than a great creative photographer. He was also a philosopher and a writer. He had an unshakeable belief in himself and his work. In short, he was a genius. When criticized for preferring landscapes and natural phenomena to cities and people, he protested in his journal:

"It seems so utterly naive that landscape—not that of the pictorial school—is not considered of 'social significance' when it has a far more important bearing on the human race of a given locale than excrescences called cities. By landscape, I mean every physical aspect of a given region—weather, soil, wildflowers, mountain peaks—and its effect on the psyche and physical appearance of the people."

Here is a good subject for a book: the influence of California's geography on its people.

With the proliferation of automobiles, roads, campers and cameras, hordes of Californians have rolled up and down and across the state, photographing nearly every square foot of landscape. There has also been an avalanche of guide books, pamphlets, folders, leaflets, and maps.

With so much familiarity and knowledge, why aren't there more great books about California? Quite simply because more than facts are needed to make a classic. Edward Weston had that something more. He was a man of vision, feeling, and power, able in some mysterious way to transmit these qualities to his photographs, which are likewise visionary, sensuous, and strong.

It is not enough merely to point a camera at nature. I once had the idea of captioning a book of aerial photographs of California's great landmarks—Shasta, the Sutter Buttes, El Capitan, Morro Rock, and so on down state. I pored over thousands of prints, all taken automatically by a commercial outfit's flying cameras. What was the result? I became bored by the monotony of outlook. A machine cannot choose.

California and the West contains only ninety-six photographs by Edward Weston, each with the power of commanding attention. They represent one man's quintessential view of California, a supreme demonstration of discriminating choice. The variety is of nearly every part of the state—orchards, vineyards, hayfields, desert flora and rocks, the dramatic mouth of the Russian River, Sierra lakes, Owens Valley cottonwoods, an old bunkhouse, a Salinas Valley barn, and beach stumps at far northern Crescent City. It even includes a humorous shot of rubber dummies on the M.G.M. lot.

Charis's log forms an ideal complement to Edward's photographs. Where he is austere, she is warm. To his fanaticism in selecting a single subject from a thousand choices, she added an easy good humor. Her log is very much her young feminine self—he was twenty-five years her senior. It is entirely her own,

232

and yet it is apparent that she was in the thrall of a tenacious man in pursuit of his own vision.

In describing the Klamath River road, she writes, "We had heard it was beautiful country, and it was—a wild river canyon, narrow, steep-sided, heavily wooded and underbrushed. We looked down in the gaps through trees to the greenish-brown water in its channel of gray and white stones. There were a few settlements, isolated cabins, now and then a skimpy orchard. A primitive area, almost untouched by logging or other forms of civilization. But it was not a photographer's road or photographer's landscape; there was too much underbrush, uninteresting growth—too little variety of form or texture."

And then she goes on to say, "It is the disadvantage of travelling with a photographer, that you become accustomed to looking at things from a photographic viewpoint. Once I would have rejoiced at the rich upholstery of underbrush, the unsettled land, the untracked mountains, the untamed river. Now, in spite of myself, I found the day-long drive down the winding river canyon monotonous."

It was Charis who drove, always ready to stop on command when Edward's eye was taken by a subject. Usually he was positive and a picture was soon shot. Sometimes, however, he would hesitate, ask her to stop, and then change his mind and they would drive on. Twenty miles beyond he would say, suddenly, "We should have stopped. Turn around and go back."

Edward Weston's vision of California was stark, clean, and honest. There was nothing bizarre or arty about it. We recognize his landscapes and their details as ones we have also seen. Or have we? They are the same and yet not the same. Something has been added, something paradoxically not to be isolated or seen. Some quality, rather, that is felt. That something was Edward Weston. It took him a lifetime of toil to find this secret of transfusing himself into his work.

California and the West was published in 1940. It was the result of a fellowship of $2,000 from the John Simon Guggenheim Memorial Foundation, the first ever awarded to a photographer. Covering a year from April 1937, it was given Weston

to make a series of photographs of the West. Most of them were taken in California, a few in Nevada, Arizona and New Mexico.

After the trips logged by Charis, the Westons settled in Carmel, and on a year's renewal of the fellowship, Edward settled in to the task of making prints of the 1500 negatives he had exposed. Today the Huntington Library possesses a comprehensive set of these master photographs. If one fancies himself as a photographer, he had better not look at Weston's prints. They are overwhelming.

Weston's work as a Guggenheim Fellow was seen by *Westways* readers of that period. Editor Phil Townsend Hanna paid the photographer for a monthly series of prints. The money received from the magazine enabled the Westons to buy a new Ford V-8 sedan, which they named Heimie. It was their mode of travel and his dark room. Theirs was a rugged experience in those years before travellers enjoyed the comfort of air-conditioned campers. The fellowship had to be carefully budgeted.

In 1939 *Westways* reprinted the Weston series in book form, called *Seeing California with Edward Weston*. It includes many prints not found in *California and the West*. Although Charis captioned the pictures bought by the magazine, *Westways* preferred, unfortunately, to supply its own text.

This *Westways* book contains a preface by the photographer which does not appear in the subsequent volume. It is characteristic of Weston's forthright manner of expression, as well as his skill as a writer and his gift for irony:

"Since my project was to photograph life, I have been questioned about the absence of human beings in my collection. Why haven't I photographed people? One reason is a personal one. For nearly thirty-five years I have been a professional portrait photographer. People were my bread and butter, and when I had the opportunity I was only too glad to have a vacation from them.

"However, I have actually done people in my own way. Wrecked automobiles and abandoned service stations on the desert, deserted cabins in the High Sierra, the ruins of Rhyolite, ghost lumber towns on the bleak north coast, a pair of high-buttoned shoes in an abandoned soda works, the San Francisco

235

Embarcadero, the statue of a leering bell-hop advertising a Los Angeles hotel—all of these are pictures of people as well as of life."

When he chose to, Edward Weston made human portraits of haunting perception. *California and the West* contains two such, of life and of death; one of Charis, the other of a dead man in the desert.

Who was Edward Weston? He was a Maine Yankee, sprung from a two-century line of New England professional men. He and his sister, sired in Illinois by a doctor father, were the first Westons born out of Maine in many generations.

Dr. Weston gave his little son a camera. *That was it.* Nothing else ever really interested him, although he worked for a time at odd jobs in Chicago, and later as a surveyor in the West to where, in 1906, he came to join his sister Mary. In California he married a school teacher, Flora Chandler, and fathered four sons.

In 1911 Weston built his own studio in Tropico, now known as Glendale, and during the next decade he achieved international fame as a photographer, specializing in Whistlerian, Japanesy portraits and compositions. He became Southern California's leading aesthetic photographer. I have a portrait he made of my father in 1920, posed against a wall-hung Oriental prayer rug, the man and the background blended in a misty tableau.

Who could have foretold the changes that Edward Weston was destined to undergo in his life and work, before he died in 1958 at the age of 72? And yet, looking back on them, they seem inevitable.

I see some of the causes as an inner discontent and necessity. Also the fate that led him in the first place to become a photographer. Another was his discovering modern painting, in 1915 at the San Francisco World's Fair. Potent factors were the women in his life, notably Tina Modotti, a ravishing Italian actress who took some of his personal work to Mexico and exhibited it at the Academia de Bellas Artes. There it was seen by painters Rivera, Siqueiros, and Orozco, those titans of the Mexican Renaissance. Their enthusiasm drew Weston, with Tina, to live in Mexico.

They went by way of New York, where he met Alfred Stieglitz, America's greatest photographer.

For three years Weston operated a portrait studio in Mexico City, assisted by Tina. He was handicapped by a lack of Spanish, too poor to leave the studio long for fear of losing commissions. He worked whenever possible with still lifes, the reason being his inability to pay models. Joined later by his eldest son Brett, Weston and Tina travelled into the hinterland, photographing the sculpture that illustrated Anita Brenner's *Idols Behind Altars*.

Favored subjects were the vegetables with which the Mexican markets abounded. Once he had three green peppers, but before he could complete a composition, Brett ate two of them.

It was a time of passionate searching, primitive living, and painful growth. And also of the dissatisfaction with his own work that marked every stage of Weston's life. Of the Mexican experience, he wrote, "I have never before had such intense and understanding appreciation. . . . The intensity with which Latins express themselves has keyed me to high pitch, yet viewing my work on the wall day after day has depressed me. I see too clearly that I have often failed. Give me peace and an hour's time and I create. Emotional heights are easily obtained, peace and time are not."

In 1925 he returned to Glendale. Shells began to enthrall him. So suggestive were his photographs of a chambered nautilus, that upon seeing them his friends back in Mexico found them even more erotically stimulating than his nudes.

Next, with Brett, he opened a studio in San Francisco. There he was commissioned by a newspaper to make a series of portraits of leading citizens. Gertrude Atherton disillusioned him. From her reputation, he expected a "forceful Amazon"; instead she appeared to him as a dowdy scrubwoman. He loathed making portraits of rich society women who insisted on retouching to remove their wrinkles.

San Francisco failed to yield the peace and the time that he craved. Eventually it was in Carmel that he found them. Once again that enchanted place exercised the magnetic power that

237

has made it our creative capital. Robinson Jeffers required only one look to succumb. Edward Weston needed several. He first saw Carmel in 1915, and again in 1925, but not until 1929 did he finally heed its call.

By then Carmel had a reputation as an arty colony. Weston did not want to be a part of it. He was a disciplined, hardworking man, hardly a bohemian. Another hesitancy in moving there came from the women that were always being drawn to him, several of whom would have liked to keep house for him in Carmel. Wise man that he was, he chose Brett, who had grown under his tutelage into a fine photographer.

Once settled in Carmel, his shingle reading for the first time "Unretouched Portaits," Weston rapidly yielded to its charm. Here is a journal entry, written soon after his move from San Francisco:

"The 1st of March I should write in Color and Capitals— I started my work again!—and in the most exciting environs,— the Big Sur. We left Carmel at dawn, and returned at dusk. . . . The coast was on a grand scale: mountainous cliffs thrust buttresses far out into the ocean, anchored safely for an eternity: against the rising sun, their black solidity accentuated by rising mists, and sunlit water. . . . My desert rocks were much easier to work with. . . . They were physically approachable, I could walk to their very base, touch them. At Big Sur, one dealt with matter from hundreds of feet to many miles distant. The way will come in time to see this marriage of ocean and rock."

"Marriage of ocean and rock." A Jeffersian phrase! The great poet was eventually photographed by Weston in the unretouched style that he now practiced exclusively. I felt its power far away in France when, in the spring of 1932, I saw a copy of *Time* with Weston's Robinson Jeffers on the cover. It had been taken against a background of the poet's tower. In great excitement I wrote to Una Jeffers, asking if I might use that portrait as frontispiece in my university thesis on Jeffers. And so it came to pass.

In Weston's journal we read what it was like to photograph Jeffers: "It was another grey day, but I now realize, knowing him better, that Jeffers is more himself on grey days. He belongs

238

to stormy skies and heavy seas. Without knowing his work, one would feel in his presence, greatness. His build is heroic—nor do I mean huge in bulk—more the way he is put together. His profile is like the eagle he writes of. His bearing is aloof—yet not disdainfully so—rather with a constrained, almost awkward friendliness. I did not find him silent—rather a man of few words. Jeffers' eyes are notable: blue, shifting—but in no sense furtive—as though they would keep their secrets,—penetrating, all-seeing eyes. Despite his writing I cannot feel him misanthropic: his is the bitterness of despair over humanity he really loves."

Another time, he wrote of reading aloud Jeffers' long narrative poem, *Thurso's Landing*, to his sons:

"I think the boys got a surprise, that great poetry could at the same time be exciting. Cole said, 'Dad, that's as exciting as a Wild West movie!'—and later—'It sounds like a song—I didn't know poetry was like that.' "

I first met Edward Weston in 1936 during the photographer's exhibition at Jake Zeitlin's Bookshop in Los Angeles. He was not obviously either a Don Juan or a genius. Small, slight, balding and shy, Weston's power was manifested only when he was engaged in the act of photographing. Then his dark brown eyes became piercing and hypnotic, irresistible to many a model.

Zeitlin was an early friend to Weston and his work, as was Merle Armitage, the impresario and publisher of noble monographs on artists. One on Weston in 1932 was the first book to be devoted to the photographer, and it remains one of the most beautiful.

After the Guggenheim fellowships, Weston was finally divorced from his first wife, and then was married to Charis, daughter of the novelist, Harry Leon Wilson. Since 1910, Wilson had lived in the Carmel Highlands. There on a piece of her father's land, at the point where Wildcat Creek crosses Highway 1, Charis and Edward built their house, and there Weston spent the remaining twenty years of his life, the last decade of which was saddened by his decline and death from Parkinson's disease.

Success of *California and the West* led the Limited Editions

Club of New York to commission Weston to illustrate *Leaves of Grass*. Together with Charis, he photographed the Bayou country, then the Atlantic farmlands. Pearl Harbor brought them hurrying home to Carmel. Charis selected captions from Whitman. Mark Van Doren wrote the foreword. And yet this ambitious two-volume edition is not Weston at his best. He had become a Californian, needful of western landscapes to fire his genius.

Before Charis left him for marriage and children by a younger man, she and Edward collaborated on still another book, *The Cats of Wildcat Hill*. It contains her writing and his pictures about their semi-domesticated cats that ranged in number from twelve to twenty. It is a basic in any collection of books about cats. Here is the way Charis ended her introduction:

"During these years we have had several hundred human visitors at Wildcat Hill, among them all ranks of cat-regarders, from cat-addicts to cat-haters—or, if you wish to be elegant, from ailurophiles to ailurophobes. A few of our guests became sneezy and red of eye, a few became so absorbed in watching the cats they forgot they had come to see us, a few paid the cats no attention whatever—although a dozen cats dispersed around a one-room house are not easy to overlook. But a visitor rarely left without having put us through at least part of what came to be called the Variable Catechism.

Q. But what do you do with so MANY?
A. We don't do anything with them.
Q. How do you *ever* tell them apart?
A. (Popular wartime variant.) How do you ever tell the men in your company apart when they haven't even different colored coats and they all have their hair the same length?
Q. You mean you actually have names for *all* of them?
A. We think it would be confusing just to name every other one.
Q. How do you keep them so quiet?
A. We teach them not to cry.
Q. I didn't know you could teach a cat anything.
A. Most people don't. Nicky, shake hands with the gentleman."

Before he was stricken with the fatal disease and could no longer hold a camera or write, Weston completed his masterful *My Camera on Point Lobos*. Just as this rugged configuration now preserved as a state park evoked some of Jeffers's greatest poetry, so did Point Lobos inspire Weston to works of luminous beauty. Cypress trunks, kelp beds, eroded rocks, and tidepool dwellers—these are seen by the photographer in clairvoyant ways that transcend their primary reality.

"Here I can work," Weston wrote of Carmel, "and from here I send out the best of my life, focussed onto a few sheets of silvered paper."

Edward Weston never lacked appreciative friends. It was in Los Angeles's Little Tokyo, early in the 1920's, that he first sold his nonportrait prints. This led him to write in his journal, "How rarely I sell to Americans! How appreciative, understanding, and courteous the Japanese!"

In addition to two of his sons, Brett and Cole, Weston taught many young photographers, including Ansel Adams, Willard Van Dyke, and William Aplin. Latterly his greatest proponent was Nancy Newhall, wife of Beaumont Newhall, director of George Eastman House in Rochester. Named by Weston as his biographer, Mrs. Newhall began her work by editing volumes of Weston's journals, called *Daybooks*, illustrated from his photographs. One is of the Mexican years, 1923-27, another of California through 1944, the third a selection from both.

His are journals to rank with those of Delacroix, the great French Romantic painter. They came from the heart, and are alive with joy and pain, the agony of change and growth, the despair of failure, and the triumph of creation. This philosophical photographer-writer, loved by many women and a good father to his four sons, was above all faithful to his genius. His journals served Weston as a safety valve, "in this day when pistols and poison are taboo."

We owe them also to Weston's habit of rising early. On February 21, 1931, he wrote, "Peace again! The exquisite hour before dawn, here at my old desk. Seldom have I realized so keenly, appreciated so fully, these still, dark hours."

His photographs need no caption, as California needs no prose to enhance its beauty. And yet are we not grateful for all that our classic authors have written in praise of the Golden State?

Reading List

EDWARD WESTON (1886-1958)

California and the West. By Charis Wilson Weston and Edward Weston.

Seeing California with Edward Weston. Los Angeles, Westways, 1939.

Edward Weston. Edited by Merle Armitage. New York, Weyhe, 1932.

My Camera on Point Lobos. Boston, Houghton Mifflin, 1950.

The Cats of Wildcat Hill. By Charis and Edward Weston, New York, Duell, 1947.

Leaves of Grass. By Walt Whitman. Introduction by Mark Van Doren. Photographs by Edward Weston, New York, Limited Editions Club, 1942. 2 vols.

Day Books. Edited by Nancy Newhall. Rochester, George Eastman House, 1961-66. 2 vols.

Edward Weston, Photographer; the Flame of Recognition. Edited by Nancy Newhall. New York, Grossman, 1965.

Photograph of Edward Weston by Mary J. Edwards, courtesy of Charis Wilson.

242

The Vineyard

IDWAL JONES

21

"THE CORE of a thing," Yeats wrote about the works of the Irish literary renaissance, "must be national or local. A great piece of literature is entirely of its own locality yet infinitely translatable."

No literature about California is more local than Idwal Jones's stories and novels of the valleys and foothills, and yet his work is so faithful to earth and man as to be universal in meaning and relevance.

In a review of *The Vineyard* in 1942, M.F.K. Fisher, who came later to live in the Napa Valley, wrote, "His novel is a long song and could as easily be of Burgundy or the Rhone as the Napa Valley."

Never a popular writer, although he wrote a dozen books in the quarter century between 1926 and 1952, Idwal Jones has fallen into a literary obscurity made even deeper by his common surname. None of his books are in print. Although they are more readily found in libraries than in bookstores, even there they are not in heavy circulation. When I went to charge out the library's copy of his first book, a novel of his native Wales and adopted California called *The Splendid Shilling*, I found that it had been called for last in 1946—by me.

Idwal Jones's largest and most faithful body of readers was made up of *Westways* subscribers. From 1935 until his death in

1964, he published there more than two hundred stories and vignettes of California literature, history, and folklore.

Though it may go dormant, writing as good as Idwal Jones's does not die. A rereading of the entire body of his work leads me to predict a revival of interest in his books.

So he was a minor writer, as one critic called him. I dislike those categories of major and minor. Publishers and their puff-men are responsible for fostering this distinction, one going as far as to place on the title-page of an author's book the subtitle "a major novel." I can't recall either the author or the novel, although I have not forgotten the publisher.

It was not in the nature of Idwal Jones's writing for it to be popular in the way most of the recent American best sellers have been. He never wrote of sex and violence. He was never influenced by fashions in fiction. "I dislike novels by and large," he once wrote. "A few I read over two or three times a year. I like Hardy; I like Arnold Bennett's *The Old Wives' Tale*. I read theology and some philosophy, and H. H. Tomlinson's essays."

Jones wrote from his own vision and viewpoint, and there is no other Californian writer, before or since, whose work could be mistaken for his. Though his surname be a common one, Idwal is not. It was borne by a Welsh king at the time of the Danish invasion in the 10th century, and it means an oilstone or hone.

His publishers were mostly unfaithful to him. Doubleday, Knopf, Viking, Duell, Morrow, all took him for a book or two, then dropped him. When finally Prentice-Hall and its percep-tive editor, Gorham Munson, added Idwal Jones to their list, it was too late. His creative arc had begun to descend, as time and age took his strength and health.

What an arc it was! A rainbow of lovely prose, the words refracted through the man's own "dome of many-colored glass." And yet he never wrote language for words alone; he was not a literary exhibitionist in the manner of Gertrude Stein. He saw life with a clear eye, and he had something to say about it. Was it a man that he saw, as in the opening lines of the story "China Boy"?

"I first beheld Pon Look twelve years ago, and even then he

was the oldest human creature in Fiddle Creek township. It was on top of Confidence Hill one August day, when the pines were withering in the terrific heat and the road was a foot deep in white dust. Pon Look came over the brow of a hill, from below.

"He waddled like a crab, leaning on a staff, and extreme age had bent his body at a right angle to his stunted legs. His physiognomy was fearsome, like a Chinese actor's in a print. His head was sunk forward, so that his ears were in line with his shoulders, and the protuberant chin was adorned with sparse, silvery hairs. For all he had the aspect of a crippled galley slave, he progressed smartly, slewing that head continually from side to side with a strange grace. He seemed to be propelling himself through the heat waves with that sculling movement. He had something alive, which he held in check with a rope. It was a large, feline animal, with a bobbed tail and a funny wicker hat fitting over its head, like a muzzle. At intervals this beast leaped into the air, and, uttering frantic cries, tore furiously at the muzzle with its forefeet. It had eyes as glittering as topazes. It was a superb catamount."

Or was it a landscape as in this passage from *Vermilion*, his long historical novel of California?

"Even before the night stars had gone, Paula was on the slope, setting fire to the windrows of slashings on the long, cleared part of the new field. In the dark, the lines of fire were furrows of carmine that had taken on a life of their own, thrumming with a dirge-like sound, helped on yard by yard by the favoring low wind . . . Some cedar trash was burning, charging the air with the sweetness of pencilwood, and on the wind came full the California winter smell, a compound of earth and grass, tarweed and anise, crumbled walnuts, the sharp rankness of wild oranges, and the medicinal tang of blue-gum leaves."

Idwal Jones died just short of his 77th birthday, in Laguna Beach where he had lived since the 1930's. An account of his work which reached zenith in 1942 with *The Vineyard*, can be written only from piecemeal sources. He was no saver of source material, and his passion was only for the book on which he was engaged in writing. "I haven't any favorite book among those

245

246

I have written," he declared. "Once a book of mine is printed, I may look into it just once."

Although all of his work is in a sense autobiographical, it is also impersonal. The filters of imagination through which he passed experience were exquisite. He was a Celtic prose poet, not an Anglo-Saxon chronicler. Munson called him a magician, a California Merlin.

Let's see what can be gathered on a short bio-bibliographical excursion before coming to *The Vineyard*, that most lyrically beautiful, deeply enchanting of all novels in California's literature, rivalled only by *To a God Unknown*, Steinbeck's hymn to the Monterey County earth and its adoring toilers.

What Jones's literary imagination did with his Welsh childhood may be learned from *The Splendid Shilling*, and from *Whistler's Van*, a book for young readers. The gist is that the boy Idwal ran away with a gypsy caravan, and gained from its members his first instruction in Romany language and lore.

His father, a slate quarryman, took his family to the New World of Pennsylvania and upper New York state. Because of improper treatment for a throat ailment which blew out his eardrums, Idwal suffered from lifelong partial deafness. Believing him thus to be unfitted for intellectual training and work, Father Jones put his son to labor in a Schenectady steel mill, an experience transmuted years later in the novel called *Steel Chips*. The ordeal also gave him tuberculosis. During recuperation in a sanitorium, Idwal learned Greek, Latin, and French.

To completely recover his health, he came to California in 1911 via the isthmus of Panama, where he joined his gold-mining brother in Tuolumne County. He later worked on the App Ranch near Jamestown. These experiences went into the second half of *The Splendid Shilling*.

Now Idwal Jones had fatefully entered the mainstream of California literature, whose headwaters are in Bret Harte and Mark Twain. In spite of his deafness—perhaps because of it—and his father's well-meaning efforts to make him into a manual laborer, Idwal Jones was destined to be a writer. Like his two great western predecessors, Jones began his career as a journalist, writing first for the weekly *Mother Lode Magnet* of Jimtown, as present day Jamestown was then known.

He spent longer on the Mother Lode than Bret Harte's day and a half, observing the characters and absorbing the lore that was to last him a lifetime. "Not to science, then, should one turn for light on the ways of life on the Mother Lode, but to local history, which for the greater part is folklore and tradition," Jones wrote in an essay for a book about the Sierra Nevada. "It is a singularly pleasant region to visit, or to dwell in permanently. Its winter is mild; snow falls rarely; the earth is a dark ochre when wet, and the grass intensely green. The trees are Digger pines, with cones the size of coconuts—and a fire of these cones, with some logs of sequoia, throws a redolence you will forever remember as the smell of the Sierra country."

It is true that Bret Harte influenced Jones, and helped shape his vision, yet Jones never imitated the master. Here is a paragraph from a tribute to Harte written by Idwal in 1936:

"For Bret Harte is master of his own world. The world on the Cyclopedean stairs of the Sierra, its pine-clad slopes, gullies, canyons resounding with the clap of water; fields of lupin, the ochre-red earth, the opal-tinted air, red-shirted Argonauts, the Heathen Chinee, the rough virtues of the camp, the elegance of Messrs. Oakhurst and Hamlin; the feel of its physical life, the thudding of shovel into the wet pebbles, the clatter of gravel into the sluice-box, and the cry of the mockingbird and oriole. Bret Harte conveyed the significance of all these."

Like Harte, Jones was drawn to the Bay city, working during World War I in the San Francisco shipyards, then going into newspaper work, ultimately to become drama critic of the *Examiner*. When his assignment was expanded to include music, he learned Italian.

Bohemian San Francisco of those years, the prince of which was the poet George Sterling, is the subject of Jones's *Ark of Empire*, a book about the Montgomery Block, a fabled building that survived many fires and the great earthquake. Jones's two-and-a-half column newspaper obituary of George Sterling, following his suicide in 1926, is a classic. Here is how it begins:

"George Sterling, touching on his fifty-seventh year, and feeling wearied, turned his face to the wall and died. He quitted this life from his little room in the Bohemian Club, and with no more regret than a bird quitting a twig. This was somewhere between seven o'clock of Tuesday night and noon yesterday. No matter when. For the curtain had fallen on the drama of San Francisco's Bohemia in which he had been master of revelry for two golden and charming decades. The Dionysian had drunk the cup to the lees, and found the end of life bitter. The reason for living was past finding out. He said goodby to no one. To say goodby would have caused his friends grief. They are many, and they all wept, for he was an exquisite poet, and a charming and loyal friend."

Jones was married in 1921 to Olive Vere Wolf, a native San Franciscan, who taught in exclusive girls' schools in Hawaii and California. Their only child was a daughter, Dilys. Publication in 1926 of his first book, and a subsequent desire for leisure in which to write more, led Jones to take his family to Europe for several vagabond years. It was primarily his wife's encouragement that led him to cut loose.

In 1928 he wrote from the south of France to Leon Gelber, the San Francisco bookseller:

"I've written a lot of stuff, none of which is important. I've got to do some potboilers now, to finance my travels up north, and to Wales, where I shall meditate a few seconds on the tombs of my ancestors, and see if there is anything I could write a book about. I'm doing some stories for Mencken; some Arabian thrillers for Street and Smith; and planning a novel to be set in a Provencal port. That's variety enough."

To my knowledge, no one has attempted the complexities of a complete Idwal Jones bibliography, including the millions of words written for newspapers.

When Jones left San Francisco for Europe, the publisher of the *Examiner*, one William Randolph Hearst, said that he would always give him a job on any of his chain of papers. And so when the Depression forced the Joneses back to America, Idwal went to work on the *New York American*, remaining there until 1933 as book reviewer, daily columnist, and feature writer.

This period was terminated, the legend goes, when Hearst happened to read one of Jones's erudite columns, and, unable to fathom it, ordered the writer fired. So back to California he came with his family, first to San Francisco, and then lured by Hollywood, to work for Paramount Pictures as a publicity writer.

Because of its urban spread, Los Angeles never fostered a Bohemian colony of which Idwal Jones had been a vital member in San Francisco. Jake Zeitlin's bookshop on West Sixth Street was the favorite downtown rendezvous for writers and artists. In addition to the poet-bookseller, members included Phil Townsend Hanna, editor of *Westways* and gourmet, Carey McWilliams, the literary lawyer destined to become editor of the *Nation*, wood-engraver Paul Landacre, impresario Merle Armitage, sculptors Gordon Newell and Archibald Garner, and printers Ward Ritchie, Grant Dahlstrom, Bruce McCallister, and Saul Marks, all of whom dwelled in the hills around Silver Lake.

Quick to perceive Idwal Jones's genius, Phil Hanna enlisted him as a contributor to *Westways*, and, starting with the issue of February 1935 and running more or less regularly for thirty years, there appeared those miniatures of Californiana, constituting now a treasury of history, legend, and lore.

In 1936 Zeitlin's Primavera Press published Jones's *China Boy*, a collection of stories about California's orientals, drawn from the writer's experiences on the Mother Lode, the Sacramento-San Joaquin deltas, and San Francisco. They are stories to rank with Bret Harte's best.

As Zeitlin's biblio-factotum, serving as a combination stenographer, window-dresser, package-wrapper, delivery boy, and bouncer, I also helped on *China Boy*. When Ward Ritchie wanted the book's cover to be composed of Chinese ideographs, I procured a photostat of some Chinese newsprint. After the book appeared it was said that the ideographic cover represented advertisements for local houses of joy. Zeitlin was uneasy until a translation revealed that it actually reported the political struggle in China.

The stories in *China Boy* are written with such skill as to appear simple. I remember when an aspiring young writer was introduced to Idwal Jones in Zeitlin's shop, and in complete self-confidence he declared that he was writing one page a day, therefore at the end of a year he would have a 365-page novel for publication. When he had left, Jones murmured to Zeitlin in the Welsh brogue he never lost, "I suppose if I were to lay a brick a day for fifty years, I would end up with a cathedral!"

I can imagine what that craftsman would have to say about today's careless prose of the Kerouac school. Like Jeffers, Jones belonged to no school. "I never discuss writing or anything I do," he wrote to a friend. "I am pretty well steeped in words and ink, and snarled up like Laocöon in miles of typewriter ribbons, but I am not articulate in discussing writing. I could no more do so than I could waste time discussing the mechanism of breathing. And I recoil from speaking of books I have done."

Idwal Jones's long residence in Southern California, exiled from his beloved Bohemia, did not wither his genius. On the contrary, it flourished south of Tehachapi. During the years from *China Boy* to the final *Chef's Holiday*, he wrote his best books.

Even to this day most eastern publishers are skeptical of California. In the late 1930's, when Jones proposed a novel about the trappers of the Sacramento delta country, he was told that unless a California novel dealt with either the Gold Rush or Hollywood, it had no hope of success. Whereupon Jones took off for Louisiana and after a short study of the Cajun trappers, he recast his book with a southern setting. It was published as *Black Bayou*. It is an example of what Idwal Jones could do when aggravated by a publisher.

Along about 1945 I was in Santa Barbara to write an article about Donald Culross Peattie, who was then engaged in helping his geographer brother, Roderick, edit anthologies of writing about the Sierra Nevada and the Coast ranges. When asked about contributors, I suggested Idwal Jones to write on the folklore of the Mother Lode and the vineyard valleys of the Coast Range. The results are vintage Jones.

Jones's auditory affliction was compensated for by acute visual and olfactory senses. He also had a photographic memory that enabled him to recall the minutiae of his travelled life. To strengthen his vision of places and people, he engaged in research.

The letter files of the State Library's California Room hold hundreds of queries from Idwal Jones, written during the years when he was living in Southern California. The UCLA library also served him. On October 26, 1948, when he was writing the book that became *Ark of Empire*, he sent this characteristic inquiry for material about Henry W. Halleck, builder of the Montgomery Block:

"I've combed the State Library and the Bancroft, getting naught but a few isolated facts and dates. The man was for 11 years Director-General of New Almaden; head of Halleck, Peachy and Billings, the greatest law firm in the West; President of the Pacific and Atlantic Railroad, etc. All this before he became Commander-in-Chief of the Federal Armies in the Civil War. I have everything on his entourage and contemporaries . . . but on Halleck himself hardly anything but the name. Huntington has his military papers, and I'll be going thru those again shortly, another tooth-combing. I'd be most grateful to know if the UCLA Library has anything on the man, any reference to his appearance, his personal life, his utterances—any shred to disprove that in his 15 years in California he was aught but a gaseous invertebrate, to quote Spencer."

Fate has its own way of weaving the web of a writer's life and work. Friendship with Phil Hanna not only led to the *Westways* series, it also brought about the writing of Jones's masterpiece, *The Vineyard*.

This is how it came about. Hanna was the founder of the Los Angeles chapter of the international Wine and Food Society. Because of an interest in gastronomy and a genius for cookery, Jones became a three-star member of the Society. This led to a study of viticulture in California, a culture which the so-called Noble Experiment of 1920-33 had nearly destroyed. With the repeal of Prohibition, the vineyards were replanted and the old tradition of wine-making revived.

In her tribute to his work in *My San Francisco*, Gertrude Atherton had Idwal Jones visiting the Napa Valley for only a single day before writing *The Vineyard*. If he told her that, the old Welsh wizard was probably indulging in Celtic hyperbole.

Jones was long familiar with the Stevenson heritage of the Napa Valley and the migratory Scottish writer's honeymoon masterpiece.

Many elements were fired in the writer's imagination to create *The Vineyard*. A love of medieval literature and legendry had acquainted Jones with Lady Juliana of Norwich, anchoress and religious writer of the 15th century, who toiled in her vineyard. His heroine, Alda Pendle, is a Californian reincarnation of the English woman who had a mystic affinity with growing things. The Regolas, father and son, were modelled on the Harazthys, the Hungarian vintners, who pioneered viticulture in California. Jones's feeling for crafts is embodied in Port, the cooper; and of orientals and their ways in Wing, the old servitor. A kiteflying contest is another means of Jones's introducing his arcane knowledge of Chinese ways in early California. On one level *The Vineyard* is a veritable treatise on viticulture—the planting, tending, harvesting, and finally the making of grapes into wine. "And still the wine her ancient ruby yields," could serve as its epigraph.

On the main level, *The Vineyard* is simply a novel, an enthralling story, in which his learning is assimilated by the writer into a few characters and the way in which they fulfill their lives in a landscape of vivid reality. "But more real than any of them," Mrs. Fisher wrote in her review, "is the vine: the tendrils and hungers and illnesses and the miraculous strength of the vine. It spreads through the whole book, and the aroma of good wine lights it."

The Vineyard is a book worthy of Robert Louis Stevenson, patron saint of the Napa Valley and its guardian Mt. St. Helena. Major novel, minor novel? What matter when it is a classic, a work of excellence, in which form and substance, characters and setting, are fused. We read the book with admiration for the writer's control over the story in its details and movement. Most artfully did he put his learning and his love of places and people into an apparently artless book. It was written in the high prime of his early fifties, in a time of economic security.

I have waited until this point to introduce another factor in Idwal Jones's ability to sustain and develop his God-given gifts as a writer. His wife played a similar role to that of the wives of Stevenson and Jeffers. Olive was to Idwal both loving wife and able secretary, a woman able to handle money, housekeeping, and also to trim the ragged edges of her husband's prose. She typed and polished his final drafts. She drove the car for him who never touched the wheel. She drew off bores when they threatened his equanimity. She guarded his need for periods of concentrated work, sometimes lasting as long as sixteen hours. When his deafness finally cut him off from all social intercourse, she was his ears. Marriage to her meant freedom to him, a confinement in which he was paradoxically free to work.

Olive Jones lives on in Laguna in a smaller house, with her two Manx cats. His books and manuscripts went to libraries, except for her copies of the books he wrote and inscribed to her.

"What was the most important thing you did for him?" I asked.

She paused before answering, and then said, "I gave him confidence, and enabled him to realize that he was more than a journalist. His early illness and the deafness made him insecure. He found certitude in me."

The Vineyard is complemented by the nonfictional *Vines in the Sun*, subtitled "A Journey through the California Vineyards," a lyrical, learned book, made even more attractive by Albert J. Camille's drawings of the vineyard regions. It is another book Stevenson would have enjoyed, for it is in the tradition of English travel books, in which his own have such a large part.

Jones does not ignore the onetime great Southern California vineyards—Guasti's at Cucamonga, the largest in the world, and Lucky Baldwin's Santa Anita, or Anaheim which was wiped out by disease, and San Juan Capistrano where vines were first planted by the Franciscans.

His one "major" novel was written in this same high decade of the 1940's. *Vermilion* is a multi-generation story of a California quicksilver mine, the Five Apostles, modelled on the New Almaden mine in the Santa Cruz mountains near San Jose. It is an ambitious novel, packed with Jones's knowledge of California history, legendry, topography, and mining. No admirer of this writer, fond of his special flavors, will fail to relish its 495 pages. The book is permeated with that intense feeling with which Jones endows the landscape. Here is an epitome of this *genius loci:* "The whole green-and-bronze region from these hills down to where Pt. Lobos thrusts its jaws into the surf had its arcana, its legends of spectres and visitants who, like the ancient gods, existed because they were believed in."

Vermilion's weakness is that its characters carry too heavy a load, and there are too many of them—a hundred in all. They do not have the convincing life of the few people in *The Vineyard*. The long time-span covered—a hundred years—also attenuates Jones's power, best displayed in vignettes, stories, short novels. A virtue of the book is that there is no explicit sex, no falling in and out of bed.

After *Vermilion* and *Ark of Empire*, Jones wrote no more California books. *High Bonnet* and *Chef's Holiday*, his two final volumes, are fictional fancies laid in France, the motherland of wine and food lovers. At his death Jones left an unfinished novel laid in Mexico of a generation ago, for which he had made a field trip to Mazatlan. This fragmentary manuscript is in the Bancroft Library which, with UCLA, harbors Idwal Jones's manuscripts and papers.

The old lung trouble recurred as he aged. His strength waned from the mid-1950's. He no longer had that power of concentration which once, in the New York days, had led him to go on typing against deadline, while a fire in the wastebasket, lit by his pipe's ashes, had set his coat to burning.

"I am not much wiser than I was before," he wrote to a friend. "I am always meeting someone who knows more than I do. I plan only to return some day to the Bay region and settle north of it, and write one more novel." He never did.

What an example he is to those who would write! Wide and deep learning of languages and customs, love of life and its people, the earth's seasonal landscapes, integrated with imagination, persistence, stamina—these were his in abundance. They are the hallmarks of his work.

Native son? Irrelevant. That Welshman, Idwal Jones, will

live among those adopted Californians who have raised the state to the level of lasting literature. *Gwin o aur*, the Welsh say, *wine from gold*. Jones the magician could perform either; he was both vintner and alchemist. It is fitting that his ashes rest in the Southern California memorial park called Valhalla.

Reading List

IDWAL JONES (1887-1964)
The Splendid Shilling. New York, Doubleday, 1926.
Whistler's Van. New York, Viking Press, 1936.
China Boy and Other Stories. Los Angeles, Primavera Press, 1936.
The Vineyard. New York, Duell, 1942.
Vines in the Sun. New York, Morrow, 1949.
Vermilion. New York, Prentice-Hall, 1947.
Ark of Empire; San Francisco's Montgomery Block. Garden City, Doubleday, 1951.

BRET HARTE
A Night at Wingdam. Foreword by Idwal Jones. San Francisco, Book Club of California, 1936. (California Literary Pamphlets, No. 6).

RODERICK PEATTIE, Editor
Pacific Coast Ranges. New York, Vanguard, 1946.
The Sierra Nevada. New York, Vanguard, 1947.
Each contains a chapter by Idwal Jones.

PRENTICE-HALL, PUBLISHER
A Toast to Idwal Jones. New York, 1947. Tributes by Gertrude Atherton, Gorham Munson, Fletcher Pratt, with bibliography.

The Cattle on a Thousand Hills

ROBERT GLASS CLELAND

22

"A KNOWLEDGE of history is able to make the whole landscape alive, to render the exploration of the humblest village an adventure of thrilling possibilities, to give a voice to the downs, and to enrich the waste with memories."

This sentence from Esmé Wingfield-Stratford's *History of British Civilization* recurs throughout the works of Robert Glass Cleland, California historian, whose *The Cattle on a Thousand Hills* is also a classic of California literature. This is what Cleland did for a vanished Southern California, in chronicling the events and portraying the persons of that pastoral era from 1850 to 1880.

No historian of our time surpassed Cleland in wedding scholarship and readability. Forty years ago in the Preface to his *Pathfinders*, a volume devoted to California's earliest explorers, he wrote, "I have sought to bring to the results of orthodox research and scholarship something of life and color and imagination."

If he were admittedly indebted to the British tradition for his philosophy of history, Cleland owed his moral view of life and his literary style to the Christian religion and the King James version of the Bible. From the fiftieth Psalm came the title of his classic: "Every beast of the forest is mine and the cattle upon a thousand hills."

Few places on earth have suffered such radical transformation in as short a time as Southern California since 1850. Wave after wave of immigration swept over it, from the Gold Rush, the cattle and sheep decades, the coming of the railroads and the real estate booms, to the oil, automotive, aviation, and industrial development of the twentieth century. Nor is the end in sight, as the flow of immigration augurs a solid city from San Bernardino to the sea, from San Diego to Santa Barbara.

The books of Robert Glass Cleland are recommended to all who would experience the sense of the past. To a mastery of the printed and manuscript sources of history preserved in the two greatest western repositories, the Huntington and the Bancroft libraries, he brought personal knowledge of and feeling for the land about which he wrote.

No ivory tower scholar he; Cleland was a rugged trailsman by foot, horse, or mule, and a passionate dry fly fisherman of western streams from Montana to Mexico. In all of his work we sense the earthy setting. His prose partakes of his own virility.

Cleland died in 1947 in his 73rd year. My knowledge of him goes back forty-five years to when he was my teacher at Occidental College in a class in English history. He was an intense and informed man, deeply grounded in Anglo-American democratic idealism. A graduate of Occidental College in the class of 1907, Cleland was a friend of his fellow student, the young poet Robinson Jeffers, and years later he wrote a vivid memoir of a camping trip they took into the wilderness of the San Bernardino range.

After graduation, Cleland went east to earn a second A.B. and a Ph.D. at Princeton University. From the time of his work for the degree, he was devoted to California history as it ensued from the union of the Anglo-Saxon and Hispanic streams. His dissertation was titled *The Early Sentiment for the Annexation of California: An Account of the Growth of American Interest in California from 1835 to 1846*. In its preface he acknowledged his debt to two men, Professor Robert E. McElroy of Princeton, who directed his studies, and Professor Herbert E. Bolton of the University of California, director of the Bancroft Library.

Although Kentucky-born, Cleland came to California at the age of four, when his father was called to a Presbyterian pastorate in Duarte, and later in Azusa. His boyhood at the foot of the Sierra Madre, with access to such trout streams as the San Gabriel and the Big Santa Anita, gave Cleland a lifelong love of his adopted land. The numerous saloons in Azusa also gave him an abhorrence of the misuse of alcohol.

His affiliation with Occidental College as professor of history, vice president and dean, continued until his death as professor emeritus. During the 1920's he established his reputation as a leading historian of California with two books, *A History of California: the American Period* and the earlier cited *Pathfinders*. A quotation from the former gives promise, amply fulfilled in the text, of more than a text or treatise:

"This volume is something more than the product of many years of research and investigation. The writer has lived in California since 1889. He has known the state when it was still in a semi-pioneer stage, and has seen it rise to its present height of cultural development and material prosperity. At one time or another, too, especially within the last few years, he has visited nearly every section of the state, from Imperial Valley to Humboldt Bay. Sometimes travelling by railroad; sometimes by automobile equipped with camping outfit; and best of all, sometimes with saddle horse and pack train, he has sought to familiarize himself with that vast empire of desert and mountain, thriving cities and fruitful valleys, which stretches a thousand miles along the Pacific, from Oregon to the Mexican boundary. For that empire, which the world calls California, the writer confesses an absorbing love; and for those who laid its foundations, an abiding admiration. This book, in the last analysis, is chiefly the product of that love and of that admiration."

Cleland's work at Princeton revealed his awareness of the sources in the Bancroft Library; and in his 1922 *History* appears the first evidence of his use of the Huntington Library and its growing wealth of western source material. That library had then recently been moved from New York to its new home in San Marino, and was little known. This inaugurated a relationship between Cleland and the Huntington that grew closer and stronger with the years, and led in 1943 to his appointment as

259

260

the Library's senior western historian and the writing of his finest books.

The Huntington Library's popular renown rests on its holdings in art, literature, and history, of British treasures such as the Gainsboroughs and Reynolds, the Shakespeare folios and quartos, and the Battle Abbey papers. Henry E. Huntington was also interested in the West and particularly Southern California, where his Pacific Electric Railway was a major factor in the unification and development of the region. His librarians, George Watson Cole and Leslie E. Bliss, had begun the amassing of source materials in California, including books, pamphlets, maps, diaries, letters, and other family papers; and it was this vein of riches that Cleland began to work in earnest and that led to his giving up administrative work at Occidental and becoming a full-time Huntington scholar.

In 1941 the Huntington Library published his *Cattle on a Thousand Hills: Southern California, 1850-1870*, and ten years later he revised and enlarged the book, extending its coverage to 1880. It has become one of the Library's best-sellers. This is *the* book to read if one wishes to know what Southern California was like in the time it embraced the state's "cow counties"; not the life of the violent pueblo described by Major Horace Bell, but rather the pastoral life of the Californios and the impact on it of American customs and institutions, and the conversion of the grazing ranchos into farms, settlements, and finally cities.

Cleland's book could have been written only at the Huntington Library, for it was the recipient in his time of the archival collection called the Gaffey manuscripts. This consisted of some 15,000 items preserved by a relative, representing letters, documents, memoranda, ledgers, and accounts of Abel Stearns, a Yankee immigrant who at the age of forty married the fourteen-year-old Arcadia Bandini and became the region's foremost merchant and rancher, from 1829 to 1871. It was hides from Stearns' Rancho Alamitos that were stock-piled at San Pedro in the 1830's and loaded by Dana and his fellow sailors.

It is one thing for a library to acquire a collection of boxes and bundles of paper and ink, then have it sorted and arranged by librarians. Such acts represent good field work and good house-keeping. It is another thing for a writer to perceive the collection with illuminating vision which will relate the parts to the whole and the whole to the land and people from which the collection came.

Such was the achievement of Robert Glass Cleland in transforming the Gaffey-Stearns papers into a socio-economic history of Southern California. Throughout the book his prose rings with Biblical overtones, as in writing of the great drought of the 1860's that destroyed the cattle industry:

"All through the long, dry summer, Southern California ranchers looked to the coming of the fall rains to save them from ruin; but the fall slipped into winter, and winter into spring, while the parched earth waited in vain for relief, and the cattle died by the thousands on sunbaked ranges and beside waterless streams and sand-choked springs. . . . The thousands of head of 'black cattle and beasts of burden,' which once carried the familiar brands of the proudest of California families, disappeared forever from the plains and valleys and rolling hills. Reduced to the unromantic realism of assessment lists and tax returns, the story of the passing of the old rancheros is written in the long-forgotten, dust-covered records of every Southern California county."

The death of a writer's wife often means the end of his creative life. Not so with Robert Cleland. When his beloved wife Muriel died in 1943, he found in his religion and work the strength not only to carry on, but also to enter his most productive years. This is not to say that her death did not affect him deeply. The Preface to *From Wilderness to Empire*, which was published soon after his loss, concluded:

"And, finally, there is one whose patience, understanding, quiet words of encouragement, and eager anticipation of the finished volume were never far absent from my thought and work. For her, life's little candle has gone out; and for me, the sunsets have lost their glory, and the shining mountains are wrapped in the shadows of the night. I wish this book were more worthy of her."

262

In addition to the consolation of religion and the urgency of his work, Cleland drew strength from nature as he experienced it in hunting and fishing. To Edward R. Murrow's series called "This I Believe," Cleland contributed a credo, "As a Watch in the Night." It told in few and simple words of the renewed faith he gained after his wife's death—faith derived from a trip in a rowboat down the San Juan River from Mexican Hat in southern Utah to Lee's Ferry on the Colorado.

It was at this time that he retired from college administration. His two stalwart sons were on their own, in pursuit of careers in medicine and chemistry. Cleland took up residence at Caltech's Athenaeum, near the Huntington Library; and until his death fourteen years later, he wrote and encouraged others to write a number of outstanding works on California and the West.

In 1944 he persuaded the Rockefeller Foundation to make the Huntington Library a grant of $50,000—at that time a lot of money—for a regional study of the Southwest. This was used to purchase further research collections, to bring scholars to work at the library on regional projects, and to publish books resulting from their research. The Southwest was defined broadly to include Utah Mormon culture and the rangelands of Texas, as well as the traditional "heart of the Southwest," Arizona and New Mexico. J. Frank Dobie was at the Library as a Rockefeller fellow to work on the manuscript that came to be *The Mustangs*. Music, utopian colonies, and the founding of San Diego were other subjects on which books were written.

Thus was carried out one of Henry E. Huntington's primary intentions in founding and endowing the noblest of all western libraries, that through the medium of scholarship, research, and publication, the treasures he accumulated on such a princely scale should be used to enlarge the understanding and increase the appreciation of the American people in their cultural birthright.

The teaching role that Cleland had played at Occidental was continued at the Huntington Library. Former students were developed as scholars through work at the Library. Cooperation between Cleland and Professor John Walton Caughey, UCLA's western historian, resulted in the training and growth of Dr. Andrew Rolle, who succeeded Cleland as professor of history at Occidental, and Dr. Glenn Dumke, who was destined to become dean of Occidental and chancellor of the California state college system. Dumke's book, *The Boom of the Eighties in Southern California*, a doctoral dissertation inspired by Cleland and carried out under Caughey's direction, is a sequel to *The Cattle on a Thousand Hills*.

Another of Cleland's achievements during his years in San Marino was to interest Alfred A. Knopf, America's most creative publisher, in issuing a series of Western Americana in commemoration of the California centennials, 1846-1850. Cleland edited two of these volumes, Bayard Taylor's *Eldorado* and Josiah Royce's *California*. He also wrote for Knopf a two-volume history of California, a young people's book on the state, a chronicle of the fur trade; and finally, a history of the Phelps Dodge copper company. After Cleland's death in 1957, Glenn Dumke updated and consolidated the two-volume work on California into a single volume, *From Wilderness to Empire*, adding a bibliographical essay on the literature about the state.

Cleland was given strong support by the staff of the Huntington Library, all of whom he thanked in the prefaces to the books written with their help. Another lay colleague of aid to him was W. W. Robinson, Vice President and Historian of the Title Insurance and Trust Co., the authority on land titles in California. Robinson's *Ranchos Become Cities*, an account of the transformation of Los Angeles County, appeared in 1939. He was called on often by Cleland when he was writing his works on the pastoral years.

I have saved till last an account of three monographs that flowed from the deep well Cleland plumbed during the San Marino years. They are models of research into primary sources, of the interpretation of data so that small themes assume larger significance, and of graceful writing. All three are concerned with the changes wrought in Southern California by the impact of the Anglos on the Californios.

The first is *The Place Called Sespe*, a history of the Rancho San Cayetano in the Santa Clara Valley of Ventura County, owned by Mr. and Mrs. Keith Spaulding of Pasadena, for whom Cleland wrote the book. First published privately in 1940, it was reissued in 1953. It is a model work of its kind.

To this day the Sespe ranch, though smaller in size than its original two square leagues, is a working ranch, lying along the Rio Santa Clara between Piru and Fillmore. If one would see a thriving remnant of pastoral-agricultural California in a region free of smog and guarded by the high mountains of the condor refuge, he should take Highway 126 from Ventura to Castaic. And read Cleland's *Sespe* before going and upon return.

The second monograph is a more ambitious history of a larger ranch, *The Irvine Ranch of Orange County, 1850-1950*. First published in 1952, this work was updated by professor Robert V. Hine to cover the events attendant upon the establishment of the University of California's Irvine campus and the Pereira Master Plan for the development of this last of the great ranchos to be broken up.

The third of these jewels in Cleland's crown is *El Molino Viejo*, a history of the Old Mill in San Marino. First built in 1816 to grind meal for the Mission San Gabriel, the mill passed through various hands, then fell into ruin. It was bought by Henry E. Huntington, and inherited by Mr. and Mrs. James R. Brehm. They restored it and gave it in 1965 to the city of San Marino. Its history and lore, and its vicissitudes over the century and a half of its existence, are told by the historian in a work of scholarship and art.

Readers will be drawn to Cleland's works for different reasons. His histories of California will remain standard references. *The Cattle on a Thousand Hills* is based on deeper, primary sources, and is thus his most substantially original work. The ranch and mill books will have fewer readers because they are more specialized and local.

And yet it is to them that I am the most attached. This is because of the way they evoke my past in Southern California.

As a boy I knew the lands of Sespe and Irvine and the Old Mill. With my father, the manager of what is now Sunkist Growers, I went along on his visits to groves and packinghouses throughout Southern California. With him I trudged down the rows of lemon groves along the Santa Clara when the mallow was lush in spring and the hills were yellow with mustard. With my brothers I fished for sharks and stingarees in the upper reaches of Newport Bay known as The Lakes, those sinuous water-ways that penetrated the lands of the Irvine Ranch.

It was as a lad that I accompanied my father to meetings with William Hertrich, Huntington's horticultural *majordomo*. While they were discussing the merits of species and specimens in planting the Huntington orchards and gardens, I gorged on persimmons and pomegranates turned orange and red in autumn. Out to the Old Mill my pals and I would bicycle to explore the hillside tunnel legend said led to the Mission San Gabriel and in which the padres hid their treasure. The ground around the deserted Mill was littered with the sweet-meated black walnuts, ours for the cracking.

On November 21, 1933, Robert Glass Cleland spoke at the Fiftieth Anniversary banquet of the Historical Society of Southern California. His address was called "The Valley of Dry Bones," which, he said, is what history is until revivified by the imaginative reader. Its peroration, with its organ tone of biblical eloquence, expresses the philosophy of history which makes his best works more than academic exercises. Let Cleland have the last word:

"Consider the Missions of California. How shall we view them? As interesting examples of architectural adaptation? As monuments to the members of an adventurous, heroic Order? As outposts of Christianity and civilization upon a barbarous frontier? They are all of these, surely, and something more. Break off a piece from one of their century-old adobe walls. Crumble it to dust between your thoughtless fingers. Then place this dust in the open palm of your hand and hold it out so that the wind from the sea will blow it away forever. Only the dust of a crumbling Mission wall, you say with an idle shrug. Yes, but a trifle

266

more. The dust you held so carelessly in your open hand was the dust of an empire, if you had only understood—the glory of an ancient, heroic, race. And the wind which blew it so utterly away? Ah, that was the wind which men call time."

Reading List

ROBERT G. CLELAND (1874-1947)
A History of California; the American Period. New York, Macmillan, 1922.
Pathfinders. Los Angeles, Powell Publishing Co., 1929.
The Cattle on a Thousand Hills; Southern California, 1850-1870. San Marino, Huntington Library, 1941. Revised & enlarged, 1951.
From Wilderness to Empire; a History of California. Revised & updated by Glenn S. Dumke. New York, Alfred A. Knopf. 1959.
The Place Called Sespe. Chicago, Privately Printed, 1940. Reissued, Alhambra, C. F. Braun Co., 1953.
The Irvine Ranch of Orange County, 1850-1950. San Marino, Huntington Library, 1952; edited & enlarged by Robert V. Hine, 1962.
El Molino Viejo. Los Angeles, Ward Ritchie Press, 1950.
"The Valley of Dry Bones"; 50th Anniversary address, Historical Society of Southern California, *Annual Publication,* v. 15, pt. 4, 1933.

GLENN S. DUMKE
The Boom of the Eighties in Southern California. San Marino, Huntington Library, 1944.

W. W. ROBINSON
Ranchos Become Cities. Pasadena, San Pasqual Press, 1939.
Land in California. Berkeley & Los Angeles, University of California Press, 1948.

Photograph of Robert G. Cleland, courtesy of Robert S. Cleland, M.D.

HELEN HUNT JACKSON

23

"IT WAS sheep-shearing time in Southern California . . ." is the way it begins.

Ramona was the first novel about Southern California. Today, nearly a century after its publication, it remains the best California book of its kind—an historical romance of a vanished way of life.

This was not its author's intention. She meant it to dramatize the plight of the Mission Indians. When Congress and the people ignored her earlier treatise on the wrongs suffered by the American Indians—*A Century of Dishonor* she called it—Helen Hunt Jackson vowed she would give them the same bitter medicine in a sugar-coated pill. Sweetness rather than bitterness is why *Ramona* is read to this day, reprinted more than three hundred times, illustrated variously, translated widely, made into films, plays, pageants; lending its name to streets, schools, towns, a convent. It has suffered somewhat the same fate as that of *Gulliver's Travels*, meant by Swift as a savage satire and become a children's classic.

Sweetness is not enough, however, to ensure a book's longevity. *Ramona* has something more. *Vitality*. That is why it has never gone unread. It possesses enormous vitality. Romantic characters though they are—Ramona and Alessandro, Señora Moreno and her son Felipe, the Franciscan Father Salvierderra, the shepherd

Juan Canito, the folksy Tennesseeans—they are all vital, and they fulfill themselves as men and women of flesh and blood.

The reader enters their lives and is swept along to the last page and its weak happy ending. The reader is at home in their homeland. Mrs. Jackson's Southern California is a real domain of earth and sky, although today it has nearly vanished, the land overbuilt, the sky obscured. The nostalgic appeal of *Ramona* is heightened with every passing year of the region's proliferation into a vast urban organism.

Whereas *The Land of Little Rain, Two Years Before the Mast,* and *The Mountains of California* were all first books, in which their authors reached heights never attained in subsequent works, *Ramona* was Mrs. Jackson's last book, coming at the end of a twenty-year career of prolific production.

She endowed it with her own life, thus illustrating Milton's description of a book as the precious life-blood of a master spirit, treasured up against Time. Its publication was followed a year later by her death.

If she had not written *Ramona*, Helen Hunt Jackson would be just another of her century's unread writers. She was a contributor to magazines and newspapers of stories, poems, travel sketches, serialized novels, under the initials "H.H." and the pseudonym "Saxe Holm." *Century* once considered devoting an entire issue of that monthly magazine to her work—poetry, fiction, travel, criticism—but dropped it because, in that Victorian age, it might have been viewed as sensational.

Writing took for her the place of living, when by thirty-five she had lost husband and two sons from accident and illness. Then destiny led this intense young woman, a native of Amherst, to Newport, Rhode Island, where in 1886 she came into the magnetic field of Colonel Thomas Wentworth Higginson, arbiter of American letters and discoverer of Emily Dickinson. His influence on the grieving widow was immediate and lasting. He encouraged her to seek surcease in writing. He corrected her work, obtained its publication, read proofs, and championed it on every occasion.

Theirs was a passionate relationship, kept from fulfilment by his being bound to an invalid wife. Higginson called her "the most brilliant, impetuous, and thoroughly individual woman of her time, one whose very temperament seemed mingled of sunshine and fire; a personality so unique and so fascinating that few could comprehend the curious thread of firm New England texture that ran through her whole being, tempering waywardness, keeping impulse from making shipwreck of itself."

What was it that led Helen Hunt Jackson finally to write *Ramona?* We can only call it fate that took her west, first to Colorado Springs in search of a climate that would ameliorate her asthmatic condition, then to Yosemite and the Big Trees. It was not only health that she found in the Rockies. There she married again, a rich railroad man named William Sharpless Jackson. He was a Quaker, and their ceremony was the traditional one of the Society of Friends.

Then in 1879, through hearing a lecture in Boston by Chief Standing Bear and Princess Bright Eyes and their group of Poncas, she became aware of the wrongs suffered by their tribe and other Indians. Until then she had never been a crusader. Women's rights, the evils of drink, and slavery—none of those three most burning issues of the age had ever aroused her to write with zealous indignation, even though her mentor, Colonel Higginson, was an abolitionist. She wrote to please, to entertain, to fill her own childless life—and to make money. She was one of the best paid writers of her time.

The Indian matter aroused her as never before. "I have done now," she wrote to Colonel Higginson, "the last of the things I had said I never would do; I have become what I have said a thousand times was the most odious thing in life, 'a woman with a hobby.' But I cannot help it. I think I feel as you must have felt in the old abolition days."

She bombarded editors with letters and articles, circulated petitions and tracts, and even blasted the Secretary of the Interior, Carl Schurz. Then, determined to concentrate her efforts in book form, she withdrew to the Astor Library in New York and there wrote *A Century of Dishonor*.

Upon its publication in 1881 she sent a copy at her expense to every member of Congress. Printed in red on the cover were these words of Benjamin Franklin: "Look upon your hands! They are stained with the blood of your relations."

Congress was not moved. There was no immediate reaction to what was essentially a compilation of raw facts and figures. A year later, however, was founded the powerful Indian Rights Association. Hers proved to be a watershed book. After it everything flowed in favor of the Indians.

From 1881 to 1885, Helen Hunt Jackson made three trips to Southern California. To write *Ramona* was not her first intention. That came toward the last, almost too late, for her time was running out. Although she did not know it, she was mortally ill from cancer. She proposed to write a series of articles on the Missions for *Century* magazine. Ever since her first visit in 1872, she had been drawn by their romantic history.

She journeyed to all of the Missions from San Diego to Sonoma, and she also researched in the Santa Barbara Mission archives and in the historical collection of H. H. Bancroft in San Francisco long before it was sold to the University of California.

In Los Angeles she spent days with the Coronel family in their home at Sixth and Alameda streets. She became familiar with life on several ranches—Guajome near San Luis Rey, Warner's Ranch, Rancho Santa Anita, Rancho Camulos, and Elwood Cooper's Ranch at Goleta. She used her repertorial skill in accumulating facts and figures and absorbing local color. She had perceptive vision, absorptive capacity, creative imagination, and physical stamina—requisite equipment for writing a masterpiece. All that was lacking was a story. That was yet to come.

In 1883 as a result of *A Century of Dishonor*, Mrs. Jackson was appointed by President Chester Arthur as a special commissioner to investigate and report upon the condition of the Mission Indians of Southern California. As colleague she chose the colorful Abbot Kinney of Sierra Madre, the founder of Venice (Calif.), whose knowledge of Spanish proved invaluable.

Together they visited the Indian reservations in the Riverside and San Diego back country, travelling by a two-horse, double-seat carriage. Helen Jackson was then a woman of fifty-three,

271

Helen Jackson.

weighing 170 pounds. When her friends warned her that such a field trip would prove too arduous, she replied, "I'll go if it kills me."

Go she did, and the subsequent fidelity of setting in *Ramona* came from the first-hand knowledge gained on that trip. She was an able field investigator and archival researcher, and best of all, a powerful writer.

Her Southern California experiences over four years' time resulted in three kinds of writing. First, the magazine articles, some of which were collected posthumously in *Glimpses of California and the Missions*. These pieces, published as they were at the beginning of the Boom of the Eighties, served as tourist guide literature.

Second was her and Kinney's *Report on the Condition and Needs of the Mission Indians*, published by the Government Printing Office in 1883, and added to the 1885 edition of *A Century of Dishonor*. A reprint of this latter book, with a lucid introduction by Andrew F. Rolle, duplicates the first edition rather than the enlarged one, thus denying readers ready access to the California report.

Third and last of these California fruits was *Ramona*. Works of creative literature form in the subconscious mind. Years may pass before they come to the surface. As we look back over Helen Hunt Jackson's life, we see how it moved toward fulfilment in the writing of *Ramona*. The timing was perilous. Although she did not know that she was doomed to die so soon, she was aware that "Time's winged chariot was hurrying near." And when she came at last to write the novel, she did so in a race against time—a race won in a photo-finish.

The novel surfaced in the autumn of 1883. She had returned home, determined to cast her urgent message in a more palatable form, but still unsure of its precise nature. Then . . . but let her tell it:

"Still I did not see my way clear; got no plot; till one morning late last October, before I was wide awake, the whole plot flashed into my mind—not a vague one—the whole story just as it stands today,—in less than five minutes, as if someone spoke it. I sprang

273

up, went to my husband's room, and told him; I was half frightened."

What an understanding husband he was, that William Sharpless Jackson! In order that she have the privacy needed to write the book, he urged his wife to leave the distractions of their social life in Colorado Springs and go into seclusion; not in a mountain retreat, but in a Manhattan hotel.

Until she finished the novel the following spring, Mrs. Jackson lived at The Berkeley in New York City. From there, on February 5, 1883, she wrote to Colonel Higginson an extraordinary letter of the book's progress, a veritable clinical report on the birth of *Ramona*. Here is another passage from that letter:

"From that time, till I came here, it haunted me, becoming more and more vivid. I was impatient to get at it. I wrote the first word of it December 1. As soon as I began, it seemed impossible to write fast enough. It racks me like a struggle with an outside power. I cannot help being superstitious about it. I have never done *half* the amount of work in the same time. Twice, since beginning it, I have broken down utterly for a week. What I have to endure in holding myself away from it, no words can tell. It is like keeping away from a lover, whose hand I can reach."

She kept dashing off requests for confirming materials to the Coronels in Los Angeles and to friends in San Diego, at the same time swearing them to secrecy. She worried a little about the liberties she was taking with chronology and setting. But surely, she reasoned, no one would be "idiot enough" to make a point of that. After all, she was not writing history.

She ignored Colonel Higginson's counsel to write slowly, as she transfused the book with her own life's blood. She wrote on large sheets of yellow paper, eschewing pen and ink, insisting that a lead pencil alone could keep pace with the swiftness of her thoughts. She was supremely confident of what she was writing, for the reason that she was at the height of her powers. Years of experience in her craft enabled her to master her demon and drive the story to its end.

"Now you will ask," she wrote him, "what sort of English it is I write at this lightning speed. So far as I can tell, the best I

274

ever wrote! I have read it aloud as I have gone on, to one friend, of keen literary perceptions and judgment, the most purely intellectual woman I know—Mrs. Trimble. She says it is smooth—strong—clear. 'Tremendous' is her frequent epithet."

"The success of it—if it succeeds—will be that I do not even suggest any Indian history,—till the interest is so aroused in the heroine and hero, that people will not lay the book down.

"Every now and then I force myself to stop, and write a short story or a bit of verse; I can't bear the strain; but the instant I open the pages of the other, I write as I am writing now—as fast as I could copy! What do you think? Am I possessed of a demon?

"Fifty-two last October—and I'm not a bit steadier-headed, you see, than ever! I don't know whether to send this or burn it up. Don't laugh at me whatever you do."

Ramona was finished by the following April. So eager was she for it to appear and make its impact that she had it serialized weekly in the *Christian Union*, instead of monthly as planned. Book publication soon followed, and this great romantic novel began its long life as a classic. The inevitable process started of the transformation of a plea for Indian justice into an idyll of California's Mexican era.

This was the irony of the book's fate. Mrs. Jackson saw it begin to happen. After reading the review in the *Atlantic Monthly*, she wrote to a friend, "Not one word for my Indians! I put my heart and soul in the book for them. It is a dead failure."

She was wrong. It was a living success, although not in the way she intended. By her early death she was spared the enormous pother over precisely what places in Southern California she had described and what characters she had intended to portray. This concern culminated in George Wharton James's *Through Ramona's Country*, a detailed itinerary in the region from Santa Barbara to San Diego.

In truth *Ramona* is a supreme example of the creative process, whereby a novelist absorbs experience and observation into the imaginative subconscious and there it is recast in the form of a story. In *Ramona* literature transcends life, the romance outlasts the reality, the book lives on after people, places, customs have long been superseded. This is what has happened in Southern California, and is why *Ramona's* power and nostalgia only increase with each passing year.

In the year of life left to her, Mrs. Jackson returned to California in search of health, and crippled with a broken leg. From Santa Monica she wrote to Emily Dickinson, the Amherst poet and recluse with whom she had grown up as a child. "This is a lovely seaside hamlet. As I write (in bed, before breakfast), I am looking straight off towards Japan, over a silver sea." Miss Dickinson replied, "Pity me, I have finished *Ramona*. Would that like Shakespeare, it were just published."

Mrs. Jackson's health did not improve. Believing her illness to be malaria, she moved to San Francisco. There she grew worse. In desperation she appealed to John Muir to find her a place in the High Sierra where she could be out of doors, at an elevation of 4,000 feet, and near to express and telegraph offices. Specifications for her outfit were fantastic: eight horses, an ambulance, two camp-wagons for tents, and a phaeton buggy; four servants, a maid, and a doctor.

"I shall do this as a gamester throws his last card," she wrote Muir, and concluded, "I believe I know every word you have written. I never wished myself a man but once. That was when I read how it seemed to be rocked in the top of a pine tree in a gale."

Muir replied with characteristic kindness, listing several possible itineraries, and concluding, "But go to the mountains where and how you will, you will soon be free from the effects of this confusion, and God's sky will bend down about you as if made for you alone, and the pines will spread their healing arms above you and bless you and make you well again, and so delight the heart of John Muir."

It was too late. She had but two months to live. By one of those turns of fate, John Muir went to call on her in San Francisco at the very hour she lay dying. The shades were drawn. Preoccupied as they were, no one answered the bell. Believing her not at home, he went away.

When Emily Dickinson heard of her friend's death, she wrote

to Colonel Higginson, "She wrote me in the spring that she could not walk, but not that she would die. Please say it is not so."

Among the many editions of *Ramona*, two are outstanding. The Monterey edition of 1900 contains an introduction by Susan Coolidge which is one of the best things written about Mrs. Jackson. It is illustrated by Henry Sandham, the Canadian artist who had travelled with Mrs. Jackson in the early 1880's and made field drawings to illustrate her *Century* articles. Sandham is the ideal portrayer of Southern California of that time. His illustrations are also found in her *Glimpses of California and the Missions*, although badly reproduced.

The Pasadena edition of *Ramona* appeared in 1902, illustrated from photographs by A. C. Vroman, whose name is perpetuated in the Pasadena bookstore founded by him.

Critics of American literature have not ignored *Ramona*. It is often coupled with *Uncle Tom's Cabin*. Even when they score it as sentimental and saccharine, they recognize its vitality and narrative power. Helen Hunt Jackson was not the naive umbrella-carrying tourist, wrongly described by Carey McWilliams in his *Southern California Country* (whose sub-title, "An Island on the Land," he borrowed from her); she was a veteran reporter and skilled writer, who knew what to see and how to describe what she saw.

When an edition of *Ramona* appeared in 1932, it was reviewed by Mary Austin, herself a champion of Indian rights and celebrant of Spanish ways. She gave it high praise, calling it, "one of the most authentic and faithful of American historical novels." Sheep shearing, hymn singing, herbal medicine, native dishes— those details of Southern California ranch life described in *Ramona*, are, Mary Austin observed, still prevalent in the Spanish Southwest. "No one who wishes to keep warmly in touch with that part of American life which gives a romantic color to history," she concluded, "should neglect the story of *Ramona*."

"It was sheep shearing time in Southern California." If one begins with those opening words, I will give odds that he will not lay the book aside until he has read it through.

HELEN HUNT JACKSON (1830-1885)
A Century of Dishonor. New York, Harper, 1881; enlarged edition with the California Mission Indians Report, Boston, Roberts Bros., 1885; facsimile of 1881 edition, with Introduction and notes by Andrew F. Rolle, Harper Torchbooks, 1965.
Glimpses of California and the Missions. Boston, Little, Brown, 1883.
Ramona. Boston, Roberts Bros., 1884; with introduction by Susan Coolidge and illustrations by Henry Sandham. Boston, Little, Brown, 1900, 2 vols., the Monterey Edition; with introduction and photographs by A. C. Vroman. Boston, Little, Brown, 1913, the Pasadena Edition; with introduction by J. Frank Dobie, Los Angeles, Plantin Press for Limited Editions Club, 1959.
"How *Ramona* was Written"; a Letter from H. H. J. to Col. Higginson, in *Atlantic Monthly*, November 1900.

GEORGE WHARTON JAMES
Through Ramona's Country. Boston, Little, Brown, 1908.

RUTH O'DELL
Helen Hunt Jackson. New York, Appleton, 1939.

ANNA MARY WELLS
Dear Preceptor; the Life & Times of Thomas Wentworth Higginson. Boston, Houghton Mifflin, 1963.

Photograph of Helen Hunt Jackson, courtesy of Huntington Library.

278

Reminiscences of a Ranger

HORACE BELL

24

WHAT IS the best way to experience the sense of a past era? If time has stood still as in southern Portugal, then one can travel and see villages and landscapes unchanged from those of long ago. This is not true of Southern California. There, over the past century, all has been changed, so that landscape and townscape are no longer the same. Even the profile of the Sierra Madre now bears a stubble of television towers. The city was once crowned La Reina de Los Angeles; and then, as her herds multiplied, she became the Queen of the Cow Counties; and finally the automobile made her the lusty jade she is today.

To relive the past, to know how Los Angeles appeared in the 1850's and how its people lived, what would one do, where would one go? To museums to look at artifacts and dioramas, early drawings and lithographs? To libraries to read Los Angeles' earliest newspaper, the *Star*, as well as books, pamphlets, reports, diaries, letters, and printed ephemera? Both, of course; and also to Hancock Park to gaze at the tar pits from which our predecessors took the *brea* with which to calk their leaky roofs.

Literature written during the early period is not plentiful. Later accounts which look back are more likely sources. Brewer's *Up and Down California* is a good one. *Ramona* is another. What a pity Southern California never had a painter to portray the scene the way Pieter Breughel did his post-medieval time. A single canvas by him is an encyclopedia of human appearance and activity.

Fortunately there is a single book about Los Angeles and its environs in the 1850's which is the best of all sources on the period. This classic work is Major Horace Bell's *Reminiscences of a Ranger*. Because of its vigorous style, lively narrative, and range of human interest, it is unique in its portrayal of time and place, and it is also written in readable prose. As W. W. Robinson testifies in *Lawyers of Los Angeles*, Bell "wrote romantically, humorously, and with great joy of his Los Angeles;" and from the noted lawyer LeCompte Davis came the tribute, "It is the only book about early Los Angeles that will live forever."

Published in 1881, Bell's *Ranger* was one of the earliest hardbound volumes produced in Los Angeles. Book culture came late to the pueblo. Today a fine copy of the first edition is worth up to a hundred dollars. There wasn't enough cloth available to bind the volume in material of a single color, so the book is found in blue, green, and red bindings, the latter probably the scarcest and also given to fading.

The UCLA Library has a salesman's dummy bound in green cloth, gold-embossed, containing only the first 49 pages, and then a dozen order-blank pages in which to enter advance subscribers' names and addresses. This item enrolled L. C. Granger of Oroville for two copies and Catharine Borkney of the same town for one. In 1966 the Huntington Library acquired six autographed letters from Bell to Lewis Granger, dated 1870 to 1893. A search today of Oroville attics might turn up those three copies of the *Ranger*. Granger was a prominent Angeleno lawyer before his move to Butte County.

The *Ranger* got off to a running start. Its job printers, Yarnell, Caystile, and Mathes, who published the *Weekly Mirror*, predecessor of the *Times*, set the type for a favorable review in the Christmas-day issue of the latter paper. Bell himself boosted it later with a blurb in his weekly newspaper, the *Porcupine*. With pardonable pride in his offspring, he wrote,

"It is unique, fresh, sprightly, combining the grave and the gay, the sad and mirthful, history as cheery as fiction, seen from the bright side of life. 457 octavo pages; gold embossed; bound in cloth; $2.00 postpaid."

Bell was right. It *is* all of those things, and is incomparably the best of all views of local life during the 1850's. Regardless of the hyperbolic, tongue-in-cheek, rhetorical style of the frontier tall-tale, which was later brought to genius by Mark Twain in *Roughing It*, *Reminiscences of a Ranger* is essentially truthful. If not in all of the things its characters said and did, then certainly in the details of what Angelenos ate and wore, their houses, occupations, sports, and pastimes, in the ways they lived and died.

Consider, for example, Bell on the adobe house: "This writer stands by the adobe house as the coolest house, the warmest house, the cheapest house, and the most earthquake-proof house (might as well try to shake down a haystack), and the best house for fandangos that ever existed in this old city of yore so famous for her fights and fandangos. Nothing but an adobe house could have stood an old-fashioned fandango. A modern earthquake is no comparison to a California fandango, especially such as we had in those good old times in this angelic city."

Then Bell goes on to describe a fandango in the precise details of dress and behavior, distinguishing it from a *baile* or private ball, the fandango being a public affair. A typical adobe house is described even to the color (green) of its wooden shutters. "No greater libel was ever perpetrated on a comfortable house than to call one of those old models of cool comfort, one of our old first-class adobes, a mud hovel."

Who was Horace Bell? How came he to write a book both useful as reference work on the period and readable as literature? Indiana-born in 1830, Bell came to California in the gold rush, and reached Los Angeles in 1852, drawn there by the presence of an uncle, Captain Alexander Bell, a prosperous land owner who had arrived ten years earlier and married into one of the Spanish families. Young Horace was encouraged to do likewise. If he would make a local marriage, his uncle promised, he would buy his nephew the Rancho San Pasqual as a birthday present.

282

If not, his only gift to him would be a horse. Horace took the horse.

It enabled him to become a member of the Rangers, a troop of volunteer horsemen organized to wipe out banditry, personified by Joaquín Murieta. At that time, Los Angeles was the toughest town in the West, a cesspool of frontier scum. Let Bell tell it as it was:

"I have no hesitation in saying that in the years of 1851, '52, and '53, there were more desperados in Los Angeles than in any place on the Pacific coast, San Francisco with its great population not excepted. It was a fact, that all of the bad characters who had been driven from the mines had taken refuge in Los Angeles, for the reason that if forced to move further on, it was only a short ride to Mexican soil, while on the other hand all of the outlaws of the Mexican frontier made for the California gold mines, and the cut-throats of California and Mexico naturally met at Los Angeles, and at Los Angeles they fought. Knives and revolvers settled all differences, either real or imaginary. The slightest misunderstandings were settled on the spot with knife or bullet, the Mexican preferring the former at close quarters and the American the latter."

Although the pages of Bell's book run with blood, he had a gift of light and humorous touch in chronicling violence, a gift lost in our bloodier era. If the T.V. hacks discovered Bell, they could keep our little ones glued to the tube for weeks on end.

Bell left town in 1855 after being whipped in a brawl, drifted north, and eventually joined Walker's filibusters south of the border. Later he became a Union scout in the Civil War and thereafter was styled Major. He fortunately took a thrifty New England wife and came back overland to Los Angeles in 1866, arriving at the end of the great drought that had destroyed the cattle industry of Southern California and its concomitant hide trade. As a Unionist, Bell was unpopular in a town of Confederate sympathizers. He is said to have had forty street fights before the Rebs left him alone.

With his uncle's help he bought land centered at Pico and Figueroa, built a cottage thereon, and became a farmer. And also a father. He and Georgia Bell brought a total of eleven children—six girls and five boys—into the world. In 1875 Bell divided his farm into town lots and cleared $8000.

In the only biography of Bell, *Fortune Favors the Brave*, Professor Benjamin S. Harrison tells an amusing story of this real estate venture:

"During the excitement of selling the lots, the Bell family sat one noon around the dinner table with several agents who were discussing with the parents the progress of sales. Mother noticed that Virginia aged four was making a muss on the red-checkered tablecloth, playing with her knife and food. She spoke sharply, 'Jinnie, what on earth are you doing?' 'I'm cutting up my gingerbread into building lots, Mamma.' "

Today the only vestige of the Bells remaining in the region of Pico and Figueroa is Georgia Street, named for Mrs. Bell. (Incidentally this family was *not* the progenitor of the Alphonzo E. Bell family of Bel-Air fame.)

It was Mother Bell's determination to raise the family's status that led Father Bell to study law and enter the Bar by examination. Starting in 1872 he embarked on a quarter-century career in the courts of Los Angeles. His lifelong sympathy with the Californios, largely dispossessed by the Yankees, led to Bell's being known as *el abogado de los pobres*. His chief handicap as a lawyer was a low boiling-point and readiness to resort to physical violence, a heritage from his youthful and wartime experiences. Tall, handsome, and muscular, Major Bell was an eyeful, whether striding along in an Inverness cape or mounted on horseback in the gorgeous uniform of the old-time Rangers.

In later years he carried on a feud with Harry Carr, who had a long career as the *Los Angeles Times'* star columnist. When Carr made fun of Bell's cape, the Major replied, "If I want to, I'll run around town in my shirt tail."

In his book, *Los Angeles, City of Dreams*, published in 1935, Harry Carr aptly contrasts two of our classic writers. "As Helen Hunt Jackson saw the leisurely pastoral life, so Major Bell saw the little pueblo from the far end of the hotel bar. He wrote with the gusto of the third *tequila* cocktail, with Mike, the bar-keeper,

284

wiping the damp off the baize table to make room for the writing materials. *Ramona* is listening to mission bells . . . a pastoral played with plaintive flutes. *Reminiscences of a Ranger* reads as though played on a cracked piano in the back room. It is a swaggering, bawdy, delightful record of a little gringo-Mexican town. Some other author is likely to produce another *Ramona* out of faded dresses packed in trunks and yellowed diaries. But no one else will ever write another *Reminiscences of a Ranger*."

Incidentally, when Mrs. Jackson was gathering the material for *Ramona*, Major Bell drove her about in his buggy, spending so much time with that compelling woman that Mrs. Bell grew jealous. The appearance of *Ramona*, however, three years after his *Reminiscences*, did not win Bell's approval. It was too romantic, he declared.

A flair for writing had manifested itself in the mid-Fifties when Bell contributed to the *San Francisco Bulletin* and later in Mexico to a Tehuantepec newspaper. After the Civil War he wrote sketches for the *Golden Era*. When he came to write his *Reminiscences*, Bell was influenced by his three literary idols, the picaresque novels, *Gil Blas* and *Don Quixote*, and the history by Bernal Díaz of the conquest of Mexico by Cortés.

It was toward the end of the 1870's that Los Angeles began to feel the excitement of its centennial. Bell was then moved to record his times as his duty to posterity. Based on the memories of Bell's daughter, Virginia, Professor Harrison tells of the *Ranger's* inception:

"One day in 1878 he closed all the doors of the back parlor, took paper and pencil, and sat down to begin his memoirs, inspired by his guns and knives in the bookcase. As he made notes he stuck them on a long nail set in a wooden block. He had no time for writing except on Sundays. Rising at five he did much of his work before breakfast, after which he continued until dinner at two, taking time out to go with his wife to church. When the children raised their voices in the house or played outside near his windows, Mrs. Bell would whisper, 'Hush, Papa's writing the *Ranger!*' "

A reader of Bell today will have difficulty in seeking to borrow the first edition from his local library, if it is lucky enough to own a copy. It will, or should be, under lock and key as rare, valuable, and well-nigh irreplaceable. More available and less valuable is the 1927 reprint, issued at Santa Barbara by Wallace Hebberd, with a foreword by Arthur M. Ellis and woodcut illustrations by James S. Bodrero.

The 1927 edition went begging in the hard times following the 1929 crash. The unsold sheets were taken over by the Primavera Press of Los Angeles and reissued in 1933 with a new title-page by a rising young typographer named Ward Ritchie. Most local libraries will have either the 1927 or the 1933 issues.

In the mid-1960's a Los Angeles advertising firm sponsored a three-volume reprint of the *Ranger*, issued as Christmas gift books over a three-year period. Designed and with a biocritical introduction by Ward Ritchie, this edition has burlesque illustrations by Gene Holtan.

According to Ritchie there is a story that most of the edition of 1881 was destroyed in a fire, but this is doubtful since in 1904 Bell sold to Holmes Book Store on Main Street some 200 copies at less than 50 cents each. Harrison tells the story that when the bookseller priced them at a half dollar a copy, Major Bell complained to Holmes, "I've got a notion to whack you with my cane."

Bibliographical history also repeats itself. Robinson Jeffers's first book of poems, *Flagons and Apples*, likewise failed to sell out the edition, whereupon the remainder of nearly 500 copies was taken over by the same Holmes Book Store. When copies could not be sold even for 10 cents apiece, Mr. Holmes took to tossing them out free at sidewalk book auctions in order to attract bidders. In piscatorial parlance I believe this is called *chumming*. Today Jeffers's *Flagons and Apples* is at the same hundred dollar premium as Bell's *Reminiscences of a Ranger*.

In 1930 Lanier Bartlett, working in a studio next to the one Ward Ritchie and I shared in the Abbey San Encino on the west bank of the Arroyo Seco, edited a group of Bell's unpublished sketches in a posthumous volume called *On the Old West Coast; being Further Reminiscences of a Ranger*. This is not vintage

Bell. The volume does not have the coherence of the orginal *Reminiscences*. These sketches and other material now in the Huntington Library were preserved by Bell's daughter Virginia, she of the gingerbread subdivision.

I have said that Bell is good reading and good reference. It is also true that it would benefit from weeding and pruning. A surplus of hyperbole could be removed without emasculating the style; incidents relating to the Civil War and Mexico could be deleted in order to make it solely a Southern California work.

As much as I relish episodes of shooting, knifing, horsewhipping, and lynching, bull and bear and cock fights, and other instances of the violence which, the Lord spare us, are still commonplace in the Angel City, I confess to deriving more enjoyment in reading about the stagecoach race from San Pedro to Los Angeles, which marked young Bell's debut; or about the stampede of herds on the Domínguez's Rancho San Pedro, caused by a runaway horse dragging a sulky; or the accounts of fandangos and rodeos; or the lyrical narrative of the Rangers' pursuit of bandits which led them to the top of the mountain known today as Old Saddleback. I quote this latter as an example of Bell at his ringing best:

"The camp was located in the valley just above the Temescal hot springs. Entering the valley we went on a full charge up the road, and turning a bend in the road just below the hot springs, we came in sight of the burning camp fires. The game had escaped. The bandits decamped, and when quiet and silence had been restored, we could hear their retreating clatter as they went up Coldwater cañon. Pursuit was impossible at night, owing to the roughness of the mountain and mountain gorge in which the robbers had taken refuge. We accordingly made our camp, fed our mustangs from the wallets of barley furnished by the provident Smith, and while some boiled coffee in their tin cups, others, fatigued with more than sixty miles gallop, were soon quietly resting in the arms of Morpheus. With a breakfast of coffee, Mexican cheese and Jurupa hard tack, at daylight we took the trail of the retreating bandits, and followed it up Coldwater cañon, sometimes in the bed of the stream, and sometimes clambering along the brink of some frightful precipice. After an infinite amount of scrambling, danger, and hard labor, we stood on the very summit of the Temescal mountain, now by some called Santiago mountain, and called by Captain Bonneville, nearly fifty years before, San Juan mountain. The day was clear and beautiful, and we were repaid for our difficult ascent by the same view as described by Bonneville, the original American explorer, who said, 'Standing on the summit of the San Juan mountain, with my face towards the sea, I behold the great Pacific ocean with its numerous islands spread out before me, while to my left are the limitless plains of San Luis Rey, and to my right the great volcano and lava fields of San Gabriel.' . . . Resting a few minutes, we followed the trail along the ridge, bearing to the east, for several miles and then descended to the plains and by the time we were well out of the canons and foothills, the sun had gently gone to rest, and another beautiful moonlight night set in. Our poor mustangs were jaded, still we pushed on, and reached San Juan Capistrano late at night."

I mentioned the stagecoach race in 1852 from harbor to pueblo. Stagemaster was Phineas Banning, who also became a member of the Rangers. He and Bell were friends, and the *Reminiscences* has several warm references to the Port Admiral, as Banning came to be known. While on a book-buying trip in a distant city, I came upon a copy of the *Reminiscences* bearing on the half-title an inscription in old-fashioned florid calligraphy: "Presented to Capt. William Palmer of the Bark *Balaclava*, with Respects of Phineas Banning 'Admiral', San Pedro, Sept. 1883." That copy is now in the Rare Book room of the UCLA Library, and the *Balaclava* is tied up on the San Francisco waterfront as a maritime museum.

A year after the *Reminiscences* appeared, Bell founded a weekly newspaper called the *Porcupine*, dedicated to exposing the evil record of office-seekers and the corrupt doings of office-holders. He apparently did not lack for material. Publication inevitably involved the editor in turmoil, threats, and counter-attacks.

288

The *Porcupine* is exceedingly rare. Only two or three libraries, including the Los Angeles County Museum, have copies, and no complete file is known to exist. The weekly ran for nearly twenty years, first under Bell's editorship, then that of his son Charles.

I was able to peruse the Huntington Library's several score issues of the *Porcupine*, beginning with Volume 1, number 1, dated November 11, 1882. As I gently turned the brittle pages there in the calm of the San Marino oasis, I felt myself borne on the time-stream in which all men, dead, living, and yet unborn, are of one timeless generation. For it was evident from reading the old Major's crackling news reports and acidulous editorials that although we have changed the natural environment, man's social behavior is the same. The police were charged with brutality. Public officials were grafting, taxes too high. Streets were being torn up. Freight trains were blocking traffic. Buildings were being erected without proper earthquake safeguards. Water supply and sewage disposal were inadequate. Postal service was deteriorating. Gambling, drinking, and prostitution were flourishing under official protection. The Indians were wiped out, the Mexicans discriminated against, children and dumb animals abused.

All through his stormy life, Horace Bell fought for the underdog and minority groups. His particular target was the prominent capitalist, E. J. "Lucky" Baldwin, into whom the *Porcupine* shot many a quill. Baldwin did not fail to respond, and it was probably he who employed an anonymous hack to write a scurrilous pamphlet on Bell which concludes as follows:

"To summarize: Bell has been a failure as a miner, soldier, farmer, lawyer, and journalist. He was never able to provide for his family till the *Porcupine* was started, and charitable neighbors who supplied his children with clothes and provisions, have come in for their share of abuse. As a blackmailer, murderer, thief, house-burner, snake-hunter, and a free-lance journalist, as a defamer of the dead, as a vituperator of good men and innocent women, he has been an eminent success. Over the grave of this fine sample of total depravity the record, if truthful, will be chiseled:

HIC JACET

HORACE BELL

who was a failure in every honorable calling in life, but was successful in everything corrupt, mean, and dishonorable."

Bell also crossed pens with General Harrison Gray Otis, the monarch of the *Los Angeles Times*, who wrote prophetically:

"The *Porcupine* made its first appearance last Saturday. True to its nature each quill was on end and deuced sharp. Somebody will be looking for the editor with a shotgun if he doesn't smooth them down a bit."

Bell managed nevertheless to survive his enemies and to live on well into the 20th century. After the death of his first wife, he made an equally happy marriage with Emily Jane Culver, the widow of the millionaire founder of the boys school in Indiana which became the Culver Military Academy. His final years were eased thereby, and he was a sedate member of Immanuel Presbyterian church, a far cry from the wild youth who raised hell in the pueblo of 1852.

The old warrior kept his salty wit to the end. In old age he declared to his daughter Virginia, "I want all you children to know that I have become a Christian. I have seen the light. Your mother's prayers have been answered. And I can truly say that I love everybody. I even love Harrison Gray Otis."

Bell died at Livermore in 1918 at the ripe age of 88. Together with his first wife, Georgia, and four of his daughters, including the devoted Virginia who lived on into her 90's, he is buried in Rosedale Cemetery on Washington Boulevard in Los Angeles, the place of which he once wrote, "Children, someday Los Angeles will be a great city. I will not live to see it, but you will, dears. And it will extend from the mountains to the sea."

For once the old Ranger was guilty of an understatement.

Reading List

HORACE BELL (1830-1918)
Reminiscences of a Ranger. Los Angeles, Yarnell, Caystile, & Mathes, 1881; Santa Barbara, Wallace Hebberd, 1927; Los Angeles, Primavera Press, 1933; Los Angeles, Advertisers Composition Co., 1965-67. 3 vols. Introduction by Ward Ritchie.
On the Old West Coast; Being Further Reminiscences of a Ranger, edited by Lanier Bartlett. New York, Morrow, 1930.

BENJAMIN S. HARRISON
Fortune Favors the Brave; the Life & Times of Horace Bell. Los Ángeles, Ward Ritchie Press, 1953.

W. W. ROBINSON
Lawyers of Los Angeles. Los Angeles, Ward Ritchie Press, 1959.

Photograph of Major Horace Bell, courtesy of Westways.

25

CHARLES F. LUMMIS's classic achievement in Californiana was not a book. His more than a dozen volumes were about other parts of the Southwest, mainly New Mexico. In Los Angeles he edited a monthly magazine, first called *Land of Sunshine*, and later *Out West*. He assumed the editorship soon after its founding in 1894, and then for the next decade he utterly dominated it. There is no better example in American literature, unless it be Mencken's *American Mercury*, of a periodical being the projected image of a single man.

Although Lummis wrote a large part of each issue, in the form of an editorial section called "In the Lion's Den," and book reviews headed "That Which is Written," as well as articles, poems, and travel features, the magazine's contents also included the best writers of its time and place. Lummis regarded his publication as the descendant of the *Overland Monthly* as edited by Bret Harte.

His *Land of Sunshine* was vital, endowed with its editor's energy and gusto. His prose was immensely readable. The magazine was also representative of the culture of its time, featuring history, literature, science, art, education, archaeology, ethnology, and local and national affairs. Lummis was discriminating, and chose for its contributors the leading contemporary writers and artists. He did not mistake entertainment, amusements, and sports for culture, and gave no space to those ephemera which dominate our later age. Although authoritative, sometimes scholarly, the style was popular without being condescending, the appeal was to an intellectual readership.

Until I came to this periodical, my rereading of California classics did not threaten my eyesight. Then suddenly I was faced with perusing nearly a hundred and fifty monthly issues. How did I proceed? Not in a public or university library, although files are to be found in the chief southland collections. I preferred to work in my own preserve of printed matter, sometimes early, sometimes late.

I was fortunate in acquiring an unbound set of the Lummis years, though somewhat imperfect from having been stored in a leaky garage. Still it was mostly legible, and read straight through it I did, in shady patio or by lamplight in the hours when the only sounds were those of the surf.

For one whose boyhood came before World War I, the reading was a nostalgic experience, a journey back in time to a landscape gone and to a vanished culture. Lummis and his contemporary boosters were all too successful. So attractive did they make local living that the population grew by thousands, then millions. The railroad was superseded by automobile and airplane, bringing urbanized congestion, air pollution and other ills coming from too many people in too small a place.

The individualism preached by Lummis and his generation was superseded by group activity. Today Southern California is one vast interlocking, interdependent, mobile community. An unbeholden spokesman such as Lummis with an independent magazine like *Land of Sunshine*, is unlikely, even inconceivable. Yet thanks to him and his legacy, we can experience a vanished age by reading about it in the pages of this unusual periodical. One of the reprint houses should fascimile the Lummis years.

The best introduction to *Land of Sunshine* is a book published by the Huntington Library, *Charles F. Lummis, Editor of the Southwest*, originally a doctoral dissertation at UCLA by Edwin R. Bingham, well proportioned and readable as many academic exercises are not, for the reason that it was written under the direction of a literary stylist, John Walton Caughey.

Charles F. Lummis's life and works are inseparable. He lived his writing, wrote his life. Flamboyant, egocentric, and abnormally vain, he was nevertheless interested in and helpful to others, quick to recognize talent and give praise.

Born in 1859, Lummis came out of New England with the blood of a crusader. His minister father started him early on Latin, Greek, and Hebrew; he was educated at Harvard in the class of 1881. There he was influenced by Professor Charles Eliot Norton, a noted teacher of art history and folklore. He married a medical student and moved to Ohio, where her family owned a newspaper. In Chillicothe he became a journalist. When they decided to emigrate to Southern California, he sent his family by train, while he proceeded on foot. Taking four months for the journey, he arrived at Los Angeles in 1885.

Before leaving Ohio he arranged with Harrison Gray Otis, publisher of the newly founded *Los Angeles Times*, to send in reports of his progress. They appeared under the byline "Lum." (Incidentally, *don't* call him "Loomis"; the "u" in Lummis is short.) Otis went out to meet Lum at Mission San Gabriel, and together on foot they made a triumphant entry into the city. Later he gathered the reports into his first travel book, *A Tramp Across the Continent*.

Lummis's overland journey was not devoid of dramatic incident, although I believe that much of the drama was added in the writing. The book is too strident to rank with the quiet masterpieces of J. Smeaton Chase and Robert Louis Stevenson. His crossing of the Mojave Desert provided background for a later evaluation of Manly's *Death Valley in '49*. Like those before him who had their first view of Southern California from the summit of Cajon Pass, Lummis was ecstatic on seeing the Promised Land.

Lummis's lifelong tendency to brag on his physique probably came from his small stature. He stood only five feet six inches and weighed between 130 and 140 pounds. There was no doubt that he was tough and strong, and yet his physical insignificance seemingly led him to overcompensate by driving himself to the point of breakdown and blindness. To add to his troubles was an affinity for romantic attachments, with the inevitable emotional wear and tear. He was thrice married. His physical breakdowns usually coincided with emotional crises, suggesting that his illnesses were largely psychosomatic.

The relationship with Otis led to Lummis's appointment as city editor of the *Times*, and in that capacity he worked himself nearly to death. To recover from partial paralysis he went to live for four years in New Mexico at Isleta Pueblo, down river from Albuquerque. Even if he had contributed nothing to Southern California culture, Lummis would be remembered for what he did for New Mexico. His *The Land of Poco Tiempo* revised as *Mesa, Cañon, and Pueblo* remain among the best works about that region.

Lummis immersed himself in the contemporary and historical aspects of a land. Spanish became his second language to the degree that his diary was written in a mixture of it and English. His scholarship led him to work with source materials. As a protegé of Adolph Bandelier he accompanied the Swiss archaeologist on field trips in New Mexico and South America. Long before Bolton's work, Lummis wrote of Anza, "His was one of the best managed expeditions ever made on this continent."

According to Lummis, it was he who first coined the phrase See America First and the generic term The Southwest. By Southwest he meant California, Arizona, New Mexico, and "further patches." His writing did more than any other to stimulate tourist travel to the region, and in recognition, the Santa Fe gave him a life pass on the railroad. His favorite seat was on the steps of an open Pullman car vestibule. When for safety reasons the Santa Fe closed the vestibules, Lummis protested, saying that if a man's fate were to fall from an open vestibule, then let the Lord's will be done.

Lummis was also a photographer, sturdy enough to carry the bulky equipment of those days into remote places. His books and the issues of his magazine derive added interest from his own illustrations. He was also an ardent folklorist. The Southwest Museum has transcribed onto more permanent forms the hun-

dreds of fragile wax cylinders of folk songs recorded by Lummis in his travels throughout the region.

Upon regaining his health, Lummis returned to Los Angeles in 1893. He lived on the south side in a cottage near 24th street. At the same time he bought what he called his ranch, three acres on the west bank of the Arroyo Seco at what is today Avenue 43. There with the help of Indian boys from Isleta, he proceeded to build his own house of stream-bed boulders, anticipating Robinson Jeffers's Tor House by a quarter century. "Any fool can write a book," Lummis declared, "and most of them do. It takes brains to build a house." He called it El Alisal (Place of the Sycamores), and it took him and his helpers fifteen years to complete. Today it is maintained as a state monument.

El Alisal is an anachronism in the land of the mobile home, built, Lummis intended, to stand for a thousand years. Until his death in 1928, El Alisal was the city's cultural heart, a rendezvous for local and visiting writers, artists, and celebrities, hosted by the aging but lively Don Carlos, clad in corduroys, sash, bandana headband and sandals, garb that he wore even when he travelled to the East and was received at the White House.

Land of Sunshine was founded as a booster monthly by Charles D. Willard, secretary of the Los Angeles Chamber of Commerce. Lummis became its editor in January 1895, and it soon bore his mark. For his first issue he wrote the lead article, "The Spanish American Face," and illustrated it with his photographs of a couple of beauties. It was characterized by such lyrical passages as, "That perfect brown is so transparent, so fine, so soft, so richly warmed with the very dawn of a flush, as no other cheek that is worn by woman. No other complexion so lends itself to the painter's canvas. Nor would I precisely advise the loveliest of my countrywomen to lay her cheek to one of perfect Andalusian brown."

With succeeding issues, the magazine's contents became richer and more varied. Format was changed from small quarto to octavo, with a cover design featuring the California mountain lion by Gutzon Borglum, one of the several young artists championed by Lummis. Others included Ed Borein, the cowboy artist, and Maynard Dixon who became one of the best of all western painters.

Lummis had nearly unerring taste for originality, quality, and performance. *Ramona* he judged as *the* California classic, Mark Twain as the greatest of all western writers. Bret Harte, Robert Louis Stevenson, and John Muir were given high rating. Nor did he overlook the early efforts of Eugene Manlove Rhodes, Jack London, Mary Austin, and Frank Norris. He picked *McTeague* and *The Octopus* as Norris's masterpieces, and lamented his early death.

His criticism of Jack London was for the young writer's inaccurate portrayal of Alaskan Indians. After first hailing Edwin Markham's poem, "The Man with the Hoe," he then gave the poet hell for quitting California for New York. "I have never known writer or artist that flocked to New York after being 'discovered' but paid for it. I never knew one whose work did not thereby show a shade of falling off in sincerity, power, and impulse." I have no doubt that if Lummis had lived until the 1940's, he would have likewise scolded Steinbeck who quit California after *The Grapes of Wrath*.

Although I lack evidence of what Lummis thought of Robinson Jeffers, we do find Jeffers's early poem, "Death Valley," in the May 1907 issue of *Out West*.

Lummis had no use for George Wharton James, his only rival as a horn-tooter. Their lives and works were remarkably similar. They came to Southern California in the 1880's, suffered woman trouble, and sought refuge in Arizona and New Mexico. Both were unconventional individualists, prolific writers, and spokesmen for Indian rights and Mission preservation. James succeeded Lummis as editor of *Out West*, although he lacked his predecessor's forceful style. Lummis was more cosmopolitan, intellectual, and polemical. As a onetime Methodist minister, James was a sentimental Christian idealist who practiced non-violence and passive resistance.

When Lummis mauled James in "The Lion's Den" for having appropriated a scientist's account of a Navajo Fire Dance, he gave his vitriolic editorial the Bret Harteian heading, "Untruthful

James." James did not retaliate, even when Lummis continued to hound him. Then in 1912, James wrote for the *National Magazine* a "profile" of Lummis which is one of the best tributes ever paid to the cocky Don Carlos. After that he eased off on his attacks on James.

Lummis gradually widened the magazine's scope to include the entire West. To be local in color yet broad in sympathy was his intent. Central and Northern California were not overlooked. An essay by Charles H. Shinn, a Berkeley faculty scientist, called "Northern California on Horseback," concluded with these prophetic words, "Often on these long journeys I have thought of Southern California's close-knit colonies, and have wondered how many years must pass before such colonies took possession of the rich valleys and warm foothills of this great, unknown northland."

Lummis recognized the importance of the young universities at Berkeley and Stanford, and published articles by their presidents, Benjamin Ide Wheeler and David Starr Jordan. He gave coverage to the San Francisco disaster of April 1906, including an eye-witness report by Mary Austin. He also offered a job to poet Ina Coolbrith who lost everything in the fire save her two cats.

Lummis led campaigns to restore the Missions, save the redwoods, and protect the Indians whose plight was first exposed by Helen Hunt Jackson. Above all, he was against Imperialism. In "The Lion's Den" he condemned both the Spanish American and the Boer wars. To write on conservation and reclamation, Lummis enlisted William E. Smythe, author of *The Conquest of Arid America*, whose monthly feature, "The 20th Century West," has pertinence to this day.

The conscience-voice of the magazine was heard loudest in "The Lion's Den." Lummis was a fearless opponent of injustice, graft, and tastelessness. His would be a strong arm today in the fight against smog and the destruction of our natural environment. It is poignant to read what he wrote after the assassination of President William McKinley and of the necessity of having a Vice President equal to the succession. In his time the nation's good fortune was in the successor's being Theodore Roosevelt, Lummis's Harvard contemporary and kindred spirit. They met in Washington, at the Grand Canyon, and in Los Angeles. "Leave it alone," Lummis reported Roosevelt saying of the Grand Canyon, "you cannot improve on it. Don't let them skin this wonderful country, as they will try to do." "They" are still trying.

As a book reviewer, Lummis ranged through current publishing, book and periodical, not merely western material. He relished nailing writers on factual errors. In reviewing Hamlin Garland's latest book, Lummis chided him for confusing a rattlesnake's tongue with its fangs and the publisher's proof reader for spelling it "broncho." ("Bronco is a Spanish word and not a Greek sister to his bronchial tubes.")

As well as being a landscape photographer, Lummis took revealing portraits of people, including John Muir, William Keith, Charles and Louise Keeler, David Starr Jordan, Jessie Benton Frémont, Frederick Webb Hodge, Frank Norris, and Mary Austin.

Throughout the Lummis files are found articles of lasting interest on the natural history of Southern California—birds, mammals, horticulture and mining, the mountains, particularly those in back of Pasadena known then as the Sierra Madre, and the offshore islands and their fauna and flora.

Several *Land of Sunshine* anthologies could be selected from these issues. They should include a few pages of the advertisements, for they are culturally revealing. At the turn of the century appear harbingers of the coming automotive revolution. In January 1901 an advertisement declares that a Milwaukee automobile will travel 10 miles on one gallon of gasoline and is good for a 50-mile trip without replenishing. In another issue we read of the board-track trestle for bicycles, following the Arroyo Seco from Pasadena to Los Angeles.

Lummis hailed the development of Henry E. Huntington's Pacific Electric Railway, although he characterized the railroad man's uncle, Collis P. Huntington as having "every element of greatness except a conscience."

In 1905 a change occurred in Lummis's life that marked the

beginning of the end for the magazine. He took on a job to which in the next five years he gave without stint of time and energy. He became Librarian of the Los Angeles Public Library. It was an unlikely appointment only to those who were unaware of Lummis's bookish bent, evidenced throughout the files of the magazine. For example, when Prescott, Arizona was considering a monument to Bucky O'Neill, a member of Teddy Roosevelt's Rough Riders who fell in the Cuban war, Lummis said to make it a public library. Instead, an equestrian statue of the hero stands to this day in front of the Yavapai County Courthouse.

Lummis's appointment aroused the wrath of the city's club-women, for he replaced a woman incumbent. He rode out the storm and settled in to become one of the best librarians this country has ever known. When it was said that he was not a professional librarian, he replied that the library already had fifty and that ought to be enough. Needed was a manager, not a clerk, and he cited railroads, insurance companies, and the Navy, all of which were managed by someone not a member of that profession.

Lummis's philosophy of librarianship is expressed in "Books in Harness," an article in the September 1906 issue of *Out West*. His concern was with every aspect of the library—its housing and technical equipment, its collections, reference services, staff organization and welfare. Many of his progressive ideas are applicable today. He visited other public libraries throughout the country, attended library conferences, and was recognized as a worthy colleague by leaders of the profession, particularly the men. His exciting, sensible annual reports can be profitably read today by library students, as well as by practicing librarians. There is no memorial to him in the library he led, and yet the record shows that in those few years he proved to be the most creative librarian California has ever known.

His administration was not without controversy within the library, the most amusing of which—and one which he lost—was his effort to tell the library staff what to eat. "No more pickles and candy lunches for the library girls," he declared, "they need three square meals eaten regularly." "Nonsense," they replied, "you smoke cigars and drink beer, and we're going to enjoy our pickles and candy." Being a librarian affected Lummis's colorful garb. During his tenure he wore store clothes. The most bizarre thing he did was to brand the fore-edges of valuable books with the letters LAPL. When chided, he replied, "We brand cows, don't we? Are our reference books less valuable?"

Without him in the editor's chair, the magazine's great period ended. In 1923 it merged with the *Overland Monthly*, and the combined periodical finally died in the Depression year of 1935. Even in Lummis's time the magazine's financial status was insecure. It was owned by a group of stockholders, including the editor, and it also depended upon loans from such patrons as Phoebe Apperson Hearst.

It was Lummis's compulsive nature to keep moving. His next, and what proved to be his most lasting accomplishment, was the founding of the Southwest Museum. Although not long after, he broke with the museum's trustees over his plan to establish a chain of satellite museums throughout the Southwest, his choice of location, design of building, and scope of program, endure to this day. High on the hill overlooking the Arroyo Seco and El Alisal, the golden building beckons young and old to enter without charge and see its beautiful collections of Indian arts and crafts of both Southwest and Northwest tribes.

Lummis was not a rich man. His declining years were frugal, and yet he continued to hold a Sunday salon at El Alisal. Toward the end attendants were wont to tuck a bill or two under their plates. He bequeathed El Alisal and its contents of books, artifacts, and papers to the Southwest Museum. The Historical Society of Southern California fittingly has its headquarters at El Alisal. The Society's origins were in the 1880's when Lum first hiked onto the local scene, and he was a lifelong member. Today the only disturbing sound comes from the Pasadena Freeway, which roars by just over the fence from the garden of southwestern natives, bearing an endless flow of the ubiquitous automobile, at once our destroyer and creator.

I went there one day last fall to commune with Don Carlos's spirit, and then I trudged up the hill to the Southwest Museum.

302

Lummis was criticized for founding it on a point of difficult access; and yet this was central in his philosophy, that the best things should be attained only by effort.

After a visit with Director Carl Dentzel, a man in the vigorous tradition of Charles F. Lummis, I settled in with the help of the devoted library staff to pore through Lummis's papers, diaries, correspondence, and scrapbooks. One of the first items encountered was a letter written in 1904 by a young Texas history instructor named Bolton, asking for permission to reproduce illustrations from *Land of Sunshine* in a proposed *Source Reader in Texas History*.

Later I climbed the caracole staircase designed by Lummis, to the top of the Museum tower, and gazed as far as the opaque atmosphere would permit. With me was Professor Dudley Gordon, a man of Lummis's build. On gala occasions at El Alisal he wears the green corduroy suit which was Lum's favorite outfit. His biography of Lummis awaits publication.

A man should be judged by his best. Lummis's best was better than most. He lived hard, fought valiantly, and met death bravely. Attacked by cancer, he wrote to Gene Rhodes a year before he died, "I am perfectly happy and resigned. I am glad I have had all I have had, and am bound to do all I can in what elbow room is left." He managed to complete a final book of poems, *A Bronco Pegasus*, and to see one finished copy before he died.

His funeral was held at El Alisal on the day after Thanksgiving, 1928. José Jarias's orchestra played "Adíos, Adíos, Amores," and Joseph Scott spoke an eloquent eulogy. After cremation, Lummis's ashes were placed in the stone walls of the house he built, even as Robinson Jeffers's were strewn at the site of his granite abode. John Steven McGroarty, the poet of the green Verdugo Hills, wrote, "The folk loitering on the high ramparts of heaven would have seen a little old fellow arrayed in corduroy, a red sash around his waist, a soft shirt and collar, and red cravat and a cowboy Stetson banded with leather on his head, a little old fellow with a face tanned by sun and wind . . ."

It is true, he was a little old fellow; he was also a mighty one.

303

Reading List

CHARLES F. LUMMIS (1859-1928)
Land of Sunshine—Out West. Edited solely by C. F. L. from January 1895 to February 1903, and with a co-editor until November 1909. *A Tramp Across the Continent.* New York, Scribner, 1892; Albuquerque, Calvin Horn, 1969. Facsimile of 1st edition, with introduction by Dudley Gordon.

EDWIN R. BINGHAM
Charles F. Lummis, Editor of the Southwest. San Marino, Huntington Library, 1955.

W. W. ROBINSON
The Story of the Southwest Museum. Los Angeles, Ward Ritchie Press, 1960.

Photograph of Charles F. Lummis, courtesy of Southwest Museum.

Boy on Horseback

LINCOLN STEFFENS

26

LINCOLN STEFFENS, born at San Francisco in 1866 and died at Carmel seventy years later, was celebrated after the turn of the century as one of the great muckrakers. He became an internationally famed journalist-reformer, and later a propagandist for the new Soviet state. "I have seen the future," he said, "and it works." His books are an example of how Time the winnower does his work. A generation after Steffens' death, most of his writing has been dated by the swiftness with which history is made in our time.

His *The Shame of the Cities* written in 1904 when he was editor of *McClure's* magazine to expose corruption in New York, Chicago, Minneapolis, St. Louis, Pittsburgh, Detroit and other boss-ridden cities, is read today mostly by students of sociology and political science. "Muckraker," a word coined in 1906 by Theodore Roosevelt in an allusion to *Pilgrim's Progress*, is no longer a familiar word, though in some cities the layers of muck lie deeper than ever.

Steffens' *Autobiography*, a best-seller during the Depression, is also dated because of its emphasis on current events. It too will probably be read more as historical sociology than as literature. And yet in its opening chapters, which recount Steffens' growing up in Sacramento and which were published as a separate book

305

called *Boy on Horseback*, he achieved a little masterpiece which bids fair to be read beyond his time.

Why is this? I believe it is for the same reason that Robinson Jeffers's poetry seems to be on the way toward surviving his age. Both dealt with permanent rather than with transient things. As long as mankind survives in its present form, boyhood will be with us. The horse might become extinct, and if it does, then our horseless successors will read *Boy on Horseback* with equine nostalgia.

Let us go back to the time of this short book's origin and see what forces converged as a burning glass which focused all that Lincoln Steffens had been on the writing of these few hundred pages. Such books do not happen by chance. They are the result of changes in a writer unbeknownst to him, and which surface in the form of a book better than anything he has ever before written. If a book is to survive beyond his time, it requires substance and form, and its writer needs leisure and some kind of withdrawal if he is to transfer his deepest self into his book and thereby give it that quality of fresh readability.

I have quoted Dr. William Carlos Williams before on this point, and I do so again, for his words are supremely relevant to the writing of Lincoln Steffens' autobiography. "Much of the world's greatest writing," the New Jersey doctor-poet declared, "has waited on a removal from the world of affairs for its doing. Concentration is what a man needs to bring his mind to harvest. To drain off the good we must find quietude."

In 1925 when Steffens began the book he was fifty-eight years old, recently married to the much younger Ella Winter, and the father of his first child, the year-old Pete Stanley Steffens, who was to be their only offspring. They were living at Alassio on the Italian Riviera, that halcyon stretch of coast east of San Remo, where the sea air is perfumed by carnations and resinous pine. He had economic security gained from success in the stock market. Behind him was a lifetime of education, experience, accomplishment, and recognition.

Lincoln Steffens' education was Californian-European, beginning with public schools in Sacramento and military academy in

San Mateo, then at the University of California in Berkeley, followed by three years of philosophical studies in Germany, France, and England. During that time his father had been his "angel," supporting his son's fluctuating desires for a career as a creative writer, or a philosopher, or a politician.

Then in the autumn of 1892 the paternal "angel" folded his wings. When Lincoln Steffens' ship reached quarantine in New York harbor, he was handed a letter by his father's agent. The English language has never been more pointedly used. It read,

"My dear son, when you finished school you wanted to go to college. I sent you to Berkeley. When you got through there, you did not care to go into my business, so I sold out. You preferred to continue your studies in Berlin. I let you. After Berlin it was Heidelberg; after that Leipzig. And after the German universities you wanted to study at the French universities in Paris. I consented, and after a year with the French, you had to have half a year of the British Museum in London. All right. You had that too. By now you must know about all there is to know of the theory of life, but there's a practical side as well. It's worth knowing. I suggest that you learn it, and the way to study it, I think, is to stay in New York and hustle. Enclosed please find one hundred dollars, which should keep you till you can find a job and support yourself."

There is probably no better way for a father to determine whether his son is a man or a mouse. Young Steffens proved to be the former. "I declared that I would never ask my father for another cent," he wrote triumphantly at the end of *Boy on Horseback*, "and I didn't. The next money transaction between us was a loan I made to him."

Thus it was that necessity made Lincoln Steffens into a reporter. His *Autobiography* gives the details of his brilliant rise, culminating in his covering the Peace Conference at Versailles. It is a story of fortune and friendship, of the right man doing the right work at the right time.

By 1925 this was no longer true. The war to end wars had ended. Muckraking was out of style. The United States was riding high on the Harding-Coolidge wave of normalcy and pros-

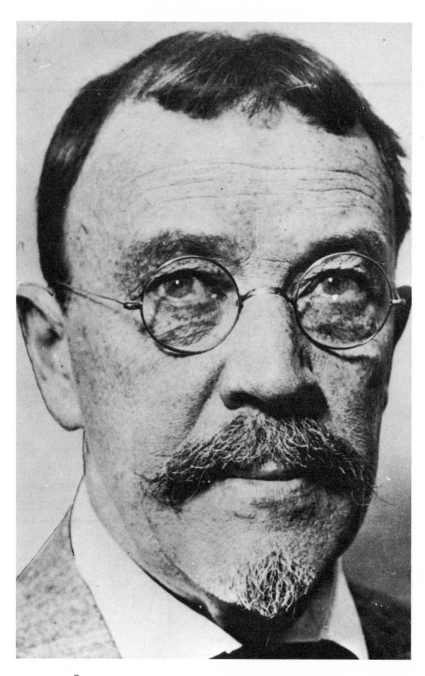

perity. Steffens found himself out of the public eye. It was a time to withdraw and take stock, and he was wise enough to recognize it.

The *Autobiography* took him five years to complete. Its success brought Lincoln Steffens back into public attention. The Depression had created a favorable climate for his skeptical style, his questioning of the classic American credo that held if you worked hard, saved money, went to church, voted with the majority, and damned the Bolsheviks, you would succeed, success being symbolized, in Hoover's words, by two cars in every garage and a chicken in every pot.

Until his death in 1936, the gadfly Steffens was a beloved devil's advocate, well known to the new generation. He couldn't be silenced or deported; he was too solidly American. Since 1902 when the state bought it, hadn't the governors of California enjoyed his boyhood home as their mansion? What could be done with a radical whose voice was gentle, who looked like a banker, and whose most subversive utterances were in the form of questions so guileless that in answering them, the prosecutor appeared ridiculous? "The strange thing about him," Clarence Darrow said at a dinner honoring Lincoln Steffens in 1931, "is his sense of humor. Everything serious that he says is a joke, and everything humorous he says is dead serious."

I am getting ahead of myself. Back to Alassio and the writing of those chapters that became *Boy on Horseback*. Their nostalgia was derived from distance in time and place. From Europe as early as 1891, Steffens had looked back on his homeland and written, "Let me get away from the grey of a German plain to the yellow and red of the Sacramento Valley. My most painful longing for home finds its cause in a yearning for our landscape."

By 1925 this longing was stronger. In another two years its power brought the Steffens family back to live in California, not in his native San Francisco or boyhood Sacramento, but rather in Carmel, that traditional sanctuary of the artist and the world weary. It was this feeling that was sublimated in those boyhood chapters, lending them intensity and impact. As a skilled writer, he knew that in their creation he had tapped a deep vein. "These first, sweet chapters," he fondly termed them.

They were written by a veteran, in control of himself and his material. This is revealed in his letters of the period. "The boy I am writing of seems to have no connection with me. I could praise him without a qualm. As a matter of fact I am showing what a goose he was, how slow my realistic intelligence was to develop. I was always naive; I am yet in some things. And I have never been disillusioned,—tragically; not so that it hurt, probably because I began to have my idealizations crushed early."

In writing of *The Journey of the Flame*—another story told of the boy when he had become an old man—I described the special vision that such a method gives to a tale. This is also true of *Boy on Horseback*. In reading it, we enter a boy's world guided by a man, and we see the world with their double sight.

Steffens answered possible criticism of his having too sophisticated a view of boyhood, when he wrote in another letter to his publisher's editor, "I am glad you don't disapprove of my mature comments here and there. They just occurred, as you guess, and I don't think myself that one minds that some of them are of today, some of earlier periods, some childish. I find that I write sometimes now as if I were the boy, naturally, I get back to that state of mind actually. Sometimes I am an outsider telling about the boy. What of it!"

Nostalgia for his homeland and the quiet certitude of life at Alassio are reflected in the pages of this book. Another element that heightened its meaning was Steffens' newfound state of fatherhood. There is no fonder father than an older man whose first child is a son. Steffens' relationship to Pete, which began a year before the autobiography was commenced, was a dominant force in the remaining decade of his life. In writing the boyhood pages, it helped him recall the relationship between him and his father. Not only to recall it, but to intensify and illuminate it, so that it became the heart of the story. Less important is his relationship with his mother and sisters. "Each of my parents thought the other didn't understand me," Steffens wrote, "and I agreed with both of them."

310

What a boyhood it was! Although his family let him run wild, they still held the end of the tether. There were limits to their permissiveness. Joseph Steffens' tolerance was short of infinite. He knew that a whip had more than one use.

Sacramento in the 1870's was a roaring river port, a trading center for ranchers, miners, shippers, and gamblers, essentially unchanged from Bret Harte's preceding decade. And there was the river. I have always believed, since seeing the world, that without a contiguous body of water—ocean, lake, or river—a city lacks soul. The mighty Sacramento, California's only fluvial body that really resembles a river, comes rolling down the great valley from its sources in the lee of Shasta, to determine the nature of the city near its mouth.

As the Mississippi was to Mark Twain's boyhood, so the Sacramento gave meaning and excitement to Lincoln Steffens' growing years. Here is how he saw it:

"Across the street beyond some uninteresting houses was another street, called Front Street, which had houses only on one side. The other side was the reeling, rolling, yellow Sacramento River—a forbidden menace and a fascinating vision. That's where the steamboats plied, the great, big, flat-bottomed cargo and passenger boats, some with side wheels, some with one great stern wheel. I did not know, I did not care, where they went. It was enough that they floated by day and whistled by night safely on that dangerous muddy flood which, if it ever got a boy in its grip, would roll him under, drown him, and then let his body come up all white and still and small, miles and miles away."

There was not only the river. Mountains owned the east. "From the Sacramento valley on a clear day," he recalled "one can see the snow-capped peaks of the Sierras, and when the young summer wheat is stretching happily in the heat of the sun, when man and animals and boys are stewing and steaming, it is good to look up through the white-hot flames at the cool blue of the mountains and let your eyes skate over the frost. All through my childhood I thirsted for those Sierras. They were a scene for day dreams and night wishes."

Yet even more than river or mountains, it was the horse that

311

dominated the boy's life, first the pony that little Lennie wanted for Christmas more than anything else in the world. "If I can't have a pony," he told his father, "give me nothing." And when his father appeared to have taken him at his word, the boy's heart nearly broke. But then the pony finally came, late because its rider had gotten drunk.

Later Lennie broke and trained a colt. We ride with him into the countryside, alone or with his pals, on adventures with bridge-tenders, battles with Chinese rice farmers, friendship with an English nobleman turned cowboy, and with a rancher's wife who had always wanted a boy like Lennie.

There is no other book in our literature that so well recreates the ambiance of central California a century ago. In it we see society changing from a gambling, mining, and ranching community, to one of farming, fruit raising, and construction, which marks the Sacramento Valley to this day.

This social milieu is secondary to the story, which is one of the boy's acting out the romance of his reading, imaginatively playing such heroic roles as that of Coeur de Lion, Byron, and Paul Revere. Then we see him outgrowing this subjective romanticism to become a realist. Credit for this growth he gives to an Englishman in San Francisco who tutored him to enter Berkeley. This man and his circle of intellectual compatriots played a part in Steffens' education akin to that of George Sterling and his group in Jack London's coming of age.

Steffens' father wanted his son to succeed to his prosperous mercantile business, or failing that, to set him up as part owner of a San Francisco newspaper. As we have seen, Steffens rejected his father's proposals and went overseas into philosophical exile. Joseph Steffens is the book's real hero, which is of course what the son intended when he came to write of his father half a century later.

After two years in Alassio, Lincoln Steffens brought his wife and son and unfinished autobiography home, first to New York, then overland to California. They wanted to settle down in a home of their own. Santa Monica was considered. Lake Tahoe proved too high for his heart. For a while they lived on the Hollister ranch at Gaviota, the home of his sister Dot, who in 1901 had married J. J. Hollister, son of the ranch's founder who was the first American to bring sheep to California. "I am working on this quiet, beautiful ranch, writing on my life . . . Life grows better and better as I live it . . . I am sure that old age is the best of life, mismanaged though it usually is. I mean to manage mine and save it, as I used to food, for the last."

Good management gave Lincoln Steffens nine more years of life. They were rich ones, settled at Carmel in the roomy wooden house called "The Getaway." There were summer trips to Europe; and after five years of writing, the autobiography was finished in France in the summer of 1930. Next he lived in Croton-on-Hudson to see it through the press, and then they came back to Carmel.

The Depression led people to question the values of the 1920's, and in this new climate Steffens regained his lost popularity, lecturing widely at community and campus forums. He was a great questioner. In Los Angeles he took the negative against Paul Jordan-Smith in a debate on Can Capitalism Survive?

Carmel was ideal soil for their growing boy, and also for the questioning father. "I may even go into politics of the place," he wrote, "and work from the outside for the schools, etc." Instead he returned to his old love, journalism, and wrote a column in *The Carmelite* and later in the *Pacific Weekly*, assuming editorship of the latter shortly before his death. He no longer had a need to travel. The world came to him for the mellow, skeptical wisdom which his widely read *Autobiography* had disseminated.

He was an old hand at outwitting the bureaucrats. A sculptor came to him for help in getting his two unlicensed Alsatians back from an overzealous dogcatcher who had impounded them. Steffens was incensed. Few dogs and certainly never any artists' dogs, had been required to be licensed in Carmel. He pondered the problem, then devised a strategy that both freed the dogs sans license yet did not cause the dogcatcher to lose face.

Steffens quickly recognized the stature of Robinson Jeffers. They met in September 1927 and began their family custom of picnicking together roundabout Carmel. ". . . it was worth a lot to meet Jeffers, who is the real thing, as his wife is too. They know what they want, and how to live and get it out of life." Anecdotes of their friendship enlivened his column. In 1928 Ella Winter edited a supplement to *The Carmelite*, devoted to Jeffers and his poetry. It remains one of the primary sources for study of the poet.

That Steffens was a skilled writer is evident in the following example of his insight and craft, speaking in a few lines volumes about the poet and his wife:

"In the smooth course of Una Jeffers' lecture on poetry to the prosaic audience of the Carmel Highlands, she forgot a word from a line she was quoting. Pausing, she appealed to her husband:

"What was the word that Yeats used, Robin?' "

" 'Tragic,' he answered, and Mrs. Jeffers repeated, 'Tragic,' and flowed on."

"Yesterday she remarked that many of her hearers had noted the incident with interest, and she asked her husband why everybody was so interested. He knew."

" 'They were all interested because they were hearing the longest address I had ever made.' "

Lincoln Steffens was ever a propagandist for his beliefs, with short patience for poets who ignored what he called the politico-economic realities of their time. Jeffers stood exempt. When Steffens remarked to him of his observation that most critics tried to fasten their own philosophy on the poet, Jeffers replied that this was true of everyone but Steffens. This puzzled Steffens. "Robin is about the only one I let go. I wonder why. Anyhow he seemed to notice my neglect or tolerance of him."

When the local paper celebrated Steffens's 68th birthday, Jeffers contributed a letter which read in part, "Dear Steff, your readers know how many pearls you gathered from the muck-heaps with that famous rake, and how much wisdom out of a foolish world; but they cannot, for instance, enjoy the ardors of a conversation between my wife and you. It is thrilling to watch you becoming ever more intellectually radical, and Una more and more instinctively Tory as the controversy develops. I listen

314

with immense enjoyment, thinking how right you both are."

It was through my work on Jeffers that I came to Lincoln Steffens' notice. When my dissertation was read by Steffens, he reviewed it in his column, concluding,

"The poet himself has not read and he will not read this book. He isn't interested in Jeffers. When I was talking to him about this thesis, he lifted his finger and hearkened. I heard a swift, short rush of twitters out in the yard.

" 'The birds hiding,' he said. 'There's a hawk soaring over us.' "

"That's what interests the prophet in his own country."

" 'The birds take to the bush when a hawk flies; the pigeons to the air, where they can dodge.' "

I returned to California in 1933 after three years of study and travel in Europe. New York and Chicago struck me as brutal, dirty places, and it was with joy that I crossed the Sierra Nevada and gained the golden valley.

Pushing on, I arrived in Carmel broke, got off the Greyhound from Monterey and stood there with suitcases and typewriter, wondering how to get the final mile to the friend's house where I had been offered lodging. I started to walk, barely able to stagger under my load, when in a typical Carmel gesture (or did he think he was impounding a drunk?), the chief of police picked me up and drove me to my destination.

Later the Jeffers took me to meet the Steffens. He saw in me one who had initially done what he had done. Now he wanted my impressions of Europe. He was an old questioner, his face deeply seamed, a listener. I was a young talker. We got along just fine.

I saw Lincoln Steffens, Ella Winter, and Pete, on visits to Carmel during the next three years. Our last meeting was on the day before he suddenly died from heart failure. It was the 9th of August, 1936.

I had known what young Athenians experienced when they were questioned by Socrates.

Lincoln Steffens was buried in the family vault at San Mateo. Life went on. In 1939 Ella Winter married Donald Ogden Stewart. They have lived for many years in London. Her autobiography, *And Not to Yield*, appeared in 1963. It is as indispensable a companion to Steffens' *Autobiography*, as she was to him.

And Pete? His father would be pleased. Pete is a journalist.

Reading List

LINCOLN STEFFENS (1866-1936)
The Shame of the Cities. New York, McClure, 1904.
Autobiography. New York, Harcourt, Brace, 1931.
Boy on Horseback. New York, Harcourt, Brace, 1935.
Lincoln Steffens Speaking. New York, Harcourt, Brace, 1936.
Letters. Edited by Ella Winter and Granville Hicks. New York, Harcourt, Brace, 1938. 2 vols.

ELLA WINTER
And Not to Yield, an Autobiography. New York, Harcourt, Brace, 1963.

Photograph of Lincoln Steffens, courtesy of Westways.

UPTON SINCLAIR

27

I HAD COME from the Library and settled down in the lounge to browse through a newly withdrawn bagful of books. A colleague in the next chair opened one eye and asked, "Well, who's your next victim?"

"Upton Sinclair," I replied.

The man opened both eyes. "You call him a classic? He was a propagandist, a glorified journalist."

"So was Defoe."

"But Upton Sinclair wrote such bad prose. How can you read him?"

"Somebody must be reading him," I countered. "Look at these books. They've all been rebound."

"Not today's students. Rhetoric has replaced reading."

On the way to my car, I joined a ring of students on the grass. "Anybody here read Upton Sinclair?" I asked.

"Who's he?"

"The author of *The Jungle*."

"I thought Walt Disney wrote it," one student said.

"You mean Kipling," objected another.

"Both wrong," I said. "Upton Sinclair was the first Ralph Nader. His novel cleaned up the meat-packing industry and led to the passage of the first Pure Food Act."

"When was that?" they asked.

"In 1906."

"Old stuff—obsolete and irrelevant. What position does he take on Southeast Asia, on air pollution, on things that really matter?"

"He's dead." I explained. "He died two years ago."

"The earth belongs to the living," a petite student pronounced. "We no longer read dead authors. Ours is a now bag."

With that I took my then bag and left the charmed circle.

Driving home, I pondered the two encounters. Is Upton Sinclair both unreadable and irrelevant? I would seek my own answers.

After much reading, I can say that Sinclair's place is secure in my pantheon of California classics. In spite of marks against him for pedestrian prose, tedious doctrine, and an inconsistent stand on pacifism, he merits entry by virtue of his vitality, his power of creative renewal, and his abiding passion for social justice. His was an unwavering conviction that the latter can be achieved and maintained only through the democratic process.

In the beginning, Sinclair's peers—Jack London, Sinclair Lewis, Ernest Hemingway, John Steinbeck—rivaled him in their productivity, but they lacked staying power; one after another they burned out. At age sixty with several score books written, Upton Sinclair undertook his most ambitious work, the Lanny Budd series of world historical novels that took a decade to write and required ten volumes to encompass four million words.

I know that sheer bulk does not make a classic, although it is true that the world's greatest novelists—Balzac, Dickens, Tolstoy—are also the bulkiest. Bulk must be lightened by spirit and animated by sympathy. Strength tempered by compassion outweighs style alone. Yet my colleague was partly right. Upton Sinclair's prose is often heavy-footed, over-earnest; and yet at his best, a zealous imagination fired his language to incandescence. These outbursts, plus a native story-telling gift and narrative drive, carry the reader through tract-like passages of moralizing.

Not only readers of English. Upton Sinclair is one of the most widely translated American writers of all time. As long ago as 1938, a bibliography listed translations into forty-seven languages in thirty-nine countries. The ensuing Lanny Budd series swelled the statistics.

Sinclair was prone to boast of his bulkiness. He was given to citing favorable opinions of his books by Einstein, Shaw, and Churchill. In his old age he compiled a volume of his correspondence from famous people, called *My Lifetime in Letters*. Rejection by academic critics never ceased to rankle in him; this was his way of proving them wrong.

Although he lived in Southern California—Pasadena and Monrovia—from 1916 until shortly before his death in 1968 in a New Jersey nursing home, two months past his 90th birthday, most of his writing is not specifically about California. Ideas interested him more than locale. He did not have Raymond Chandler's poetic view of prosaic things. He lacked the gift of metaphor. Language to Sinclair was primarily an instrument for changing society.

In *Oil!* Upton Sinclair refined a novel of high California octane. As well as a social document of Southern California in the 'teens and 'twenties, it is a human tale of narrative power that sweeps the reader along through more than five hundred pages. His prose may resemble the Big Muddy, but it flows, it carries the reader with it.

In surveying the long, controversial, and prolific career of this writer, we see the wide plain of his ninety books to be dominated by three creative peaks. First *The Jungle* in 1906, then *Oil!* in 1927, and finally the Lanny Budd decalogue of 1940-49. These times of massive upthrust were the result of Sinclair's creative imagination erupting. Or to put it differently, certain events fired the rockets that launched him into high orbit.

The lesson to be learned by aspiring writers from these phenomena is that when they occurred, Sinclair was prepared to take advantage of and to control them. His response was disciplined and fruitful. He left no unfinished work. His career is a classic case-study of a writer both born and made. Whatever judgment we pass on the quality of his prose, we recognize him as a good craftsman. What he set out to do, he did.

Upton Sinclair was marked by genius, and he knew it. In his

319

Autobiography written at eighty-four, he tells of an early awareness of having been given extraordinary gifts, of realizing that
he was in the hands of a force outside himself. At the same time,
he had the strength and the stamina to control and direct this
force.

Critics called him humorless. It is true that his zeal for social
justice was excessive and indomitable, and yet he was also capable of self scrutiny. "Any psychiatrist would have diagnosed me
as an advanced case of delusion of grandeur, messianic complex,
paranoia, narcissism, etc.," he cheerfully confessed. When his
mother urged him to go with the current and write what people
liked, he replied that there was something in him that drove him
to write what he believed and what other people ought to believe,
always something unpopular, something difficult.

Until his first marriage at twenty-two, he led a chaste life, but
not without a constant struggle against temptation. Instead of
warping him, Sinclair found in this a source of intensity and concentration. He was his own psychiatrist. A drunkard father led
him to a lifelong abhorrence of alcohol.

Born at Baltimore in 1878 of impoverished genteel lineage—
Wallis Warfield was a cousin—he was educated at the College of
the City of New York and Columbia University. He thought of
a legal career. He was also musical. Edward MacDowell was his
teacher. He played the violin, though never very well. His compulsion to write manifested itself in a primitive way: he sold
jokes to magazines for a dollar apiece. Then discovering that he
was uncommonly fluent, he became a pulp writer under the
pseudonyms of Ensign Clarke Fitch, U.S.N. and Lieutenant
Frederick Garrison, U.S.A. He thus earned forty dollars a week
grinding out a 30,000 word novelette every seven days.

What did this spate of writing teach him? "It taught me to
shape a story, and to hold in mind what I had thought up; so it
fostered facility. On the other hand it taught me to use exagge-
rated phrases and clichés; and this is something I have fought
against, and not always successfully."

The *Autobiography* tells of his conversion to Socialism and his activity as a pamphleteer. He was marked for life by a naive idealism, a childlike simplicity and innocence. "I write in a fine glow," he confessed, "expecting to convert my last hostile critic; and when I fail, the shock of disappointment is always as severe as ever." And yet he was never disillusioned, never became embittered. I knew him in his very old age, and I have never met a more joyous man.

Publication of Lincoln Steffens' *The Shame of the Cities* led Sinclair to criticize his fellow muckraker for not having gone far enough in condemning Big Business. It also led the two men to lifelong friendship, with Steffens ever the teaser and chider.

"In 1914," Sinclair wrote, "he came out to Croton where we had rented a little house, and spent several weekends with us. Once I took him for a tramp in the snow before he had had his coffee. He appealed to my wife never to let that happen again, and she promised."

In 1933, when Sinclair's book on William Fox appeared, Steffens wrote him, "Dear Upton, you are a dear. Always looking for yourself in other men; and seeing what you look for. Here you are finding a prophet, a leader, and showman in William Fox. Well, he and I know that it's you who are the showman, leader, and prophet. You, Upton, not Fox. But I do love you and your size and your faith and,—and all that; as I love all your fiction."

In reviewing Steffens' *Autobiography* and Sinclair's *American Outpost*, Edmund Wilson contrasted the one's skepticism with the other's certainty. "Sinclair ends by inspiring us with respect," he concluded. "A fundamental earnestness and sweetness take the curse off his attitude of moral superiority; a devotion to values beyond his own interests outweighs his egoism."

Sinclair's zeal for Labor led him in 1904 to visit Chicago, where the stockyard workers were on strike. He went with a publisher's advance to write a novel about the strike, as thirty years later John Steinbeck returned to Salinas to transmute the lettuce workers' strike into the novel called *In Dubious Battle*.

For two months the young writer haunted the stockyards, slaughter houses, and packing plants. "I went about white-faced and thin, partly from undernourishment, partly from horror."

He called on Jane Addams at Hull House, and his trying to convert her to Socialism led her to remark that here was a young man who had a great deal to learn.

He came upon the characters for his novel by seeing a Lithuanian wedding party entering the back room of a saloon. "I stopped to watch, and as they seemed hospitable, I slipped into the room and stood against the wall. I watched them, fitted them into my story, and began to write the scene in my mind, going over it and over, as was my custom, fixing it fast. I went away to supper, and came back again, and stayed until late at night, sitting in a chair against the wall, not talking to anyone, just watching, imagining, and engraving the details on my mind. It was two months before I got settled at home and first put pen to paper; but the story stayed, and I wrote down whole paragraphs, whole pages, exactly as I had memorized them."

The Jungle brought Upton Sinclair instant fame. "I aimed at the public's heart," he said, "and by accident I hit them in the stomach." It led to the speedy passage of the pioneer Pure Food Act. With *Uncle Tom's Cabin* and *The Grapes of Wrath*, it is a landmark in American literature. And yet it came into print only after five publishers had turned it down and Sinclair had issued it himself. Jack London fired a salute in its praise, saying, "It is alive and warm. It is brutal with life. It is written of sweat and blood, and groans and tears." The eminent Walter H. Page of Doubleday, Page and Co. finally assumed publication of *The Jungle* and gave it widespread dissemination.

President Theodore Roosevelt became its champion. He summoned Sinclair to the White House. This only inflamed the writer's zeal for Socialism. It wasn't long before Roosevelt was to protest, "Tell Sinclair to go home and let me run the country for a while."

With money earned by *The Jungle*, Sinclair founded a New Jersey cooperative called Helicon Home Colony. A lad named Sinclair Lewis worked there as a chore-boy. Fire destroyed Helicon Hall. Sinclair went away to recover, went all the way west to Carmel. There Lincoln Steffens wrote to him from Boston, "You are in my state, you know. California, the most beautiful kept lady in the Union, and you are in a beautiful place in that beautiful state." Steffens urged him to go on to Sacramento and call on his parents and see the old family mansion.

"I did not visit Sacramento until a quarter of a century later," Sinclair wrote afterward, "when I was the Democratic Party's candidate for Governor. The Steffens mansion had become the official residence of the Governor. I climbed, as I remember, four tall flights of stairs, and I said, 'God save me from having to live here.' My request was kindly granted."

It was poet George Sterling's chronic drunkenness that led Sinclair to quit Carmel and return east.

After eleven years of marriage and one son, David, Sinclair divorced his wife for unfaithfulness. With his second wife, Mary Craig Kimbrough, he returned to California in 1916. They sought warmth. Coronado proved too cold. "We decided we wanted to get away from ocean winds; and I had met a tennis professional who lived in Pasadena and who assured me I would find plenty of tennis there. So we made the move and found ourselves a brown-painted, two-story house on Sunset Avenue [overlooking the Arroyo Seco], a remote part of town. It was covered with a huge vine of red roses, and roses were as important to Craig as tennis was to me."

Tennis was Sinclair's way of expending the energy that overflowed his writing. He was a crack player. I know, for I saw him play against my father at the Live Oaks Tennis Club in South Pasadena. My job was to chase balls driven out of the court. I can see them both in their Sunday white ducks, dripping sweat. I did a bit of running too.

I also remember my father, a staunch Republican, saying to my mother, "That Mr. Sinclair plays to win. I wish he had a better eye for the base line."

During his first ten years in Southern California, Upton Sinclair pursued an unpopular way as a Socialist writer and supporter of organized labor. He was disliked by the ruling establishment, especially Harry Chandler's *Los Angeles Times*. The bombing of the *Times* building in 1910 was still a bitter memory. In 1923 Sinclair and friends were jailed, under the since repealed

Criminal Syndicalism Act for reading aloud in public from the Bill of Rights.

All the while Sinclair was unknowingly approaching the second creative peak of his career, the conception and writing of *Oil!* Neither a foreword to a paperback edition of the novel, nor his *Autobiography*, tells as much about the writing of the book as does Craig in her autobiography, *Southern Belle*. She is specific. The book came from her having owned several lots on Signal Hill before the big strike. As drilling approached her land, she and her husband made trips to the area to join with neighboring lot owners in dealing with would-be lessors. "Here were a score of 'little people' suddenly seized by the vision of becoming 'big people,' driven half-crazy with a mixture of greed and fear."

The Sinclairs made half a dozen trips to Long Beach, and each time she would apologize for dragging him away from his writing. And then she noticed that he had a notebook with him, in which he was making a pencil smoke. "On the way home I said, 'What's this—are you going to write about it?"

" 'Gosh!' he said, his favorite expletive. 'Don't you see what we've got here? Human nature laid bare! Competition *in excelsis!* The whole industry—free, gratis, for nothing! How could I pass it up?' "

She went on to describe how the fire spread. As it did with *Ramona* and *The Grapes of Wrath*, the novel consumed its author in a year-long, creative obsession. Sinclair interviewed oil-men, lawyers, workers; he watched drilling, gushers and fires, read books and briefs. And then he wrote—a gusher of words, Craig called it, pouring from a deep source.

It was not only a story of oil in Southern California; he widened it to include university life, Hollywood, religious cults, labor strife, the corruption of public officials; and even wider to treat of World War I, the Russian Revolution, and the Harding-Fall-Doheny scandal. *Oil!* is the largest scale of all Californian novels. Readers will identify many of the local citizenry—educators, publishers, oil men, movie stars, evangelists. They are not caricatured; merely drawn from life, revealing themselves by their own actions. As well as for its human story of Bunny Ross and his father, beginning with boyhood to the death of the parent and tracing Bunny's awakening social consciousness, *Oil!* is to be read as a social document.

Oil! is Sinclair's most sustained and best writing. Those who believe that he wrote only pedestrian prose should read those pages describing the bringing in of a gusher, or the fighting an oil well fire, or his vision of the Signal Hill field at night—"it looks like Fairyland but is a Slaughterhouse." In such passages he achieved a prose of powerful fidelity.

Sinclair sent a copy of the book to Gertrude Atherton. "I had a lot of extra work to polish off after I finished my novel," she replied, "but I have got round to *Oil!* at last. I find it extremely interesting and no doubt it will be absorbing later on; the signs are all there. I doubt if anyone else could have written it but Balzac."

Oil! was banned in Boston for sexual not political reasons. The passages objected to make pallid reading today. With his flair for publicity, Sinclair had several hundred copies printed in which the offending pages bore a superimposed black fig leaf. Wearing an advertising sandwich board in the shape of a fig leaf, he proceeded to sell the Fig Leaf edition on the streets of Boston. The chief of police summoned Sinclair, and said that what had shocked him the most was a passage about birth control.

"I recall the soft voice of the old chief pleading," Sinclair recalled, " 'Now surely, Mr. Sinclair, nobody should write a thing like that.' I told him I earnestly wished that someone had done me that favour when I was young. I believed in birth control and practiced it, and I am sure that the salvation of the human race will depend on it—and soon."

Today the Fig Leaf edition of *Oil!* brings up to $500 in the rare book market.

In 1934 Upton Sinclair scared a majority of California voters into defeating him as the gubernatorial candidate. Their fright was escalated by a massive billboard campaign into which the other candidate's backers poured large sums of money. Sinclair was quoted out of context, so that he appeared to be an atheistic revolutionary, an advocate of free love and the nationalization of children. Today, a generation later, most of his Epic platform (End Poverty in California) is state and national law. He was also ridiculed as an amateur politician who, if elected, would wreck the state's economy.

A hero in defeat, he came back with a best-selling pamphlet, *I, Candidate for Governor, and How I Got Licked,* and then embarked on a nationwide lecture tour. The truth is he was profoundly relieved to have lost the election. He was above all a writer.

In 1938 the creative pressure had built up to the point where it again sent him into orbit. When the first volume of the Lanny Budd series, *World's End,* was the Literary Guild choice for July 1940, the Guild's magazine, *Wings,* included a statement by the author, telling how the book had been triggered by the Munich crisis of 1938. "This is the end, the end of our world," Sinclair declared. He went on to tell of the book's creation, in words reminiscent of Helen Hunt Jackson's describing the writing of *Ramona:*

"I was walking up and down in my garden one night, and something happened; a spring was touched, a button pressed— anyhow, a novel came rolling into the field of my mental vision; a whole series of events, with the emotions that accompanied them, a string of characters, good and bad, old and young, rich and poor. I have had that happen to me before, but never with such force, such mass and persistence. There was no resisting it, and I didn't try. I spent the next thirty-six hours in a state of absorption. I slept little, but lay in bed and 'saw' that theme; I ate little and talked little—I have a kind and long-suffering wife, and when I tell her what is happening to me she lets it happen. I trod the garden path hard under my feet, and filled sheets of paper with notes of characters, places, events—the whole panorama of *World's End.* Ultimately I had nearly a hundred type-written pages of notes, a small book in themselves."

"I am one of the fortunate ones in this land of ours. I live where the sun shines most all of most days, and in the morning I can take my typewriter out into the garden. I can wear a pair of bathing trunks and a white canvas hat while I walk up and down

327

behind jasmine and rose hedges with the people of my books as they live their adventures and say their say. I suppose a psychologist would describe what goes on in the mind of a novelist as controlled multiple personality. These imaginary persons are more real to me than the people I meet in the outside world, for the latter keep me guessing, whereas the former are my grown-up children; they do what they please, and while they often take me by surprise, I am able to understand them instantly."

"In a historical novel like *World's End* I cannot, of course, leave everything to my imaginary characters. I have to spend a part of my day reading books to refresh their memory as to places and events. In the evening, propped up in bed, I revise the morning's manuscript, or stroll in the garden and invite the next chapter to unroll itself. This, I take it, is the ideal life for the writer. Sticking to it, day in and day out, rarely seeing anybody or going anywhere, I can produce a thousand words a day, and at the end of a full year I have a thousand pages. It is the hardest kind of work, yet also the most delightful play."

The complete account is reprinted in the appendix to the tenth volume of the Lanny Budd series, *O Shepherd, Speak!* The third volume, *Dragon's Teeth*, won the Pulitzer Prize. His having never received the Nobel Prize irked Sinclair. He was a repeated contender. In supporting a petition of Sinclair's advocates to the Swedish Academy in 1931, G. B. Shaw concluded, "Mr. Upton Sinclair is not a Henry James: he is rather a Daniel Defoe; and though Daniel still lives in his works after two hundred years, his contemporaries put him where several respectable Americans would like to put Mr. Sinclair: in the pillory."

Craig saw to it that her husband's proliferating archives were religiously preserved. By the end of the 1950's they were an enormous accumulation of manuscripts, books, pamphlets, magazines, documents, photographs, a quarter million letters, etc. They constituted one of the most complete and valuable literary collections ever formed. The Sinclairs wisely wished the material to be kept intact. The Huntington Library passed up an opportunity to buy the collection. The reason was, Sinclair said, the institution's ultra-conservative board of trustees.

UCLA was in the Sinclair "dog-house" because of an incident in 1938 that had understandably offended the author. A prominent local doctor had offered to lend the library his Upton Sinclair collection, to be exhibited in honor of the writer's 60th birthday. The offer was declined. Whereupon the doctor's collection was presented as a gift to the Occidental College Library.

After I had become Librarian of UCLA, I had a visit in the 1950's from David A. Randall, Librarian of Indiana University's Lilly Library, an institution established by the pharmaceutical tycoon. Randall is one of the country's most imaginative and aggressive collectors. I wondered what he was doing in my territory. I soon found out. As we were chatting in my office, a long distance call came in for Randall from Needles on the Colorado River. He listened for a moment, then hung up with a chuckle. "I told them to phone me," he said, "when the moving van had crossed into Arizona. I was afraid you'd have your Highway Patrol stop it."

"What have you made off with?" I demanded.

Another chuckle, as Randall made his exit. "Uppie's eight tons, that's all."

Now that I have recovered from the shock, I really can't complain. Indiana has given tender loving care to the great collection. There it remains at Bloomington, down in the limestone country, a primary source for scholars to study the creative lifework of a Marylander become Hoosier by way of California. Words Van Wyck Brooks once wrote to Upton Sinclair constitute a fitting epitaph: "You are obviously something on a large scale that literature has to include, though you don't fit into any of the usual categories."

After forty-eight years of marriage, Sinclair lost Craig to death. The story is movingly told in his *Autobiography*. As she lay dying, Craig told him he must find a good woman to care for him, as she most lovingly had done for nearly half a century. He proceeded to do just that. In 1961 at eighty-three, he married May Hard Willis, a seventy-nine-year-old widow, the sister of the president of Scripps College.

They made a grand couple in the years that were left to them,

I dined with them not long after their marriage. It was at the Hotel del Coronado. Upton Sinclair was the main speaker at the annual conference of the California Library Association, and we were honoring him and his wife at a private dinner of the association's officers. It was a formal affair, and the trim old man was handsome in evening dress. All but one of us dined on prime rib. Sinclair ate what he had been eating twice a day for many years: a bowl of boiled rice with mashed bananas and peaches.

Seated next to him, I said, "Mr. Sinclair, I once chased tennis balls for you fifty years ago."

He laughed. "It was good exercise for us both!"

The reformer in him was still active. "My dear boy," he said, "if you want to live as long as I have and write as many books, you'll stop eating dead animals and try some of this."

Well, I didn't say I would, but I might yet—if the price of beef keeps rising.

Reading List

UPTON SINCLAIR (1878-1968)
The Jungle. New York, Doubleday, Page, 1906; New American Library, Signet Classic, with an afterword by Robert B. Downs, 1960.
Oil! New York, Boni & Liveright, 1927; New York, Washington Square Press, 1966, with a new preface by the author.
World's End. New York, Viking Press and Literary Guild, 1940.
O Shepherd, Speak! New York, Viking Press, 1949.
My Lifetime in Letters. Columbia, University of Missouri Press, 1960.
Autobiography. New York, Harcourt, Brace, 1962.

MARY CRAIG SINCLAIR
Southern Belle. New York, Crown, 1957.

Photograph of Upton Sinclair, courtesy of Lilly Library.

28

CARMEL AGAIN. During the first half of this century many of
California's creative roads led to that village on the Monterey
coast, though seldom in a straight line. No route was more cir-
cuitous than that of Harry Leon Wilson, whose serial stories in
the *Saturday Evening Post* were read with delight by millions
and made Bunker Bean, Ruggles, Merton Gill and the Montague
Girl into household names.

It was in the year 1910 when he was forty-three years old, that
the wandering Wilson came to harbor in Carmel, bought twelve
acres of wooded ocean-front and built thereon a roomy residence
he called Ocean Home. There in what is now the Carmel Highlands he lived until just before his death in 1939.

Of the many Carmel writers, Harry Leon Wilson and Robinson Jeffers remained the longest and became the most noted. No
two writers could have been more unalike. Was Wilson destined
to celebrate that coast in prose as Jeffers did in poetry? He was
not. Although not oblivious to the region's beauty, he never used
its setting in his writing. People, not places, were his passion. He
is a writer who does not illustrate the thesis that California's
landscape and literature are inseparable.

Harry Leon Wilson's life and work are classic examples of the
unpredictability of literary achievement. Up to the time when
he lived in Hollywood to gather material for a movie novel, who

could have predicted that his ultimate renown, at least in his adopted state, would be determined by *Merton of the Movies*, one of the first and still one of the best Hollywood novels?

Let me retrace the route that led from Wilson's birth and boyhood in the small town of Oregon, Illinois, to fortune, fame, and love and, finally, to the loss of much of all three. On first glance the stages of his journey are a series of non sequiturs; and yet, on looking closer, we can see a connecting thread between them.

Wilson's father was the publisher of two country newspapers. Harry was the printer's devil. As a reader he began with dime novels and graduated to Bret Harte and Mark Twain. *Roughing It* became his favorite book, partly responsible for his ultimately becoming a westerner. At seventeen he left home to work as a stenographer in the Union Pacific's Omaha office. Then his answering an ad took him to Denver as "leg man" to the regional manager of the Bancroft publishing organization. This led to a year of traveling salesmanship for the historical sets produced in H. H. Bancroft's "factory."

The year 1887 found him in California, charmed by San Francisco's setting and climate and by the Hispanic vestiges in Los Angeles. Yet California did not hold him; he was not ready to enter its stream of literature.

His wanderings took him east again, back to Omaha and another try at working for the Union Pacific. Since the Colorado year, Wilson had been selling jokes and short pieces to *Puck*, the American version of the English *Punch*. His was a literary debut similar to Upton Sinclair's. He became increasingly successful in this apprenticeship, and it finally led to his being offered a job in New York by the editor of *Puck*, the eminent Henry Cuyler Bunner.

For the rest of his life, Harry Leon Wilson was a writing man. In the good American success story tradition, he rose to succeed Bunner as editor of *Puck*. During the Gay Nineties he was one of New York's liveliest bon vivants. His first book, *Zig Zag Tales*, was a collection of pieces written for *Puck*.

A first marriage, to a Denver sweetheart, failed because of Wilson's fondness for multiple loves. He next married a divorcée, an illustrator named Rose O'Neill Latham, and went to live on her family's Ozark farm. There he wrote three moderately successful novels, notably *The Boss of Little Arcady*, the glamorized setting of which was his hometown of Oregon. Jack London once called it his favorite novel.

Then at a magazine publishers' convention, Wilson's fate led him to share a suite with the two most influential men of his life, George Horace Lorimer, editor of the *Saturday Evening Post*, and Booth Tarkington, the Hoosier writer. There followed a sharp turn in Wilson's route. Together with their wives, Wilson and Tarkington went to Italy in 1905 to share a villa on the isle of Capri. The next year in Paris they collaborated on *The Man from Home*, a play whose success on Broadway and on the road made their fortune. For five years each author received royalties of $200 a week.

From 1906 to 1909 the Wilsons lived in Paris. Five more plays were written with Tarkington. Theirs was an uneasy collaboration. "He is extremely quiet," Tarkington said of Wilson, "unless you differ with him about something unimportant."

Wilson's second wife, Rose O'Neill, was the originator of the Kewpie Doll. It is said to have made her a million dollars. Given to baby talk, she was the model for the Baby Talk Lady in Booth Tarkington's *Seventeen*. Wilson did not like her mode of speech. He told her that if she did not eschew it, he would leave her. One morning the story goes, she approached with an armful of freshly cut roses and said to her husband, " 'mell my pitty wosies." Whereupon he packed his bag and caught the first boat to New York.

He proved to be fed up with both Manhattan and marriage, although the truth seems to be that Rose found him too moody to live with. After divorce they remained lifelong friends. His two greatest thrills, Wilson once said, were coming to New York and getting out of it ten years later.

Back to the West he went, on a pack trip deep into the Canadian Rockies. Hunting and fishing filled his days. After four months he emerged from the wilderness a confirmed westerner. In San Francisco he chartered a boat and set out down the coast, deter-

333

334

mined to find his ultimate place even if it took him all the way to Chile. He didn't have that far to go. From Monterey the way led, as Jeffers's did four years later, over the pine-forested hill to Carmel.

There he fell in with the earlier bohemians, notably Jack London and George Sterling. Outdoor sports, rather than writing, were their bonds. As a working writer, Wilson believed that writing is better done than talked about. He was inducted by Sterling into the Bohemian Club of San Francisco and its summer encampment at the Grove on the Russian River. Unlike Upton Sinclair, who in Carmel a year earlier had been disgusted by George Sterling's fondness for alcohol, Wilson enjoyed matching drinks with the thirstiest. He was built like a rock. Editor Lorimer called him Old Ironface.

Whereas Sterling lived in a cabin in the pinewood, Mary Austin in a tree house, and Jeffers subsequently in his stone dwelling on Mission Point, Wilson went south of the village to build his big brown-shingled Ocean Home. From it he wrote to George Ade,

"I'm five miles in the country, surrounded by scenery and climate that are what people expect to find when they make for the Riviera; back yard full of wooded mountains, and front yard, after you cross the rocks, reaching clear over to Japan . . . I've tried to get Tark out, but the poor lump believed the trip from Council Bluffs on is still made in wagons and interrupted by hostile Sioux."

Although the scenery, climate, and fellowship with kindred spirits combined to anchor Wilson in Carmel, none of these elements was used by him in his writing. "A fiction writer has two passions: people and words," he once declared to an interviewer. "If he has a gnawing, insatiable curiosity about the people he meets, the words will come to fit them."

Some writers (Somerset Maugham and D. H. Lawrence are prime examples) live on people around them; and then, having devoured them, they move on to new feeding grounds. Not Harry Leon Wilson. It was not that he didn't recognize colorful copy in Carmel's characters.

"It is a literary and artistic colony," he wrote to an eastern friend, "whose post-office handles more rejected manuscripts than any other of its size in the country. Naturally the town is a hot-bed of gossip and all uncharitableness, with a 'forest theatre' complicated by amateur acting and amateur authorship, and very funny. A book should be written about it, but I can get insurance on my house only for about two thirds of its value. Besides I want to live here."

By 1912 Wilson was ready for his third marriage. An unconscious predilection for a young girl seems to have determined his choice. His first wife, the Denverite, had a daughter, Helen, by a previous marriage whom Wilson adored. His choice of a third wife was of the age his former stepdaughter would be in 1912— seventeen. He was forty-five. He chose Helen Cooke, the prettiest girl in Carmel and wise beyond her years. She had lived with her mother in Upton Sinclair's Helicon Hall, the utopian colony established with the profits from *The Jungle*. When it burned down, it was said, from careless furnace-tending by young Sinclair Lewis, some of the residents, including the Cookes and Lewis, moved to Carmel. As suitor for the daughter's hand, "Red" Lewis lost out to Wilson.

The girl married the man of the world under the impression that he would show her the world. She did not know that he was in revulsion from too much worldliness. She came to realize her error, as Wilson firmly domesticated her. She soon bore him a son, Leon, and a daughter, Charis, the latter destined eventually to make a similar May-December marriage with Edward Weston.

Ocean Home became a country establishment—horses, two cows, chickens, a vegetable garden, and myriad flowers that made it a showplace. In spring and summer five gardeners were needed to maintain it. And money to keep it going. Wilson proved capable of earning—and spending—it.

In the fulfilment of a fruitful marriage and the Carmel setting, what did Harry Leon Wilson produce in the next decade, 1912-1922, those prime years during which he reached zenith? He wrote his best work in the form of three comic novels that brought him wealth and popularity. All bore alliterative titles:

Bunker Bean, *Ruggles of Red Gap*, and *Merton of the Movies*. It was in the first of them that the flapper made her American debut.

They were tailored for the *Saturday Evening Post*, a lucrative result of that first meeting with its editor. This weekly was dear to the hearts and influential on the minds of millions of middle-class Americans. Like the *New Yorker* a generation later, its pages of equally interesting text and ads are a window into the country's materialistic being. And like the *New Yorker*, the *Post* paid top rates to its star contributors. By 1922 Wilson was receiving three thousand dollars for short stories and thirty thousand for novels; a decade later, he was paid sixty thousand dollars for a single novel, *Two Black Sheep*.

His treasury of material continued to be his midwestern origins. Although *Ruggles of Red Gap* has a vague northwestern setting suggested perhaps by his Canadian Rockies experience, its Ma Pettingill is a pedigreed midwesterner. Ruggles the butler—predecessor of P. G. Wodehouse's Jeeves—is a more composite character, expressing Wilson's prejudices as a repatriated American. As for Merton Gill, he is the classic midwestern tenderfoot in California; his is the greenhorn story that has no end. To witness its latest chapters, one has only to take a Gray Line tour of Los Angeles, Hollywood, and Beverly Hills, and watch and listen to the passengers.

Merton of the Movies is an odd book, differing from others in the Wilson canon in its exotic setting, its satirical purpose and also somewhat mysterious conception and creation. In spite of initial success as a *Post* serial, a Broadway triumph in the Marc Connelly and George Kaufmann acting version starring Glen Hunter, and a threefold life as a movie with Glen Hunter, Stuart Erwin, and Red Skelton as its successive stars, *Merton* is today a neglected book. It has never been reprinted after the first edition of 1922 and a reissue in 1923 with illustrations from the Glen Hunter stage version. None of the films stressed the book's satire, dwelling instead on the pathos.

This neglect is not unaccountable. Since his first acceptance by such diverse critics as William Dean Howells and H. L. Mencken,

Harry Leon Wilson has been snubbed by the coteries that dominate our literary criticism. For them *Merton* just won't do. It is too corny, juvenile, and pathetic. True, *Merton* is not without faults. The chief one is that requirements of serial publication led Wilson to over elaborate some passages.

And yet *Merton* is the work of a craftsman, in loving control of his material and its form. Behind the false-fronts, the fun and games and the hyperbole, there is an indictment of Hollywood and the fans who create it that has never been bettered and is still pertinent. In a town that produced such larger than life characters as Sam Goldwyn and Clara Bow, who can call Merton Gill and the Montague Girl unbelievable?

"Certainly I put a lot of genuine movie dope into it," Wilson wrote to Julian Street on October 27, 1921, "the first time a lot of it has been fictioned, I believe, and the producers, I am persuaded, will consider that I have not treated their art with becoming seriousness . . . Not until I got into the writing of it did I feel repaid for my four-months' sentence served on the lots down there. Then I knew that I had not suffered and sacrificed in vain."

It remains uncertain why and how *Merton* came to be written. In the only book about Wilson, thorough as it is and based on the writer's papers preserved by Wilson's son Leon, George Kummer sheds no light on the matter. When I queried Leon Wilson, he replied, "I know not where he got *Merton*, or why he went to Hollywood."

I believe that it was George Horace Lorimer, his editor and friend, who suggested that Wilson write a movie novel. This belief is derived from Lorimer's introduction to a memorial edition in 1919 of *Buck Parvin and the Movies; Stories of the Moving Picture Game* by Charles E. Van Loan, Wilson's fellow contributor to the *Saturday Evening Post*.

"I first met Van some years ago when the moving-pictures were young and a trifle smudgy-faced," wrote Lorimer. "During a visit to Los Angeles, I was struck with the possibilities of this new field for the fiction writer. But when I looked up Van with the idea of suggesting a series of stories to him, I found that he had anticipated me."

Does it not seem likely that Lorimer then made a similar suggestion to Harry Leon Wilson?

When writers go to Hollywood, it is usually because they are hired to write scenarios. They do this for money. This was not true of Harry Leon Wilson. He had money. He went there unbeholden in 1920-21 to write a novel about Hollywood, and he went in style. The family's home was on Harvard Boulevard near Sixth Street. Although a member of the Bohemian Club, Wilson was no bohemian, at least not since he settled in Carmel as a country gentleman. In Los Angeles as in Carmel, his home was one of comfort and grace. A Japanese couple served, and at formal dinners the woman wore native dress and sang to the guests. Helen Wilson was gowned by Magnin, though she was sometimes fearful of having exceeded her allowance.

It was the springtime of the movies, when making them was an art not an industry. Those of us who lived there then have memories of casual times. Scenes from Mary Pickford in *Pollyanna* were shot near our home in South Pasadena, and she smilingly autographed a glossy picture for little me. Another of my big moments was when the western star, Jack Holt, gave me a ride in his Pierce Arrow roadster.

"This was the era," Leon Wilson wrote me, "when slapstick comedy sequences were staged almost anywhere. I remember seeing several, here and there on the streets; and one afternoon the classic routine of dozens of people getting out of the back of a limousine was staged in front of our house."

According to Leon, his father's mentor in Hollywood was Nat Deverich, a pioneer actor, director, producer, and agent. When I sought to find Deverich, I learned that he had died in 1963. I did locate his widow, the former D. W. Griffith actress, Loretta Blake, a charming and still beautiful lady. She recalled Harry, his wife, and their children. I learned much of the man, his silent manner, and the gleam in his eye which responsive women never missed. But nothing about him as a writer. He attracted no attention as such in Hollywood. Movie people were not readers.

As well as playing golf with him nearly every day, Deverich gained entree for Wilson to various studio lots. In an unpublished fragment among his papers, Wilson describes how he gathered material for *Merton:*

"The details of him [Merton Gill] filled themselves in as I hung around the Hollywood studios, watching, listening, for an always exciting four months. What would be his adventures, his shocks, his tragedies, his triumphs? Those movie lots told me day after day, and I tried to put them down. If Merton is real, all the credit to that incredible Hollywood. If he isn't the fault is all mine. No excuse for a writer worth his salt who can't see a dozen characters in that exciting atmosphere. It still excites me. I wish I had Merton to do all over again."

"He loved Hollywood parties," Loretta Deverich recalled, "and yet he was never really a part of them. Although he was the last to leave, he often just sat and stared, his rugged face expressionless. He was a very attractive man."

And he listened. Some of the dialogue in *Merton*, particularly that between producers and directors, might have come from those parties. Wilson had the gift of looking, listening, and remembering. To help him remember, he made notes on scraps of paper, which he accumulated in a desk drawer.

Leon Wilson describes the way his father used these accumulated notes. "If he ever sifted through the piles later, preparing to write a novel or story, I don't know. I suspect he simply picked up a few handsful of the stuff and read them through for a starter. In the early 1930's his desk once got jammed up with the stuff, so he emptied the drawers on the floor of an unused room off his study, and there the pile rested for many months: a heap of penciled scraps perhaps 8 or 10 inches high and 4 or 5 feet around. Nothing organized or specific: just the accumulation of lifetime habit." And then a sentence to horrify librarians. "Late in his life, when no other paper was convenient, he wrote on and ripped out the endleaves of whatever book he was reading."

Wilson's planning of content and form, the creative process, went on constantly in his head. This he never discussed with anyone, nor did he ever read passages aloud. He was self-contained. When his mind was working on a story, he was given to pacing.

"We children could hear him pacing the diagonal of his

upstairs study," Leon wrote me. "Seemed to go on forever. Reason tells me today that he probably paced for half an hour, then sat at his desk and played another of his many games of solitaire. He also paced downstairs after supper. We children would be sitting quietly to one side, perhaps our mother was there too, knitting, reading, or keeping us quiet, and H. L. would be pacing the diagonal of the living room and library, back and forth, with unvarying speed. And out of that came *Merton* and all the rest."

No evidence of *Merton*'s writing has apparently survived; no notes, outline, draft, manuscript, typescript—nothing. He left few traces of his workmanship. Working steadily with stops only for food and sleep, Wilson could write a hundred thousand word novel in thirty days. The published book was his inexorable goal. Like Mozart's music, Wilson's creative work was completed by the time he sat down at the typewriter. The rest was a mechanical process. The Bancroft Library is to be the repository of those papers that did survive and have been preserved by Leon.

The satire of *Merton of the Movies* is tempered by compassion. The book is a disillusioned midwestern view of moviemaking. Although richly detailed, it is not a journalistic report. It is Hollywood filtered through and projected by the unique equipment of Harry Leon Wilson.

What we don't find in Wilson as we do later in Raymond Chandler, is the poetry of place, the lay of the land; but as I said, people and words, not places, were what concerned H. L. Wilson.

I am not a *Time*-style reviewer who pads space with plot summaries. If one has read *Merton*, he will recall its story. If not, I hope that what I have written will lead him to read it. The problem will be to find a copy. A public library is the likeliest place. Copies are rarely seen in bookshops. I found mine years ago in London. *Merton's* hold on readers endures. I heard of a nineteen-year-old girl who has read it thrice.

Wilson's arc reached zenith with *Merton of the Movies*. After that, the descent began. It is sad when a writer lives beyond his prime. Wilson's decline can be seen as a failure of character. His was not equal to the stresses put upon it by life. His third marriage failed. Authoritarian by nature, he became obsessed by jealousy. When playing in a Carmel amateur theatrical, Helen was ardently kissed by the leading man, her husband challenged the actor to a duel with gloved fists. The ludicrous affair saw him bested by the younger man. His marriage ended in 1928 with Wilson's being divorced for infidelity.

Wilson's ambition was to write a serious novel. This he never did. He remained the prisoner of his early success as a humorist. The limitations of the *Saturday Evening Post* were an inhibiting factor. Who pays the piper, calls the tune; and it was George Horace Lorimer who paid, all too well. *Merton of the Movies*, that pathetic tale of the small town boy who yearned to be a tragic actor and became instead an inadvertent comic, can thus be read as Wilson's own heartbreak story. It is a book of more than one level of meaning.

Not only his marriage failed. Even worse, by 1930 he had written himself out. Unlike the Canadian Rockies, the Depression was a wilderness from which he never emerged. His ultimate failure was to have a serial rejected by Lorimer. Wilson's last appearance in the *Post* was in 1935, four years before his death.

"I rarely go to the movies," he wrote, "except by the mischance of being polite to others who like to go. What has been calculated to please 25,000,000 people isn't likely to enthrall me. When I do go, I prefer the silent films. Can't get a sense of reality from the talking ones; merely weird to me; like dead people talking out of a cistern."

In 1935 a need for money led him to accept M.G.M.'s offer to come to Hollywood at $1250 a week, as consultant on a film of *Ma Pettingill*. He could take it for only three weeks. Used to commanding, he could not tolerate waiting. The film was never made. Later he walked out on a screening of Charles Laughton in *Ruggles of Red Gap*, revolted by the audience's "yelling idiot laughter."

Though domineering, sometimes cruel, Wilson was never stingy. Cavalier with money, he made (though only after she sued him) a handsome settlement on Helen. Long years after their divorce, he sent money to Rose. Generosity to an improvident brother and the upkeep of Ocean Home finally bankrupted

342

him. To compound his sorrows, a car accident impaired his nervous system. Then his memory failed.

He turned to his son and daughter for help. Charis was then married to Edward Weston. She and Leon attempted to straighten out their father's tangled affairs. When the bank foreclosed on Ocean Home, they moved him into Carmel in the care of a practical nurse and her husband. There he improved, and resumed his old ways of notetaking and pacing and sitting at the window, staring out to sea. He was seventy-two. Old Ironface had come to the end of his journey. He died in his sleep on the night of 28-29 January, 1939.

Edward and Charis managed to buy a couple of acres of Ocean Home from the bank. Across Wildcat Creek from the old brown residence they buried the ashes of Harry Leon Wilson.

Reading List

HARRY LEON WILSON (1867-1939)
  The Boss of Little Arcady. Boston, Lothrop, 1905.
  Ruggles of Red Gap. New York, Doubleday, Page, 1915.
  Merton of the Movies. New York, Doubleday, Page, 1922; Theater edition, 1923, illustrated from photograph of scenes from the play.

GEORGE KUMMER
  Harry Leon Wilson. Cleveland, Western Reserve University Press, 1963.

JOHN WILLIAM TEBBEL
  George Horace Lorimer and the Saturday Evening Post. Garden City, Doubleday, 1948.

Photograph of Harry Leon Wilson by Edward Weston, courtesy of Charis Wilson.

29

I HAVE NEVER counted the novels about the movies. W. W. Robinson estimates there are upward of fifteen hundred. At UCLA, Caroline See wrote a mammoth dissertation called *The Hollywood Novel*, in the course of which she analyzed three hundred of them.

I wrote about *Merton of the Movies* for its portrayal of Hollywood in the springtime period, for mirroring the moving pictures at the time of their romantic origins. I was drawn to it because it was written about the era when I was entering my teens, an avid movie-goer and collector of glossy photos of my favorite stars.

Time passed. Hollywood and I aged. Movie-making became a business rather than an art. As a result of its worldwide influence, people were lured to Hollywood for a variety of reasons in a kind of second gold rush. They came to act, to write, or merely to look.

Although *Merton of the Movies* is a satire on that magnetism of Hollywood, it is sugar-coated. Harry Leon Wilson was a people-watcher, not a people-hater, yet he was not moved by any particular pity for the human plight. He was no Dostoevsky. He came to Hollywood a successful writer with a ready buyer for all that he wrote and a reading public eager for his stories, and he wrote a book easily sold and easily read.

That was in 1920. Sixteen years later when Wilson return to

Hollywood springtime was over, for him and for Hollywood. If he had not been old and written out and nearly bankrupt, he might have created a powerful anti-*Merton* novel. It was too late.

The shortness of life and the longness of art bring other times and other writers who in turn reach their zenith and descend. At the time of Wilson's return to Hollywood in the depth of the Depression, a young writer was also there, out of work as a scenarist and toiling on what was to be his fourth and final novel. It was published in 1939 at almost the very time of Harry Leon Wilson's death.

Like *Merton of the Movies*, Nathanael West's *The Day of the Locust* is about the power of Hollywood to lure people and then destroy their illusions. Unlike *Merton*, it is a sordid story, both pitying and pitiless, and with a relentless hold on the reader. At the end of *Merton*, the book's characters resume their changed lives. They were not destroyed by disillusionment.

On the contrary, *The Day of the Locust* ends in a kind of holocaust; its characters do not know resurrection. It was not written to entertain. West wrote it from a compulsion to formalize a tragic view of life. He perceived Hollywood and its product as the pure epitome of all that is wrong with life in the United States. His treatment of it is equally pure.

The book was a publishing failure. A year later West was killed in an automobile accident in the Imperial Valley near El Centro, leaving only plans for more novels. *The Day of the Locust* has had a better fate than the unreprinted *Merton*. In 1950 New Directions reissued it in its New Classics series, and since that rebirth it has had a thriving life in paperbacks and translations, widely read and discussed, its author becoming the subject of legend and cult.

Nathanael West's three earlier novels—*The Dream Life of Balso Snell*, *Miss Lonelyhearts*, and *A Cool Million*—were also resurrected. An accumulation of critical writing about his work was capped by a richly detailed, brilliant biography, *Nathanael West, the Art of His Life*, by Jay Martin, a professor on the University of California's Irvine campus. It is based on the papers preserved by West's brother-in-law, S. J. Perelman, the humorist.

346

Nathanael West was not an autobiographical writer. From his four short novels one could only guess at who he was and what his life had been. He wrote about others than himself, and yet it was always he who selected and shaped what he saw of life. Although we cannot reconstruct his life from his books, in reading them we gain insight into his nature as man, artist, and philosopher. In reading Martin's biography we are enabled for the first time to perceive the heroism of West's drive to be a writer—an unsuccessful writer, at least in his lifetime, as judged by the fate of his books, all of which were commercial failures.

I am sometimes asked by people how to go about becoming a writer. They seem hopeful that there is a formulated method, a secret way to success. There has been no answer other than to say, "If you want badly enough to be a writer, you will write, come hell or high water. If you have talent, it will become apparent, and with practice you will write well."

As West proved, popular success does not necessarily follow. Posthumous recognition? Few writers have the stoicism of Robinson Jeffers who declared that the best fate that could happen to a writer was not to be bothered in his lifetime with adulation, "the smoke that smothers the flame." Few have the fortitude of Stendhal, reconciled to his writing having to wait a century for final judgment.

Now I will say to questioners, "Study the lives, development, and creations of the writers in this book. You will see that there are as many ways to become a writer as there are writers."

What was the way followed by Nathanael West? To answer we must go back to the time and place of his birth: October 17, 1903, New York City. As the first child of Russian Jewish immigrants named Weinstein, he was called Nathan. His lifelong nickname of Pep was a sarcastic reference to his lethargy in schoolboy sports.

His father prospered as a contractor, builder, and operator of New York real estate, including hotels and apartment houses. He assumed that his son would follow in this field. Pep had other desires. For him higher education meant time to defer what his family expected him to do. Although intelligent, he failed to make a good record in high school. To gain admission to Tufts College in Boston, he forged credits on his transcript, sent it in and was accepted. A later transfer to Brown University in Providence was equally shady. His Tufts record, showing two years of completed work, was actually that of another student who bore the same name of Nathan Weinstein. While at Brown he added his mother's maiden name for good measure, to give himself the impressive cognomen Nathan von Wallenstein Weinstein. Throughout his life West took a cavalier attitude toward the facts of life—dates, statistics, places.

While at Brown, West pursued literary and artistic interests, without any goal other than to defer the ultimate fate of entering his father's business. During summer vacations he worked as a timekeeper on family projects, which only served to increase his distaste for the construction and management field. His relationship to his father recalls that of Lincoln Steffens' of a generation earlier. West also was sent to Europe after graduation from Brown in 1926. The cost of this cultural vacation in France was paid by a paternal uncle, for his father was already feeling the creeping effects of the approaching Depression.

It was at this time that the young dilettante legally changed his name to Nathanael West. All through school he had played variations on his original name, in what seemed to be a psychological quest for his true identity. He was a complicated, bizarre, eccentric person.

West stayed in Paris only three months before the declining family fortunes compelled him to return. Although he was beginning to think of himself as a writer, he found it more practical to work in one of the family hotels as night room-clerk and later as manager. This surrender was justified by the free time it afforded him to write.

His early efforts were derived more from literature than from life. His first book, *The Dream Life of Balso Snell*, was published in 1931 by a "little magazine." Readable only as a literary tour de force, it is interesting as a stage in West's development. He had to purge himself of too much schooling and reading in French literature. His first efforts were not promising of the artist destined to write a classic novel about Hollywood, California.

West's success with educational credentials other than his own makes understandable his interest in literary hoaxes. He said later that he had once gone to a second-hand bookstore and bought a hundred copies of outdoor western magazines of the genre of *Field and Stream* and then, using scissors and paste, had composed a master story from the fragments of many. The tale is probably apocryphal.

Success in a less extravagant vein resulted in his first published work in a national magazine. "A Bare-Faced Lie" appeared in the *Overland Monthly*, an appropriate place considering that it was a tale in the burlesque manner of Bret Harte-Mark Twain, in a periodical whose first editor was Bret Harte. That issue of July 1929 was dedicated to the memory of Charles F. Lummis and contained a gathering of tributes to him. It also announced the appointment of Robert Gordon Sproul as president of the University of California.

If literature is to live, it must be drawn from life, not literature. This does not eliminate the need for literary refinement. Slabs of life do not make literature. Nor is the journalistic treatment of the newspapers enough to hold readers beyond a day. The secret of literary immortality is in the selection and rearrangement of raw material, then its passage through the writer's filters, the result being what we call style.

Looking back over it in the Martin biography, we can see the cunning way that West's life led from literary literature, by way of experience, to living literature as embodied in his second book, the now celebrated *Miss Lonelyhearts*. Once again the Depression was the prime mover, compelling West to embrace life itself, rather than imitations of it. Concurrently with John Steinbeck and Raymond Chandler, Nathanael West was created as a writer by the economic catastrophe that destroyed many less hardy ones.

The key person in West's life was his Brown classmate, S. J. Perelman, who became even closer to him through marriage to his sister, Laura. In the 1920's, Perelman was established in New

349

York as a humorous writer for *Judge* and *College Humor*. West looked to him as his model of a successful writer, all the while West was working as hotel manager and writing unsaleable stories.

Then occurred the event that coalesced West's gifts into a single creative act. Perelman asked West to have dinner in Greenwich Village with him and Laura and a woman writer from the *Brooklyn Eagle* who contributed a daily column of advice to the lovelorn. She had an accumulation of letters written to her that she thought Perelman might make literary use of. They read them at dinner. Let Jay Martin tell what happened:

"If any one moment in his life could be regarded as absolutely crucial in West's discovery that he was an artist, it occurred during this night of March 1929. He was overwhelmed by the letters, all his elaborate personal defenses were swept away in a flood of intellectual exaltation and emotional receptivity. Perelman could not use the letters; but *he* would, West said. He believed he could do something—not comic, certainly not comic, though perhaps using comedy to heighten the tragedy in them."

In writing *Miss Lonelyhearts*, West brought to the letters a refinement of the material that passed before his eyes in the hotel. During the three years that it took him to complete the short book, the Depression deepened. As manager he was torn by sympathy for down-and-outers and deadbeats and duty to make them pay up. The novel was an effort to ameliorate the heartbreak of those lovelorn letters and the even closer views of human suffering afforded by his vantage point.

West's dream was to make enough money from *Miss Lonelyhearts* to enable him to take a year off and live in the country and there do nothing but write. It was not to be. If the Depression made him into a creative writer, it also blighted any economic success. Publication of the book in April 1933 by the prestigious firm of Liveright, four years after its conception, could not have been at a worse time. The country's banks were closed by presidential order. Liveright went into bankruptcy.

It was a heartbreaking experience for West. Although his book was a critical triumph with a resulting public demand for it,

Liveright's printer seized 2000 of the 2200 copies printed and re-fused to release them to bookstores until he had been paid. When several movie studios sought to buy the story, they found the legal rights in a snarl. By the time copies were made available, it was too late. The fickle public's interest had cooled. The edition was remaindered for 75 cents a copy.

Late in 1932 the Perelmans and West had bought a Bucks County farm where West intended to settle with the profits from his book. Fortunately everything was not lost in the Liveright debacle. Darryl Zanuck finally obtained rights to the book and bought it for $4000. In the meantime the Perelmans had left the farm for Hollywood where he wrote the classic *Horse Feathers* and *Monkey Business* for the Marx Brothers. West followed, as a script writer for Columbia Pictures. His first reaction to Holly-wood was in a letter to Josephine Herbst, written in the summer of 1933:

"This place is just like Asbury Park, New Jersey. The same stucco houses, women in pajamas, delicatessen stores, etc. There is nothing to do, except tennis, golf, or the movies. In other words, phooey on Cal. Another thing, this stuff about easy work is all wrong. My hours are from ten in the morning to six at night with a full day on Saturday. There's no fooling here. All the writers sit in cells in a row and the minute a typewriter stops someone pokes his head in the door to see if you are thinking. Otherwise, it's like the hotel business."

After a vicious attack on *Miss Lonelyhearts* by the puritanical trade paper *Harrison's Reports*, in which the novel was denounced as a degenerate book, Zanuck toned it down into the film called *Advice to the Lovelorn*.

Books as deeply conceived and meticulously written as *Miss Lonelyhearts* are not that easy to kill. They have a way of out-living the so-called major novels. Consider what Raymond Chan-dler said in 1949 in a letter to a friend:

"I've always enjoyed reading Marquand and have always felt while doing so that he came as close to being an artist as any writ-er could who wasn't one. But somehow his successful soufflés always make me think of little lost books like *Gatsby* and *Miss*

Lonelyhearts—books which are not perfect, evasive of the problem often, side-stepping scenes which should have been written (and which Marquand would have written at twice the necessary length) but somehow passing along, crystallized, complete, and as such things go nowadays eternal."

On this first trip to Hollywood, West stayed only a few months. By fall he was back on the farm, still on leave from the hotel, eager to write his third novel. It was not about Hollywood. He never worked that fast. It would be nearly six years before *The Day of the Locust* was finished.

West was feeling the full impact of the Depression on the American success story to which he had been conditioned in the 1920's. His new book, *A Cool Million*, took the form of a burlesque satire on the Horatio Alger story of rags to riches. It recounted the crazy adventures of Lemuel Pitkin, in a land torn by economic distress and threatened by crackpot movements. Harcourt, Brace rejected the manuscript. It was then published by the small house of Covici, Friede, which also issued Steinbeck's *Tortilla Flat* in that same year of 1934.

A Cool Million flopped and was remaindered for 25 cents a copy. As *Balso Snell* was the springboard to *Miss Lonelyhearts*, so was West's third novel an essential detour on the way to his final masterpiece. These first three novels earned total royalties of $780.

He next tried the Guggenheim Foundation in an application for a fellowship to enable him to write "a narrative of ideas." Despite sponsorship by F. Scott Fitzgerald, Malcolm Cowley, Edmund Wilson, and George S. Kaufman, West failed to receive an award.

Back to Hollywood he went in the summer of 1935, hopeful of being rehired as a script writer. He wasn't. He lived at the Pa-Va-Sed apartment hotel on North Ivar Street. It was a time of discouragement, personal suffering, and despair. He was ill from prostatitis. When his money ran out, his brother-in-law supported him.

"I spend my time thinking of how much money I owe you," he wrote to Perelman, "and how it seems to be impossible for me to get on my feet again. My new book will be a failure. I can't possibly get a job. I have deteriorated mentally. I have nothing to say, and no talent for writing, then I get up and take two more tablets of morphine, against the doctor's orders. I fall asleep for half an hour—then wake up and find myself laughing quietly."

It was from such depths that *The Day of the Locust* was born. Its characters were those living in the same hotel. West's sanctuary was the nearby Stanley Rose bookshop, which served as a Hollywood artists' rendezvous in the same way that Jake Zeitlin's bookshop did for downtown Los Angeles. He came to know police reporters and the Mexican-American underworld. Did he and Raymond Chandler ever meet? The latter's detective, Philip Marlowe, had his office in the same neighborhood.

Thanks to Perelman and Laura, West survived. Then in 1936 his fortune improved. Republic Pictures hired him at $200 a week, with a contract rising in five years to five times that figure. He proved successful as a scenarist. In the Martin biography is an appendix listing his film work in the four years of life that remained to him. He was able to pay back all that Perelman had loaned him, and also to save money.

He continued to work on the Hollywood novel, first called "The Cheated." Before it was finished, Broadway lured him. In 1938, with Joseph Schrank, he wrote an anti-war play called *Gentlemen, the War!* The timing was wrong. Hitler was marching. Anti-war sentiment had been replaced by concern for the fate of humanity. The play closed after two nights.

A return to Hollywood was the only way to recoup. His novel was now in proofs, to be published by Random House. Its final title was possibly derived from the references to locusts in the Book of Exodus. Already his mind had turned to his next work. "Will you be able to work in Hollywood?" a friend asked him. "Yes," he replied, "I'll be writing, but a writer needs to lead a writer's life. It isn't just a sitting down—it's the whole business of thinking and reverie and walking and reading, and you can't do that in Hollywood, so I don't know what my future will be. But I'm going to be working."

The Day of the Locust was published in May 1939. As usual

West had high hopes for it, and yet he was prepared for another failure. In that same year he wrote to George Milburn, ". . . all my books always fall between the different schools of writing. The radical press, although I consider myself on their side, doesn't like my particular kind of joking . . . and the literature boys, whom I detest, detest me in turn. The highbrow press finds that I avoid the big, significant things, and the lending library touts in the daily press think me shocking. . . The proof of all this is that I've never had the same publisher twice . . . because there is nothing to root for in my work and what is even worse, no rooters."

In spite of favorable reviews, *The Day of the Locust* failed to regain its cost to the publisher, including an advance on royalties of $250. It sold only 1464 copies in the first year. Again West's dream of financial ease, in which he could write at his own pace, was ended by the necessity of returning to work in the studio.

Then as his short life drew to a close, West was married to Eileen McKenney, the subject of Ruth McKenney's highly successful *My Sister Eileen*. They were blissful during a marriage destined to last for less than a year. She shared the passion for hunting that he had developed on the Pennsylvania farm. They hunted wild boar on Santa Cruz Island, duck in the Tulare sloughs, quail and dove on the Colorado desert. He planned to write a book of shooting sketches in the manner of Turgeniev.

Then in December 1940 they crossed the border at Mexicali to hunt dove. They headed home on the 22d, driving a Ford station wagon. West had never been a good driver. He was both impulsive and absent-minded, and up to then, lucky. Homeward bound for Christmas after their successful hunt, what was in his mind? Plans for the unwritten books that someday would be successful? One was for a South Seas novel in the manner of Conrad.

Whatever the cause, he ran through a stop sign at the intersection of Highways 111 and 80, and crashed into a westbound car. He and his wife were killed. He was 37, she 10 years younger. They left her little boy by an earlier marriage, and their hunting dog Julie.

354

And the book I judge to be a California classic. Why do I? Because the words of Raymond Chandler about *Miss Lonelyhearts* are equally true of *The Day of the Locust*: "crystallized, complete, and as such things go nowadays eternal."

In writing it West was compulsively moved to sublimate his own suffering and despair, and to transfer the burden onto his characters, so that it is they who know disillusionment and disaster. We recall Robinson Jeffers's "Apology for Bad Dreams": by creating tragic characters the poet believed he was warding off evil from his own house.

Who were West's characters? Not the Hollywood high and mighty. Two years were to pass before they became the targets of Budd Schulberg's *What Makes Sammy Run* and F. Scott Fitzgerald's posthumous *The Last Tycoon*, the best of the anti-bigshot novels. As in *Miss Lonelyhearts*, West was moved in the *Locust* to portray the little people, the moths drawn by the Hollywood flame: a middle-aged midwesterner, a dwarf, a teen-age whore and her seedy clown-father, a bratty child actor whose role is to trigger the climax, a Mexican cockfight promoter, and a studio draughtsman with the ambition to paint a masterpiece, a gala canvas to be called "The Burning of Los Angeles."

The Day of the Locust is like a series of paintings by Hieronymous Bosch, etched in brilliant detail, terrible and compassionate, and rising to the apocalyptic denouement of an orgiastic movie premiere. It is a very short novel, and the economy is deliberate. Four years of painstaking and painful revision went into its writing. In comparing it with today's overblown novels, I am reminded of these lines by Thomas Bailey Aldrich:

> What mighty epics have been wrecked by Time
> Since Herrick launched his cockle-shells of rhyme!

Although West drew on the life around him as the material of his book, his own life was transformed into something impersonal and universal. Nothing has ever equalled his description of the set and filming of "The Battle of Waterloo." Here the fakery, fantasy, and dream world of the movies pass before us like a

355

panoramic painting, a dream dump, a Sargasso Sea of the imagination. Yet the novel is not overloaded with Hollywoodiana; everything in it was selected for its essential truth.

How much the pornographic novelists could learn from Nathanael West! Although his themes are sex and violence, alienation and disillusionment, they are handled fastidiously, surgically. With his command of language, he had no need of four-letter words.

Although West was radical in his sympathies—an early version of a chapter in the *Locust* was printed in 1936 in Lincoln Steffens's *Pacific Weekly* and West addressed the Western Writers Congress in the same year—he was never a political or propagandist writer. He was instead an artist, with character to retain his integrity and stamina to complete his work, until Death interfered.

". . . because there is nothing to root for in my work and what is even worse, no rooters."

If only he could have lived to see how wrong time has proven him!

Reading List

NATHANAEL WEST (1903-1940)
The Dream Life of Balso Snell. New York, Contact Editions, 1931.
Miss Lonelyhearts. New York, Harcourt, Brace, 1933.
A Cool Million; the Dismantling of Lemuel Pitkin. New York, Covici, Friede, 1934.
The Day of the Locust. New York, Random House, 1939; New Directions, 1950, with an introduction by Richard B. Gehman.
Complete Works. New York, Farrar, 1957.

JAY MARTIN
Nathanael West, the Art of His Life. New York, Farrar, 1970.

Photograph of Nathanael West, courtesy of S. J. Perelman.

After Many a Summer

ALDOUS HUXLEY

30

IT WAS in the month of May 1926 that England's witty young writer, Aldous Huxley, first passed through Los Angeles, homeward bound after a trip around the world. He stayed only a day or two, sightseeing with an English poet, Robert Nichols, who was living there. It was long enough, however, to provide him with the mocking vignettes that come at the end of *Jesting Pilate*, the book he wrote about his global tour.

From a compartment on the Chicago-bound Santa Fe train, Huxley wrote a thank-you letter to his host, which concluded, "How delightful it was to see you again, my dear Bob, after all these years—and how still more delightful to think that you will soon be returning to civilization. Hollywood is too altogether antipodean to be lived in; it gives you no chance of escape. Italy seems to be clearly indicated."

Huxley's "escape" from Hollywood lasted a decade, during which his reputation as a man of letters became worldwide. Then in 1937 he returned to Southern California and there he lived for the rest of his life, apparently reconciled to his fate. He died at 69 on November 22, 1963. It was the day of President Kennedy's death, which meant that the death of Aldous Huxley went virtually unnoticed in the world press.

What drew him back to the place he had once ridiculed as Joy City? What kept him there for 26 years? And finally, what literary use did he make of Southern California? My answers to these questions are the subject of this chapter.

No writer can escape being moulded by the social forces of his time. As the 1930's deepened, Huxley perceived the world's drift toward another global war. He was a true European, married to a Belgian, fluent in French and Italian, and a devotee of Spanish art. He embraced a pacifist philosophy, at the same time recognizing that mankind has never long remained at peace. In 1932 his *Brave New World* was a biting forecast of life in the ultimate scientific utopia. It and the earlier *Point Counter Point* are probably his best known novels.

The Spanish Civil War, harbinger of a wider conflict, was the deciding factor that turned the Huxleys again toward the New World. They were concerned about the education of their only child, Matthew, who in 1936 had reached the age of 18. In his son's desire for premedical schooling, Huxley saw a realization of his own ambition to be a medical scientist. He had been thwarted when, at 16, an attack of keratitis had resulted in temporary blindness and lifelong eye trouble.

He sought a calmer, surer future in the United States for his son, as well as for himself and his wife. Another reason for his emigrating was a wish to visit Frieda Lawrence, the writer's widow, on the New Mexican ranch celebrated in novels, stories, and essays by D. H. Lawrence, whose friend and literary executor Huxley had been.

And so the summer of 1937 found the Huxleys at the Lawrence ranch in the Sangre de Cristos, northwest of Taos. There on the aspened slope of Lobo Mountain he wrote *Ends and Means*, a philosophical summing up to that time of his early 40's.

Then another factor entered the field of forces that were pulling Aldous Huxley back to the land he had once so wickedly satirized. It was personified by the rising young Los Angeles bookseller-poet-art entrepreneur, Jacob Israel Zeitlin, known to his friends as Jake. The son of a Fort Worth rabbi, he had run away from home at 18 to become a vagabond troubadour in the manner of Carl Sandburg and Vachel Lindsay. Arriving in Los Angeles in the mid-1920's, Zeitlin's first employment was as a gardener on the E. L. Doheny estate. Little did Mrs. Doheny know that the bohemian runaway was destined eventually to sell her some of the rarest of the treasures housed today in the Doheny Memorial Library at St. John's Seminary, Camarillo.

Ten years later as the lord of his own bookshop on West Sixth Street, Zeitlin was negotiating with Frieda Lawrence to act for her in the sale of her late husband's manuscripts. On a visit to the New Mexican ranch he arranged for them to be sent to Los Angeles for cataloging. At the same time he persuaded Aldous Huxley to let him represent him in the sale of the movie rights to Huxley's books.

At this point I came on the scene, newly graduated from library school and becalmed on the sea of the Depression. In the hope of writing a book about D. H. Lawrence, I had assembled a large collection of his books and the books about him. Zeitlin needed a cataloger for the Lawrence manuscripts. I needed a job. Need more be said? The catalog was finished in a month, subsidized by Dr. and Mrs. Elmer Belt, printed by Ward Ritchie, and published by the Los Angeles Public Library where, thanks to Librarian Althea Warren, I had obtained temporary employment. The work's distinction was a foreword by Aldous Huxley.

Not only did Zeitlin arrange for the sale of some of Huxley's published works to Hollywood, he set the stage for Huxley's becoming a film writer, and on a more exalted level than that on which Nathanael West was then struggling to survive. Huxley's assignments included adaptations of such classics as *Pride and Prejudice* and *Jane Eyre*. He also wrote the scenario for *Madame Curie*. He declined to adapt *The Forsyte Saga*, declaring that ". . . even the lure of enormous lucre cd. not reconcile me to remaining closeted for months with the ghost of the late poor John Galsworthy." His version of his own memorably titled story, "The Gioconda Smile," became a film called "A Woman's Vengeance."

Before going further with Huxley's career in Southern California, let me introduce Mrs. Huxley. She was the former Maria Nys, a petite Flemish girl he had first met in 1915 when she was still in her teens. They were married in 1919. Maria was to him

359

 Aldous Huxley
August 2nd
1962.

360

what Una was to Robinson Jeffers and Olive to Idwal Jones—wife, lover, housekeeper, chauffeur, reader, typist, and of supreme importance, a buffer between her husband and the hangers-on and would-be disciples who are always attracted to great writers.

Nowhere is Maria Huxley's native shrewdness and good humor better revealed than in the rambling letter she wrote to a friend soon after their return to Southern California. In it she tells first of arriving on the east coast, then driving south and across Texas. The contrast with Italy and France caused cultural shock. She lamented the absence of "towns with monuments and ravishing quarters and café terraces to rest on when one is tired. In this country there is nothing but the earth and its population and nowhere to rest and sit when one is tired of that."

She goes on about Huxley and his fellow Englishman, Gerald Heard, who were off lecturing. Heard's shortness and Huxley's six feet four led her to describe them as "a sort of Mutt and Jeff on war and peace and religion and so on."

The dry air of Southern California was healthful for her and the clear air of that pre-smog era was good for his eyesight. Lecturing and film-writing proved lucrative sources of income. Much of his earnings went to help less affluent members of his and her families. And they found intellectual companionship, testified to in Maria's letter:

"We have met here all the very eminent world of The Technical Institute of Pasadena, gone up Mount Wilson and looked at the sky with professor Hubble . . . we have met scholars on Bacon [Walter Arensberg] and novelists and sociologists and on the same day we have met Gary Cooper or Anita Loos or Charlie and the whole pattern becomes fantastic and improbable . . . Yesterday we had a very *intellectual* dinner with Charlie Chaplin, Paulette Goddard, a very good and very handsome hostess and Upton Sinclair one of the guests."

The varied range of Huxley's writings was the result of an interest in all aspects of life. In spite of defective eyesight he saw more than most people do. When his eyes were too fatigued to read, Maria read to him. He mixed with all kinds of people from

whom he learned many curious things. He continually wrote—
essays, articles, stories, novels, treatises and tracts, book after
book up to the week of his death, when he was writing an essay
on Shakespeare and Religion. If he had written only essays, his
place in literature would be secure. He was in the great tradition
of English essayists.

Through my work on the Lawrence manuscripts, I came to
friendship with Aldous Huxley. Eventually as Librarian at
UCLA, the staff and I served his research needs, notably on the
scholarly *Grey Eminence*, a biography of Cardinal Richelieu's
priestly collaborator.

Modest, unassuming, and appreciative, Aldous Huxley was
the model library user. Many a time I saw him at the catalog,
scanning the cards held within an inch of his eyes. His voice was
high, bell-like though not effeminate, and very English. Students
were quick to recognize his striking appearance, the tall thin
body, the leonine head. Sometimes they asked for his autograph.
He was never annoyed, never condescending.

"Conversation with him was always a memorable experience," Jake Zeitlin recalled, "because, by lifting you up to his
level rather than talking down, he gave you the feeling that you
too were brilliant, and also because you were conscious that profound and witty things were being said, yet said as if they were
commonplace. One could not be trivial with him or talk of
trivialities."

Although it was not then the in-word it has become, *charisma*
was his in abundance.

In 1943 we exhibited Zeitlin's peerless collection of Huxley's
works (preserved today at UCLA), and the writer opened the
show with a talk to the students on book collecting.

Thus we see that it was a combination of world events, family
need, climate, libraries, and friendships that brought Aldous
Huxley back to Southern California and kept him based here for
the rest of his life.

Now to the question, what literary use did he make of the region? With his gift for satire and the wealth of material it offered, we would have expected him to write a novel about Holly-

wood. Most every visiting writer did. Huxley did not, at least not about Hollywood as such. Perhaps it was a wish not to bite the hand that was feeding him so well.

Other flamboyant manifestations of Californiana were the subject of his one principal novel about the region, written soon after his return to Los Angeles. *After Many a Summer Dies the Swan* is the longer American title, *After Many a Summer* the English. The title was drawn from a line by Tennyson in the poem "Tithonous," the myth of the fair Trojan boy who asked the goddess of dawn for immortality. His mistake was in not asking also for perpetual youth and vigor.

After Many a Summer appeared in October 1939. That last year of the dying Thirties, verging to the immolation of the Forties, was a great one for the California novel. In addition to Huxley's, it saw publication of *The Grapes of Wrath*, *The Big Sleep*, and *The Day of the Locust*.

In Huxley's letters we read of the inception of this novel. On 19 February 1939 he wrote from 1320 North Crescent Heights Boulevard to a friend:

"Did I tell you that I had put aside the long, elaborate novel for the time being and am hard at work on a short phantasy, in the manner, more or less, of *Brave New World?* It seems to be going pretty well, and I hope to have it finished in time for early autumn publication. The book, as I hope it will be, is a phantasy, but built up of solidly realistic psychological elements; a wild extravaganza, but with the quality of a most serious parable. I hope it will get itself written fairly smoothly and expeditiously. After that I shall write the eight lectures on religion which I have to deliver this year in Calcutta for a thing appropriately called the Gosh Foundation."

From where the Huxleys had moved to 701 South Amalfi Drive in Pacific Palisades, he wrote to his brother Julian on July 30:

". . . I am momentarily free, having finished the book I have been working on for these past months. It is a kind of fantasy, at once comic and cautionary, farcical, blood-curdling and reflective."

"In the intervals of writing, I have been working on my eyes, taking lessons in seeing from an admirable teacher here who was trained by the late Dr Bates, the deviser of the method that bears his name. Optometrists loathe the method, because it endangers a hundred-and-fifty-million-dollar-a-year spectacle industry."

In that same momentous year as the world teetered on the brink of war, Huxley was not the only one to hit the bull's-eye on California's prime target: Hearst and his castle at San Simeon. It was the year that Orson Welles, Hollywood's boy wonder, was making *Citizen Kane*, one of the few Hollywood movies to win an unfading blue ribbon.

With literary license Huxley moved San Simeon to the western San Fernando Valley, and from the San Joaquin he transported a band of Steinbeck's Okies to serve as Hearstian serfs in the orange groves at the foot of the castle. Hearst's friend, Marion Davies, is as recognizable in Huxley's novel as she is in Welles' film. The other characters were also drawn from life. The philosopher, Mr. Propter, owed his being to Gerald Heard. Dr. Obispo, the Levantine villain, is said to have been modelled after a Hollywood physician.

The novel's central theme was inspired by Hearst's notorious fear of death and a corresponding desire to prolong his life. Here Huxley drew on knowledge gained from his biologist brother, Julian. Carp were known to be alive after two hundred years, apparently with no signs of senility. *Voila!* Put a man on a diet of carp guts and he might live indefinitely. The macabre plot sees Huxley slyly ridiculing himself as the young English intellectual, Jeremy Pordage, imported by Jo Stoyte (the name he gave to Hearst) to catalog twenty-seven crates of an English titled family's ancestral Hauberk papers.

In the course of his work, with the oily Dr. Obispo reading over his shoulder, Pordage comes on clues that lead Obispo, the lord of the castle and his lady, to England, where they discover the Fifth Earl and his housekeeper still alive in their third century— but, horrors, degenerated to a simian state. Huxley was scientifically warranted in theorizing that the great cells in the brain which make us human do not replace themselves, and that the older we grow, the more apelike we become.

The novel also includes Huxley's composite of two of the Southland's leading educators merged into an unctuous college president named Dr. Mulge, whose voice is a blend of vaseline and port wine. This did not endear the author to his models.

Renamed Beverly Pantheon, Forest Lawn comes in for only a glancing volley. It was an attraction to which Huxley always took visitors to Southern California. It was left to his fellow countryman, Evelyn Waugh, to immortalize the Glendale necropolis in *The Loved One*, that subterranean masterpiece of mortuary Californiana. Incidentally the manuscript of this novelette, and Waugh's other papers, are enshrined in the University of Texas. Waugh was in Southern California for only three months. Movie studio work and ecclesiastical affairs (he was a devout Catholic) occupied most of his time, so that he nearly missed seeing his ultimate target. Then in a diary entry of April 7, 1947, written upon his return to England, we read this: "I found a deep mine of literary gold in the cemetery of Forest Lawn and the work of its morticians, and intend to get to work immediately on a novelette staged there."

In *After Many a Summer* Huxley relieved himself of any further need to satirize the Southern California environment. A decade later when he wrote a second novel with a local setting, too much had happened, namely World War II and the Atomic Bomb, to permit the kind of gruesome slapstick he had exploited in the first novel. The disillusionment of *Brave New World* was now much deeper. From his own scientific interests and reinforced by what he had learned from Julian, he foresaw the barbarism into which the world would most likely fall if the Bomb were ever widely used.

We first read of his plan for a post-nuclear novel in a letter of 26 March 1947, from Wrightwood in the San Bernardino mountains, to Anita Loos. Ever since Huxley was first enchanted by *Gentlemen Prefer Blondes*, they had been friends. They also collaborated on scenarios such as that for *Jane Eyre*.

"I potter around with the beginnings of a historical novel—only to wonder whether I know enough about the period to do it as I should like to do it. Going to the other extreme, I think that perhaps I may write something about the future instead—about, among other things, a post-atomic-war society in which the chief effect of the gamma radiations had been to produce a race of men and women who don't make love all the year round, but have a brief mating season. The effect of this on politics, religion, ethics, etc. would be something very interesting and amusing to work out."

By February 1948 the book was finished. Again literature, this time Shakespeare's *Measure for Measure*, was drawn on for the title, *Ape and Essence:*

> Man, proud man,
> Drest in a little brief authority—
> Most ignorant of what he is most assured,
> His glassy essence—like an angry ape
> Plays such fantastic tricks before high heaven
> As make the angels weep.

In a minor sense this is Huxley's Hollywood novel. Cast in scenario form, it prints a rejected script rescued by the narrator when it falls off a passing truck en route to the studio incinerator with a load of similar discards. A quest for its author leads to the Mojave Desert, across the mountains from Pasadena where, at Llano, the Huxleys lived for a time in the early 1940's.

The setting is the Los Angeles plain in the 21st century, where an exploring party from unbombed New Zealand finds a community of barbaric survivors. One scene transpires in Pershing Square where books from the former Public Library are being used to stoke the communal ovens.

"All the scholar in Dr. Poole, all the bibliophile, is outraged by the spectacle."

" 'But this is frightful!' " he protests.

"The Chief only laughs."

"In goes *The Phenomenology of the Spirit*, out comes the corn bread. And damned good bread it is."

366

"He takes another bite."

The book's closing shot is of Dr. Poole and the girl Loola flee-
ing over the San Gabriels to sanctuary in the desert.

By the early 1950's Aldous Huxley might have agreed with
Robinson Jeffers, whose life at Carmel, before the death of Una
in 1950, had attained a state of happy monotony, in which the
poet confessed himself willing to go on living for several centuries. "But," Jeffers observed, " good and evil are very cunningly balanced even in the most favored lives, and I would not
feel cheated if I were to die tomorrow, although it would be
annoying."

Evil days now came upon Huxley. In 1953 Maria developed
cancer. Two years later she died. Unlike Jeffers and Raymond
Chandler, who were also dependent on their wives, Huxley bore
his loss without suffering creative collapse. He did however go
deeper into experimentation with mescaline and LSD. One of
his motives seemed to be a desire to attain a higher state of being
in which he might be reunited with Maria. Grief does strange
things to the reasoning mind. *The Doors of Perception* is the book
he wrote about these experiments.

If he were alive today, Huxley would be appalled at the extent
of drug usage. *Après lui le deluge.*

He wrote less. The great vision that had sustained him through
so many creative works was fading. "I always have the feeling,"
he wrote in the elegiac vein into which he fell after Maria's death,
"when I read history, or see or listen to or read the greatest works
of art, that, if we knew the right way to set about it, we could do
things far more strange and lovely than even the strangest and
loveliest of past history."

Writing had never been other than hard work. He once said
that he knew of no short cuts to good writing except repeated
rewriting. His surviving manuscripts and typescripts bear evidence of this practice of painstaking revision. And so with a
diminished drive, he found lecturing an easier outlet for his
ideas. He lectured successfully throughout the country from
Santa Barbara to M.I.T., and abroad.

As George Wickes observed in his catalog of Huxleyana at

367

UCLA, "he played an important role in the life of the University of California at Los Angeles, Santa Barbara, and Berkeley, with his wisdom, his wide-ranging intelligence and vast learning. He was not a brilliant lecturer, but his mind was always stimulating—original, perceptive, inquiring. It was not an academic mind, and for that reason all the more stimulating to an academic audience. Learned in half a dozen different fields, he constantly brought his learning and intelligence to bear on the problems of mankind. He was a man of rare gifts."

Although he gained companionship in a second marriage, the creative flame never again burned as brightly. It was a time of Indian Summer. "The terrible sadness of Maria's last months and the sense of amputation which followed her death have retreated," he wrote to a friend, "and my memories of her are now happy, grateful, and tender memories."

After his marriage to Laura Archera in 1956, they moved to a house on Deronda Drive, high in the hills above Hollywood, It had, Huxley said, "an incredible view, with virtually no smog . . . hills which remind me a little of Greece by their barrenness, their steep-sided narrow valleys and the unsullied sky overhead." He did not see Nemesis lurking in the brush-covered terrain.

There were two more bitter draughts to drink before Aldous Huxley finally gained the peace of death. In 1960 he developed cancer of the tongue, which spread later throughout his body. Then in 1961 the hill house and its contents were destroyed by a swift, erratic brush fire. The house was replaceable; its contents were not. They included his annotated library of 4,000 volumes, the manuscripts of most of his books; his diaries; letters from such famous contemporaries as André Gide and D. H. Lawrence; and most precious of all, Maria's letters and the memorabilia of their long loving life together.

"It is odd to be starting from scratch at my age," he wrote to Robert M. Hutchins, "with literally nothing in the way of possessions . . . I am evidently intended to learn, a little in advance of the final denudation, that you can't take it with you."

He had time only to save the manuscript on which he was working, the novel published in 1962 called *Island*. It was his last work, a vision of the utopia he foresaw in a culture of controlled drug usage and mesmeric medical therapy. *Island* is, alas, not an autumnal masterpiece. It was too late. Winter had come. He had suffered too much from disease, death, and destruction.

If it is true that *Island* does not rank as one of Huxley's best books, no one devoted to this writer of unwavering integrity and unceasing moral searching can read it without being deeply moved by the pity of its circumstances and all that went into it. His conduct to the very end was marked by nobility.

Aldous Huxley was never self-deluded. He knew what he had and had not wrought. In the course of *Island's* composition, while he lived and worked in the shadow of death, he wrote in a letter:

"I am always haunted by the feeling that, if only I had enough talent, I could somehow poetize and dramatize all the intellectual material, and create a work . . . which would be simultaneously funny, tragic, lyrical and profound. Alas, I don't possess the necessary talent."

Not true. Talent he had, and in a measure far beyond most writers. What he lacked, at the end, was strength enough and time. During his prime, when he possessed those precious assets, he achieved a worldwide audience and fame. These he still has, for his books have won him immortality. They speak with his voice.

Reading List

ALDOUS HUXLEY (1894-1963)
Jesting Pilate. New York, Doran, 1926.
After Many a Summer Dies the Swan. New York, Harper, 1939.
Ape and Essence. New York, Harper, 1948.
The Doors of Perception. New York, Harper, 1954.
Island. New York, Harper, 1962.
Letters. Edited by Grover Smith. New York, Harper, 1969.

JULIAN HUXLEY, Editor
Aldous Huxley, 1894-1963, a Memorial Volume, New York, Harper, 1965.

GEORGE WICKES, Editor
  Aldous Huxley at UCLA; a Catalogue of the Manuscripts . . . with . . .
  Three Unpublished Letters. Los Angeles, University of California
  Library, 1964.

*Drawing of Aldous Huxley by Don Bachardy, courtesy of Josephine and Jacob
Zeitlin.*

Farewell, My Lovely

RAYMOND CHANDLER

31

WHO WOULD have picked an obscure middle-aged, pulp-maga-zine contributor to be the one who would write, *bang! bang! bang! bang!* four detective-story novels that would win for him the prose laureateship of Los Angeles?

This was Raymond Chandler, and his unlikely feat was con-summated in a span of hardly more than four years, from 1939 to 1943. When he died at La Jolla in 1959 at the age of 71, the *Times* of London ended its obituary with this solemn pronounce-ment: "His name will certainly go down among the dozen or so mystery writers who were also innovators and stylists; who, working the common vein of crime fiction, mined the gold of literature."

What was it that worked this alchemy, this transformation of common material into literary masterpieces? so that W. H. Auden wrote of Chandler that his books should be "read and judged, not as escape literature, but as works of art." Why choose Raymond Chandler and not S. S. Van Dine or Dashiell Hammett or Erle Stanley Gardner, all of whom wrote mysteries with a Californian setting?

The answer is partly to be found in a letter Chandler wrote to Gardner, a kind of pupil-to-master letter, for it was from analyz-ing one of the latter's stories in the early 1930's that Chandler first learned the technique of his craft. What he says of Gardner reveals what Chandler sought to do, and did, to a degree that Gardner never did:

"When a book, any sort of book reaches a certain intensity of artistic performance it becomes literature. That intensity may be a matter of style, situation, character, emotional tone, or idea, or half a dozen other things. It may also be a perfection of control over the movement of a story similar to the control a great pitcher has over the ball. Every page throws the hook for the next. I call this a kind of genius."

Such was the genius of Raymond Chandler.

In those four miraculous novels, *The Big Sleep, Farewell, My Lovely, The High Window*, and *The Lady in the Lake*, Chandler stopped the Los Angeles kaleidoscope; he arrested its spinning, so confusing to most writers who have tried to see the city clearly; and then he fixed in prose of poetic intensity the brilliant bits and pieces, until we find in his "Big Four" a glittering mosaic of greater Los Angeles from San Bernardino to the sea.

The unlikeliness of Chandler's achievement is only superficial. We have only to delve a bit to discover the logic in his life that led slowly, surely, inevitably, up to the four-year rocket-burst of creativity and subsequent worldwide acclaim, followed, alas, by a descent from zenith to a lonely, miserable nadir, the passionate thrust of his prime all spent.

Who was Raymond Thornton Chandler? Chicago-born in 1888 of an American father and an Irish mother, taken to England by the latter when her husband became an alcoholic, young Chandler received a classical education at London's Dulwich College and language training at private schools in France and Germany. A wealthy Irish uncle got him placed in the Admiralty, from where Chandler made his escape with the intention of becoming a poet and essayist; and as such he contributed to various London periodicals around the year 1910.

In order to maintain his American citizenship Chandler returned to the United States in 1912 on borrowed money, and made his way from New York, via St. Louis, to Los Angeles. There he picked apricots for ten hours a day, and then changed jobs to one of stringing tennis rackets for Spalding on a fifty-four hour week. It does not seem to be known why he came to Los Angeles.

In 1917 Chandler enlisted in the Canadian army's Gordon Highlanders, served overseas, and was discharged in 1919 at Vancouver, B.C. He worked then as an accountant in an English bank in San Francisco, but soon returned to Los Angeles and lived with his mother in an apartment hotel on Bunker Hill, at the top of the short funiculaire called the Angels Flight. It was a similar dwelling, The Cumberland, that was our first home in Los Angeles when, after several winters in Riverside, my parents moved permanently in 1911 to Southern California. The Angels Flight was my childhood paradise. A round-trip ride cost 5 cents.

When Chandler's mother died in 1923, he married a woman eighteen years his senior. This was his only marriage and it lasted until his wife's death, thirty years later. His books were their children.

Chandler entered the oil business as an accountant, rose to auditor, and finally became the executive director of several small companies. This prosperous phase of his life lasted for ten years. More important than his material earnings was a familiarity gained with the life and landscape of greater Los Angeles. Unlike most novelists who write about Southern California, he knew the differences, large and small, between Azusa, Rialto, Hueneme, and Escondido, between Pacific Palisades and Malibu. "Business is very tough," he wrote, "and I hate it. But whatever you set out to do, you have to do as well as you know how."

The Depression resolved his ambivalence. Along with hundreds of other ventures, the oil companies failed. By 1933 he was 45 and broke. On the surface, a literary career leading to immortality was unlikely. And yet, just as it orbited Steinbeck, the Depression was also Chandler's launching pad. Let him tell it, in a letter he wrote years later to his English publisher.

"Wandering up and down the Pacific Coast in an automobile, I began to read pulp magazines, because they were cheap enough to throw away and because I never had at any time any taste for the kind of thing which is known as women's magazines. This was in the great days of the *Black Mask* and it struck me that

374

some of the writing was pretty forceful and honest, even though it had its crude aspect. I decided that this might be a good way to try to learn to write fiction and get paid a small amount of money at the same time. I spent five months over an 18,000 word novelette and sold it for $180. After that I never looked back, although I had a good many uneasy periods looking forward."

Founded in 1920 by H. L. Mencken and George Jean Nathan, *Black Mask* was the aristocrat of the pulps. Taken over in 1926 by the erudite Captain Joseph Shaw, it became the cradle of the new hard-boiled school of American prose fiction, whose "big daddy" was Ernest Hemingway. In the crime genre it was Dashiell Hammett whose stories and serialized novels were the glory of *Black Mask*. Like Chandler, Hammett soared swiftly and high between 1929 and 1932 with his "Big Five": *Red Harvest, The Dain Curse, The Maltese Falcon, The Glass Key*, and *The Thin Man.*

We see the pen handed to Chandler in the year following Hammett's last novel. "I did not invent the hard-boiled murder story," Chandler wrote. "I have never made any secret of my opinion that Hammett deserves most or all of the credit."

Let the *Times* settle it. "Chandler's mature thrillers became something of a cult among intellectuals. They were praised by literary critics, who normally despise crime fiction. Their originality has been confirmed by a host of imitators; but it would be untrue to say he founded a school, rather he defined a school. Dashiell Hammett was his master. He admired Hammett's effect of realism, his sharp, aggressive attitude to life, and style of writing which, Chandler insisted, was not personal to Hammett but inherent in the American language for him that can get it."

The same determination that made him succeed in business, accounts for Chandler's triumph as a writer. He set out to do the best he knew how to do. The stories and novelettes he sold to *Black Mask* led inevitably to the novels that carried his fame worldwide, translated as they were into many languages, including Finnish and Japanese.

My choice of *Farewell, My Lovely* is arbitrary. It might just as well be one of the other three, although it is true that *Farewell*

375

was Chandler's favorite. The four books are really one book, an encyclopedia of Los Angeles.

I once reread them in four consecutive days, and then went wandering around the city in search of Chandlerian survivals. Except for smog, the weather is the same. Flora is unchanged, only more of it. Hydrangea, grevellea, acacia and pepper, deodar and eucalyptus—he included them all as bits of the mosaic. Architecture is altered though not completely unrecognizable. Is there still a violet light atop the green-patina tower of Bullock's Wilshire? My wandering was by daylight. Many backwater areas, bypassed by the freeways, remain pure Chandler of the 1920's.

What distinguishes his treatment of Los Angeles from that of most other novelists is his wealth of precise observation and power of description. His vision was clear, with prose to match it. Through his transparent language we see landscape and life in exact register without blur.

As I said, he stopped the kaleidoscope. His pages glitter with brilliant descriptions. They are like the view of the city from aloft, either in the sharp light of late afternoon or after dark, when a day of Santa Ana has swept the coastal plain of smog and the Queen of the Angels is her former naked self.

Time and place are of the essence in a Chandler novel. Consider the openings of the four novels:

"It was about eleven o'clock in the morning, mid-October, with the sun not shining and a look of hard wet rain in the clearness of the foothills."

"It was a warm day, almost the end of March, and I stood outside the barber shop looking up at the jutting neon sign of a second floor dine and dice emporium called Florian's."

"The house was on Dresden Avenue in the Oak Knoll section of Pasadena. There was a heavy scent of summer on the morning and everything that grew was perfectly still in the breathless air they get over there on what they call a nice cool day."

"The Treloar Building was, and is, on Olive Street, near Sixth, on the west side. The sidewalk in front of it had been built of black and white rubber blocks. They were taking them up now to

376

give the government, and a hatless pale man with a face like a building superintendent was watching the work and looking as if it was breaking his heart."

There is not a paragraph in any of them that does not have this same concentration on reality as Chandler recalled it. This is a hallmark of extraordinary writing. The reader recognizes the world that he too inhabits and which he sees even more clearly with the added vision given him by the extra perceptive writer.

By literature, Chandler meant any sort of writing that reaches a sufficient intensity of performance to glow with its own heat. "There must be magic in the writing," he said, "but I take no credit for it. It just happens, like red hair." His pages have this magical glow and give off heat that comes from the incandescence of his own style. He took the American vernacular as it is concocted in the melting pot of Los Angeles and made it an expressive instrument. I could fill pages with his characteristic similes and metaphors.

Chandler's stories are melodramas, which is to say they are exaggerations of violence and fear in which emotion is overcharged and time and event are compressed beyond probability. And yet they are relevant to the milieu they transform.

Horace Bell's *Reminiscences of a Ranger* chronicled the frontier violence of Los Angeles in the 1850's. By the time Chandler arrived nearly a century later, the frontier was gone, but violence was still there, though not as brutally revealed. Now in the 1970's it stalks the streets and campuses again, and who's to be our laureate?

Yet Chandler's novels are not merely violent, any more than Jeffers's narrative poems are that and nothing more. Both writers are moralists. Jeffers's background was Presbyterian, Chandler's Quaker. The private eye, Philip Marlowe, is a crusading knight, fighting evil both individual and social. All four of his adventures in detection have "happy endings." We come to share his contempt for corrupt city administrations, crooked police departments, smut bookshops, quack doctors, phony yogis, and miscellaneous grifters, grafters, pimps and peepers. We adore his blonde secretaries and reporters, modelled, it is said, on his own blue-eyed wife, Cissy. Indeed his books are social moralities, in a class above what Chandler called the "comic books" of Mickey Spillane. They are therefore fit reading for young and old and those between.

It is true that Chandler was taken more seriously in England than in America, and I find myself turning repeatedly to the British press for confirmations of my judgment. In a special issue on crime fiction in 1961 the *Times Literary Supplement* said:

"No morality play could condemn the wickedness of man and the trampishness of woman, or point to the high-powered doom under the bonnet and the skeleton beneath the mink, more emphatically than do many of the products of the American school of Raymond Chandler."

Not only does Chandler describe environment with poetical realism, his people are vividly alive, even the most minor such as bartenders, elevator men, and parking lot attendants. His major characters, especially detectives, are gloriously real and threaten to walk off the page into our own lives. He created an enthralling human menagerie. Read Chandler and then go downtown to the Central Library and sit on a bench in the park. His characters will pass by, and some may even sit down beside you. Or visit the Strand in Venice and linger in one of the little oceanfront shelters. There too will be encountered Chandler's people, on the move or at rest. He captured the social milieu of Southern California just as truly as Lawrence Durrell did that of Egypt in his Alexandria Quartet, another tetralogy of poetical intensity also written in a burst of creative power.

After *The Lady in the Lake*, what did Chandler write in the remaining sixteen years of his life? How did he meet one of Cyril Connolly's enemies of promise, Success? The answer is a sad story, for his was an unhappy ending. "Everything a writer learns about the art or craft of fiction," Chandler said, "takes just a little away from his need or drive to write at all. In the end he knows all the tricks and has nothing to say."

This is all too true of him. In a little more than four years of concentrated creativity, Chandler said it all and at such a level that never again could he regain that height. *The Little Sister*, *The Long Goodbye*, and *Playback* are what was left after the cream had been taken off. They are the tail of the rocket, the tricks without the magic. And yet every Chandler addict will read them and long for more.

In 1943 Chandler began to work as a Hollywood screenwriter. He remained only a few years. *The Little Sister* represents his disillusionment. Before this occurred, he landed twice on target with the scenario (with Billy Wilder) for James M. Cain's *Double Indemnity*, featuring Barbara Stanwyck and Fred Mac-Murray, and an original screenplay, *The Blue Dahlia*, in which Veronica Lake starred. Both won Academy awards.

"They don't want you until you have made a name," Chandler wrote later about Hollywood, "and by the time you have made a name, you have developed some kind of talent they can't use. All they will do is spoil it, if you let them. The best scenes I ever wrote were practically monosyllabic. And the best short scene I ever wrote was one in which a girl said 'uh huh' three times with three different intonations, and that's all there was to it."

In 1946 he and his wife moved to La Jolla, and in 1954 she died, at the age of 84. When Jeffers lost Una, his grief was assuaged by his sons and daughters-in-law and their children. Huxley likewise was fortunate. Chandler had no one. "She was the beat of my heart for thirty years," he wrote to a friend, "she was the music heard faintly at the edge of sound. It was my great and now useless regret that I never wrote anything really worth her attention, no book that I could dedicate to her."

He was lost without Cissy; he drank heavily, attempted suicide, and wandered around Europe, declaring "All that is really the matter with me is that I have no home, and no one to care for in a home, if I had one." He too died in La Jolla, on March 26, 1959, twenty years after the publication of *The Big Sleep*. He and his wife are buried in Mount Hope Cemetery, San Diego.

Before Chandler died, the UCLA Library persuaded him to deposit his papers on the Westwood campus. Augmented by material from his agent, Helga Greene, they served as the basis for the only book about Chandler, Philip Durham's *Down These*

Mean Streets a Man Must Go. Also in the UCLA Library are the *Black Mask* archives, presented by its editor.

In 1962 Dorothy Gardiner and Katherine Walker edited a volume of Chandler's letters, called *Raymond Chandler Speaking.* Not since Somerset Maugham's *The Summing Up* has there been as good a book about the art and craft of writing. It is rich with *obiter dicta* on writing and writers, including praise of Maugham's *Ashendene,* Hemingway's *Across the River,* and Erle Stanley Gardner's *The Case of the Velvet Claws.* In 1949 Chandler wrote to a critic, "You cannot have art without a public taste and you cannot have a public taste without a sense of style and quality throughout the whole structure of society."

Although Chandler's view of himself was serious, it was never self-satisfied nor pompous. His opinion of the popular picture magazines was deadly. In reply to a questionnaire from one, prying into his personal life and writing habits, he replied:

"Yes, I am exactly like the characters in my books. I am very tough and have been known to break a Vienna roll with my bare hands. I live in a French Provincial chateau on Mulholland Drive. It is a fairly small place of forty-eight rooms and fifty-nine baths. I dine off gold plate and prefer to be waited on by naked dancing girls. I have fourteen telephones on my desk, including direct lines to New York, London, Paris, Rome, and Santa Rosa. My filing case opens out into a convenient portable bar, and the bartender, who lives in the bottom drawer, is a midget. I am thirty-eight years old and have been for the last twenty years. I do not regard myself as a dead shot, but I am a pretty dangerous man with a wet towel. But all in all I think my favorite weapon is a twenty dollar bill."

Although I never knew Raymond Chandler, I do know Philip Marlowe, and I believe that Marlowe's hard-boiled decency, his gallantry toward women and other downtroddens, represent Chandler's alter ego. Creative literature comes from the blood and marrow of a writer's being. He gives his life that his books may live. This Raymond Chandler did in his tetralogy of which *Farewell, My Lovely* is the finest part.

Reading List

RAYMOND CHANDLER (1888-1959)
The Big Sleep. New York, Alfred A. Knopf, 1939.
Farewell, My Lovely. New York, Alfred A. Knopf, 1940.
The High Window. New York, Alfred A. Knopf, 1942.
The Lady in the Lake. New York, Alfred A. Knopf, 1943.
The Raymond Chandler Omnibus. Foreword by Lawrence Clark Powell. New York, Alfred A. Knopf, 1964. Includes "The Big Four."
Raymond Chandler Speaking. Edited by Dorothy Gardiner and Katherine Walker. Boston, Houghton Mifflin, 1962.
Killer in the Rain. Introduction by Philip Durham. Boston, Houghton Mifflin, 1964.

PHILIP DURHAM
Down These Mean Streets a Man Must Go; Raymond Chandler's Knight. Chapel Hill, University of North Carolina Press, 1963.

Photograph of Raymond Chandler, courtesy of Alfred A. Knopf.

Index

Index

390

California Classics

And meanwhile the beautiful, the incredible world in which we live awaits our exploration, and life is short, and time flows stanchlessly, like blood from a mortal wound. And there is all knowledge, all art. There are men and women, the innumerable living, and, in books, the souls of those dead who deserve to be immortal.

Aldous Huxley, JESTING PILATE

Copyright © 1971 by Lawrence Clark Powell
Library of Congress Catalog Number 75-149085
ISBN 0378-07781-3
Printed in the United States of America
Designed by Ward Ritchie
Illustration by Don Perceval

Second Printing 1972

California Classics

THE CREATIVE LITERATURE
OF THE GOLDEN STATE

by Lawrence Clark Powell

The Ward Ritchie Press
Los Angeles